# Switching Theory

## Volume II:
## Sequential Circuits and Machines

# Switching Theory

## Volume II:

## Sequential Circuits and Machines

### Raymond E. Miller

*IBM Thomas J. Watson Research Center*
*Yorktown Heights, New York*

John Wiley & Sons, Inc., New York · London · Sydney

# *Preface*

Switching theory includes mathematical models and techniques for handling problems associated with networks of elements which are capable of exhibiting only a finite number of signal values. Examples of such "digital circuits" are digital computers, communication switching systems, and digital control systems. In *Switching Theory*, which appears in two volumes, my purpose is to present a unified treatment of the subject, with emphasis on those aspects related to the synthesis and analysis of switching circuits. Although I have made no attempt to describe every technique which has been developed for switching circuit design, each of the selected subjects is treated in detail. In addition, the approach is aimed at both describing certain techniques not covered in previous books and giving a broad introduction to the various disciplines in switching theory. The separation of material into two volumes provides, I believe, greater flexibility in their use. The underlying theory, rather than detailed cookbook procedures for designing special circuits, is stressed. These concepts and mathematical techniques are fundamental to the methods of analysis and design of switching circuits; they also form the basis for future developments in switching theory itself. Much of the material is of very recent origin and, consequently, has not appeared previously in a book. This is to be expected, since the subject is rapidly expanding, and very often current texts are badly outdated.

I have written both volumes primarily for advanced undergraduate and graduate study in electrical engineering, computer sciences, and related courses, although each volume can also serve as a reference book. To meet this double purpose, I have included a considerable number of exercises, extensive references to original papers and other works, and a short discussion of references at the end of each chapter. This material should prove valuable to those students and people interested in doing further research on particular topics. Each volume contains sufficient material for a one-semester course, and combined can be used for a one-year course.

A word about the selection of subject matter is appropriate. To provide some background for Volume I, an introductory description of digital computers and some other digital systems is given in Chapter 1. Chapter 2 is concerned with an extensive development of Boolean algebra, its basic connections with switching circuits of various types, and its relationship to other mathematical structures. Special types of functions and functional forms of importance to switching theory are also discussed. Chapter 3 treats the most common type of circuit minimization problem—that of two-level circuits. For the first time in a book the formulation is presented in terms of the cubical representation, rather than in the more commonly used chart or functional forms. Both geometric visualization and algebraic formalism of the cubical representation are given. Because connections with functional forms and chart forms are discussed and these techniques are readily available in many references, I feel that the use of cubical representation will give the reader a broader understanding of this classical problem of switching theory. Chapter 4 discusses two methods for treating multiple output circuits as well as the theory of functional decomposition and its application to gate-type circuit design, an important concept which has not been treated in previous texts. Some standard approaches to bilateral switching (relay-type) networks and an application to cryogenic circuits appear in Chapter 5.

Volume II consists of Chapters 6 through 10. Chapter 6 introduces various models for sequential circuits and machines and discusses the relationship between them. To my knowledge one of these models, the formal language of regular expressions, has never been discussed in a text on switching circuit theory. State minimization of sequential machines is treated for general incompletely specified machines, and state minimization for completely specified machines is developed as a special case in Chapter 7. Chapter 8 discusses various approaches to state assignment for synchronous sequential machines, including the theory of partitions for reduced dependence. In Chapters 9 and 10 an extensive theoretical treatment of asynchronous circuits and speed independent circuits is given.

I am indebted to many people for their direct and indirect aid in making it possible to write this book. The references and reference notations at the end of each chapter indicate my indebtedness to the many researchers in the field who are cited in the literature. I particularly want to thank Professor G. D. McCann for inviting me to the California Institute of Technology, during 1962 and 1963, for it was during this year of teaching a course on switching theory that the first draft of this book was written and many improvements were suggested by the students. Initial drafts of several chapters were also written for a course at the University of Illinois during the fall semester of 1960; and I am grateful to Professors D. E. Muller and A. H. Taub for inviting me to visit the Digital Computer Laboratory and teach this course. In connection with this teaching I wish to acknowledge the assistance of IBM Corporation, and thank Dr. H. H. Goldstine and Dr. C. C. Elgot for enabling me to accept these invitations and providing continued encouragement and support. Finally, I thank Mrs. M. A. Kenny for her patient and expert typing of the final manuscript, the editors of John Wiley and Sons for their immeasurable help in all phases of the preparation, and my wife Marilyn for her patience and continued encouragement.

*December 1964*                                          R. E. MILLER

# Contents

# Contents for Volume One

*xi*

**CHAPTER 3   COMBINATIONAL SWITCHING CIRCUITS:**
**NORMAL FORM CIRCUIT DESIGN          134**

**CHAPTER 4   MULTIPLE OUTPUT AND MULTILEVEL**
**COMBINATIONAL CIRCUITS          197**

# 6

# Some Models and Elementary Properties of Sequential Machines

## 6.1 INTRODUCTION

In Volume I we discussed various theorems and methods pertaining to the analysis and synthesis of combinational switching networks, whose outputs can be expressed as switching functions of the inputs. In the various models for combinational networks one assumes that timing for the inputs, internal signals,* and outputs can be ignored. Although this assumption is often valid, in some situations the timing of the signals is of primary importance. For example, the behavior of the relay circuit of Figure 3.2.9, which contains an internal relay, depends on the relative operation times of contacts on the internal relay. Similarly, the behavior of the logical circuit of Figure 3.2.10 depends on the timing of signals on the feedback lines. One may be interested in obtaining sequences of outputs for certain sequences of inputs, where the output at any point in a sequence may depend not only on the inputs to the network at that instant of time but also on the previous inputs that have been applied to the network. Another way of expressing this dependence of the outputs on the inputs is saying that the network outputs depend on both the present inputs to the network and on the past history of inputs into the network. In this volume we shall describe various models and properties of these networks. The networks are called *sequential switching networks*† and their mathematical models *sequential machines*.

As we saw in Figures 3.2.9 and 3.2.10 the relative timing of the internal signals of the circuit and the timing of the input signal can effect the sequence of outputs produced by the circuit. Thus, as we discuss sequential

---

* The voltage levels or other electrical measurements of the lines in a circuit are assumed two-valued and assigned the Boolean values 0 and 1. We shall call these 0 and 1 values the *signal values* or *signals*.

† We shall usually drop "switching" here, and simply call such networks *sequential networks* or *sequential circuits*.

network realizations for sequential machines in this and the following chapters, various assumptions on the timing of the circuits are also provided that enable us to describe sequences of inputs and outputs for sequential networks.

For the outputs of a switching network to depend on the previous inputs to the network, the network must be able to preserve information about the previous inputs. We thus introduce the concept of "states" of a network, where the "state" corresponds to some memory of the past inputs; then the dependence of the outputs on both present inputs and past inputs can be expressed as a function of the present inputs and the "state" of the network. To demonstrate this idea, let us consider a simple example of a sequential switching network. Consider a simple-minded cat that catches mice for food, whose behavior can be defined as follows. This cat has either a "searching" mode or a "chasing" mode of operation. In the searching mode he walks straight ahead keeping his eyes open for the sight of a mouse. He can sense a mouse either on his left side or right side. When he sights a mouse, he turns in the correct direction, either left or right, and changes to his chasing mode, running after the mouse until he catches it. On catching the mouse, he returns to his searching mode and repeats these actions. The "inputs" to this cat are three, labeled as

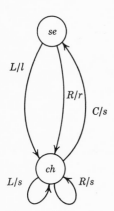

Figure 6.1.1 State diagram for a simple-minded cat.

$L$ = sighting a mouse to the left.

$R$ = sighting a mouse to the right.

and             $C$ = catching a mouse.

The two modes of operation can be called the "states" of the mouse, labeled as

$se$ = search mouse.

$ch$ = chase mode.

The outputs of this cat are either to turn left $l$ or right $r$, when the inputs are $L$ and $R$, respectively, or to not turn $s$. In a model for this cat's behavior, we represent the states by circles, and the inputs and outputs are represented on directed lines between these states to indicate the change of state due to the sighting of a mouse and the output required to start chasing the mouse, as shown in Figure 6.1.1. Such a model is called the *state diagram* for a sequential machine.*

Looking at the state diagram, note that the cat ignores the distraction of

* Sequential machines and state diagrams will be defined more rigorously in Section 6.4.

other mice when he is in the chasing mode by staying in the chasing mode and going straight after the mouse he first saw. Also note that when in the *se* state we have not specified what the cat might do if an input *C* occurred, that is, we do not anticipate that the cat will catch a mouse without first seeing it.

Although our main interest in the theory of sequential machines in the following chapters is in the analysis and synthesis of electrical sequential switching networks, the theory is applicable to many diverse fields; the simple-minded cat example illustrates how certain elementary behaviors of an animal can be described by a sequential machine. Some further examples of other applications of sequential machines are given later.

Our approach to discussing sequential networks and machines is as follows. First, in Section 6.2, we develop a model for describing the terminal behavior of sequential networks. This model consists of a combinational network plus some idealized timing elements and simplifying assumptions on internal delays of the elements within the network. We then briefly describe how such a model may be implemented in logical circuitry assuming somewhat more realistic, but controlled, timing of the elements in the circuit. In Sections 6.4 through 6.6 we next introduce two general sequential machine models for sequential circuits. In Section 6.7 it is shown that a formal class of expressions on input symbols (called regular expressions) is precisely the class of expressions which can be represented in finite sequential circuits.

The sequential machine model developed in this chapter serves as a means for giving a precise statement of the design requirements for a sequential circuit. We then turn to studying procedures for obtaining suitable sequential circuit designs from the sequential machine model. In Chapter 7 we study "state minimization"—a theoretical problem for sequential machines that also determines the minimum possible number of memory elements required for a circuit design. In Chapter 8 we discuss "state assignment." The state assignment of a sequential machine reduces the design problem to that of a multiple output combinational circuit design when strict timing controls on the circuit are assumed (that is, synchronous circuits). Finally, in Chapters 9 and 10, we discuss "asynchronous sequential circuits," ones where it is possible to maintain correct operation even under considerable variability of element timings.

## 6.2 A BASIC MODEL FOR SEQUENTIAL SWITCHING NETWORKS

We can represent a sequential network schematically as in Figure 6.2.1, where the network has $n$ input signals $x_1, x_2, \ldots, x_n$ and $m$ output signals

$z_1, z_2, \ldots, z_m$. We assume that both $m$ and $n$ are finite. This schematic diagram appears identical to that of Figure 3.2.1 for a combinational circuit. In the combinational circuit each output $z_i$ can be expressed as a Boolean function of the $n$ inputs, giving $z_i = z_i(x_1, x_2, \ldots, x_n)$. In particular, we are concerned with switching functions for the $z_i$ of binary variables $x_1, x_2, \ldots, x_n$. For sequential networks each input $x_i$ and each output $z_j$ also assume only a finite number of values; and as in combinational networks, we are often concerned with the particular case that each $x_i$ and each $z_j$ assume only the binary value 0 or 1 at any particular instant of time. The principal difference, then, between combinational networks

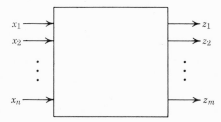

Figure 6.2.1    Terminal model for a sequential switching network.

and sequential networks is that for the latter we consider also the behavior of the inputs and outputs in time, that is, temporal sequences of inputs and outputs. Thus we can consider each $x_i$ and $z_j$ of Figure 6.2.1 as a finite-valued, time-dependent signal. Rather than using time as an explicit variable, however, we use the concept of the "state" of the sequential network and make the output of the sequential network at any time $t$ depend on the inputs and the state at time $t$. The use of the state allows us to remove time as an explicit variable of the inputs and outputs, as is noted in the state diagram realization of the simple-minded cat of Section 6.1.

As mentioned previously, the "state" stores certain information about previous inputs in the sequential network. This information is thus available as an internal signal or a set of internal signals within the sequential network. For practical purposes, a network can have only a finite number of states, since each internal signal is assumed finite valued, and there are only a finite number of internal signals. Therefore we call this network a *finite-state sequential network* and its mathematical model a *finite-state sequential machine*. Each state of the network may be represented by a different set of internal signals. We designate these internal signal values by $k$ internal variables $y_1, y_2, \ldots, y_k$, where each of them is finite valued. Thus, if each of the $k$ internal variables is binary valued, we can represent at most $2^k$ states with the $k$ internal variables. For example, if $k = 3$, then the various sets of signals to represent states are $(0, 0, 0)$, $(0, 0, 1)$, $(0, 1, 0), \ldots, (1, 1, 1)$. The outputs can then be expressed as Boolean functions of the inputs and internal variables as

$$z_1 = z_1(x_1, x_2, \ldots, x_n, y_1, y_2, \ldots, y_k),$$

(6.2.1)
$$z_2 = z_2(x_1, x_2, \ldots, x_n, y_1, y_2, \ldots, y_k),$$

$$z_m = z_m(x_1, x_2, \ldots, x_n, y_1, y_2, \ldots, y_k).$$

With the introduction of these internal variables $y_1, y_2, \ldots, y_k$, we must also specify how they behave in the circuit in order to describe it completely; that is, we must specify this internal behavior. To do this we restrict ourselves to a strictly *deterministic* behavior by insisting that if we are in some state (a set of values for $y_1, y_2, \ldots, y_k$) and obtain an input (a set of signals on $x_1, x_2, \ldots, x_n$), there will be only one possible transition to some new state. We can express this mapping as assigning new values to the $y_i$, calling them $y_i'$. This gives the set of functions

$$y_1' = y_1'(x_1, x_2, \ldots, x_n, y_1, y_2, \ldots, y_k),$$

(6.2.2)
$$y_2' = y_2'(x_1, x_2, \ldots, x_n, y_1, y_2, \ldots, y_k),$$

$$y_k' = y_k'(x_1, x_2, \ldots, x_n, y_1, y_2, \ldots, y_k).$$

The set of equations (6.2.1) is called the *set of output equations* and (6.2.2) is called the *set of next state equations*.

In each of these equations we assume that the inputs $x_1, x_2, \ldots, x_n$ and internal variables $y_1, y_2, \ldots, y_k$ are given at some instant of time $t$. Equations (6.2.1) specify the outputs $z_1, z_2, \ldots, z_m$ at the same instant of time $t$, possibly by using a combinational circuit with $m$ outputs and $n + k$ inputs. Equations (6.2.2) specify the next state $y_1', \ldots, y_k'$ which is to be used with the next set of inputs to form another set of outputs. Various methods of synchronizing the networks are used to insure that the internal signals representing states and the input signals entering the network actually occur simultaneously at the time instant $t$ so that Equations (6.2.1) and (6.2.2) are meaningful. A particularly simple method of synchronization is having the network controlled by an external synchronizing source (or clock) which supplies a signal to the network to indicate discrete intervals of time $t$, $t + \Delta$, etc. We can assume without any loss of generality that these discrete intervals of time are all equal, as indicated by $\Delta$. Then Equations (6.2.1) and (6.2.2) are interpreted as the following idealized circuit.

If signals $x_1, \ldots, x_n, y_1, \ldots, y_k$ occur at time $t$, then $z_1, \ldots, z_m$ are outputs at time $t$, and $y_1', \ldots, y_k'$ (the next state) will be available as the present state at the next synchronizing interval $t + \Delta$, in other words, after a delay of time $\Delta$ the $y_i'$ values become the $y_i$ values. A network using such a clock for synchronizing is called a *synchronous sequential network*. We can depict this synchronous network, then, as a combinational circuit plus $k$ delay circuits of delay $\Delta$, as shown in Figure 6.2.2. Here we assume the combinational circuit outputs react instantaneously to the combinational circuit inputs; that is, there are no internal delays in the combinational circuit. The state of this sequential network is stored in the $k$ delay elements shown below the combinational circuit.

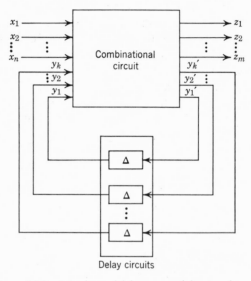

Figure 6.2.2　A basic model for sequential networks.

This basic model for a sequential network can be considered to be a canonical form for sequential networks, since any deterministic finite-state sequential network can be represented in the form of the basic model, where exactly the same sequence of inputs and outputs is obtained from the basic model as from the deterministic finite-state sequential network. This is because states can be obtained for the deterministic finite-state sequential network, and these states may be encoded by a set of internal variables $y_1, \ldots, y_k$, so that Equations (6.2.1) and (6.2.2) describe accurately the outputs and next states of the network; also, these equations can be considered as describing a basic model of the network as shown in Figure 6.2.2. We illustrate this by a simple example.

Consider the one input, one output sequential switching network shown in Figure 6.2.3. To describe precisely the behavior of sequential networks constructed from decision and delay elements, we must assume certain specific temporal characteristics for the inputs, decision elements, and delay elements. We make the following idealized assumptions in discussing the network of Figure 6.2.3 and later present somewhat more practical methods of simulating such timings.

We assume that both delay circuits $\Delta_1$ and $\Delta_2$ have a time delay of exactly $\Delta$ and that the binary input values are fed into the network spaced

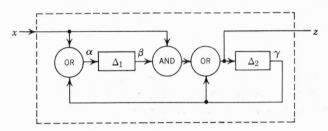

Figure 6.2.3   A simple sequential network.

exactly at $\Delta$ units between successive inputs. In addition, we assume as in previous chapters that the AND and OR decision elements have no internal delays. Finally, we assume that both $\Delta_1$ and $\Delta_2$ have outputs of 0 at the beginning of our analysis (from $t = 0$ to $\Delta$, $\beta = \gamma = 0$). This pair of signals $(0, 0)$ on $\beta$ and $\gamma$ is thus the starting "state" of the network. With

**Table 6.2.1.**   Signal Values from
$t = 0$ to $\Delta$ for Figure 6.2.3

| Input | State | | | |
|:---:|:---:|:---:|:---:|:---:|
| $x$ | $\beta$ | $\gamma$ | $\alpha$ | $z$ |
| 0 | 0 | 0 | 0 | 0 |
| 1 | 0 | 0 | 1 | 0 |

these assumptions, using a truth table formulation, we can determine the signals on $\alpha$ and $z$ from $t = 0$ to $\Delta$ for both $x = 0$ and $x = 1$ during this first interval of time. These signals are shown in the truth table of Table 6.2.1.

During the next time interval $\Delta$ to $2\Delta$ if $x = 0$ from 0 to $\Delta$, then $\beta$ and $\gamma$ will both be 0 since signal $\beta$ at time $t + \Delta$ is equal to signal $\alpha$ at time $t$, and signal $\gamma$ at time $t + \Delta$ is equal to signal $z$ at time $t$. If $x = 1$ from $t = 0$ to $\Delta$, however, then from $t = \Delta$ to $2\Delta$ signal $\beta = 1$, since $\alpha = 1$ from 0 to $\Delta$; but signal $\gamma = 0$, since $z = 0$ from 0 to $\Delta$. Thus we have another state of the network represented by $(1, 0)$, that is, signals $\beta = 1$ and $\gamma = 0$. We must then again analyze the network with signals $\beta = 1, \gamma = 0$ under both possible inputs $x = 0$ or 1. This gives

| Input | State | | Output | |
|:---:|:---:|:---:|:---:|:---:|
| $x$ | $\beta$ | $\gamma$ | $\alpha$ | $z$ |
| 0 | 1 | 0 | 0 | 0 |
| 1 | 1 | 0 | 1 | 1 |

so that when $x = 1$ we obtain the new condition of $\alpha = 1$ and $z = 1$, which at time $\Delta$ later becomes $\beta = 1, \gamma = 1$ which is a new state $(1, 1)$. Analyzing again with this state $(1, 1)$ gives

| Input | State | | Output | |
|:---:|:---:|:---:|:---:|:---:|
| $x$ | $\beta$ | $\gamma$ | $\alpha$ | $z$ |
| 0 | 1 | 1 | 1 | 1 |
| 1 | 1 | 1 | 1 | 1 |

Since no new states arise, we have completed the analysis, giving states $(0, 0)$, $(1, 0)$, and $(1, 1)$. Note that the condition $\beta = 0, \gamma = 1$ never can arise starting from $\beta = 0, \gamma = 0$ no matter what sequence of inputs is applied to the network.

Given the encoded states $(0, 1)$, $(1, 0)$, and $(1, 1)$, we can leave the encoding of the states exactly the same when interpreting Equations (6.2.1) and (6.2.2) by letting $\beta = y_1$, $\gamma = y_2$, $\alpha = y_1{}'$, and $z = y_2{}'$. From the

**Table 6.2.2.**    Truth Table for Network Behavior

| State | | Input | Next State | | Output |
|:---:|:---:|:---:|:---:|:---:|:---:|
| $\beta$ | $\gamma$ | | $\alpha$ | $z$ | |
| $y_1$ | $y_2$ | $x$ | $y_1{}'$ | $y_2{}'$ | $z$ |
| 0 | 0 | 0 | 0 | 0 | 0 |
| 0 | 0 | 1 | 1 | 0 | 0 |
| 1 | 0 | 0 | 0 | 0 | 0 |
| 1 | 0 | 1 | 1 | 1 | 1 |
| 1 | 1 | 0 | 1 | 1 | 1 |
| 1 | 1 | 1 | 1 | 1 | 1 |

preceding analysis we obtain the truth table of Table 6.2.2. This table defines the output equation as

$$z(x, y_1, y_2) = xy_1 \lor y_2$$

and the next state equations as

$$y_1'(x, y_1, y_2) = x \lor y_2$$
$$y_2'(x, y_1, y_2) = xy_1 \lor y_2.$$

The basic model represented by these three equations is shown in Figure 6.2.4. The behavior of this network can be described as follows. The output remains at $z = 0$ until two adjacent inputs of 1 occur in the input sequence; then $z$ becomes 1 and remains 1 thereafter no matter what inputs occur.

From the analysis we have also determined all the possible states and transitions between states starting from state $(0, 0)$. We note that the conditions $(0, 1)$ cannot be reached from $(0, 0)$ by any possible input sequence. However, analyzing the network as if started in state $(0, 1)$, we obtain

| $x$ | $\beta$ | $\gamma$ | $\alpha$ | $z$ |
|---|---|---|---|---|
| 0 | 0 | 1 | 1 | 1 |
| 1 | 0 | 1 | 1 | 1 |

As was done in Figure 6.1.1 a state diagram may be also constructed for the network, as in Figure 6.2.5. The four states, shown as circles, correspond to the four possible pairs of signals on the output lines of the two delay elements. The input-output values are shown on the directed lines between circles, where the symbol above the / corresponds to the signal on the input $x$, and the symbol below the / corresponds to the signal on the output $z$. Thus, for example, if we start in state $(0, 0)$ and have an input of $x = 1$, then the state becomes $(1, 0)$ and the output value is 0. This behavior is exactly that indicated by the second row in Table 6.2.2.

The idealized timing characteristics which we assumed are somewhat impractical. For example, decision elements whose outputs require no time to react to input changes cannot be constructed. Furthermore, it is not possible to balance perfectly the delay times of a set of delay elements, as was assumed in describing the operation of Figures 6.2.2 through 6.2.4. For these and other reasons, it is more common to use sets of electronic memory elements called "flip-flops," rather than delay elements, to represent the states of a sequential network and to provide an externally

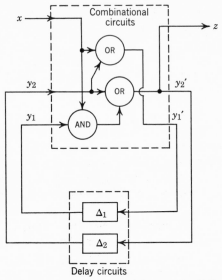

Figure 6.2.4   Basic model for the sequential network of Figure 6.2.3.

timed synchronizing source, called a clock, for synchronization of the sequential network. We now describe how flip-flops and clock signals can be used to accomplish the behavior required for the basic model of Figure 6.2.2.

First, we give a simple explanation of a flip-flop. As an example, consider the logical diagram shown in Figure 6.2.6. The inputs to this flip-flop are labeled by $x_1$ and $x_2$, and the outputs by $w_1$ and $w_2$. (Note that this is a circuit with feedback and could be redrawn in the basic format of Figure 6.2.2.) Consider the signal values on the lines as shown in the

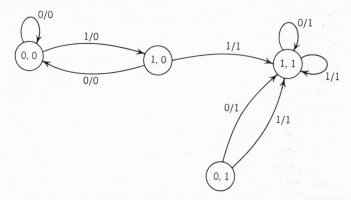

Figure 6.2.5   State diagram for networks of Figures 6.2.3 and 6.2.4.

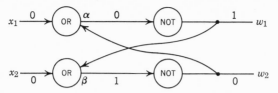

Figure 6.2.6   A logical diagram of a flip-flop.

figure. As is easily checked, each logical element is stable, that is, with its given inputs the output assumes the value designated by the Boolean function of the element. If input $x_1$ changes from 0 to 1, however, then $\alpha$ will change to 1, followed by $w_1$ changing to 0, followed by $\beta$ changing to 0 and then $w_2$ changing to 1. If the $x_1$ value again changes to 0, we have a stable condition with $x_1 = x_2 = 0$ and $w_1 = 0$, $w_2 = 1$. Thus, by controlling the inputs $x_1$ and $x_2$ to this circuit, we can change the output conditions from $w_1 = 1$, $w_2 = 0$ to $w_1 = 0$, $w_2 = 1$ and vice versa, where the output condition remains stable when the inputs are both 0.

Many different electronic circuits have been designed to provide this or similar logical behavior. This, however, is not the place to discuss these circuits. Instead, we wish to show how such a flip-flop may store a state variable for a sequential network. Obviously, if we assign the flip-flop output $w_1$ to equal a state variable $y_j$ we can set $w_1$ equal to either 0 or 1 by controlling the inputs. One method is shown in Figure 6.2.7. Assume that we replace each delay element of Figure 6.2.2 by the network shown in Figure 6.2.7 and the outputs of the flip-flops represent some state of the network. If inputs are applied to the combinational circuit and the clock pulse signal is equal to 0, after sufficient time the elements within the combinational circuit will stabilize. At this time, the correct outputs appear on outputs $z_1, z_2, \ldots, z_m$. Furthermore, if the clock pulse is then

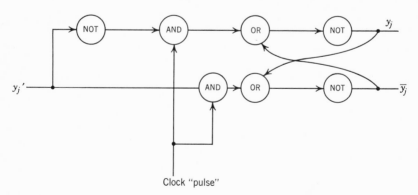

Figure 6.2.7   Flip-flop use as state variable.

changed temporarily to a 1, the flip-flop output $y_j$ will assume the value of $y_j'$. By controlling how long the clock pulse remains a 1, it is possible to set the flip-flops to their new values and not have any of these newly set $y_1, \ldots, y_k$ signals change any of the $y_1', \ldots, y_k'$ signals before the clock pulse returns to 0.*  Here we have simulated the delay elements with this arrangement of flip-flops and the clock pulse.  The clock pulse forces all state variables to change simultaneously, and the time between clock pulses allows time for new inputs to be applied and for the combinational circuit elements to react.  This type of sequential circuit operation is termed *synchronous*, because of the clock pulse to synchronize the circuit timings.  Also, the time between clock pulses is the $\Delta$ time interval of the basic model.

In describing this circuit operation we have referred to the input and state signals as values that remain constant during the operation, that is, *level-type signals*.  Similar behavior could be described by considering the signal values to be *pulses* of only short-time duration that progress through the circuit.  There is considerable literature on "pulse-type" and "level-type" sequential circuits which we shall not treat in detail here.  The example using flip-flops in this section and the two other types of sequential networks given in the next section illustrate sufficiently the various possible circuit implementations, since we are interested primarily in the logical behaviors of these networks.  Although the detailed electronic circuit realizations may be quite different, the basic logical behavior of these circuits is so similar that the same sequential machine models may be interpreted to apply to each type of circuit.  We therefore concentrate on the models for sequential machines.

In some types of sequential networks, the time required to obtain the next state variables $y_1', y_2', \ldots, y_k'$ may not be precisely known or controlled by an external synchronizing source.  In this instance, certain precautions must be taken in designing the network so that correct operation is obtained with some degree of independence from the actual times of reaction of the various network elements.  Detailed consideration of these networks, known as *asynchronous sequential networks*, appears in Chapters 9 and 10.

### 6.3  SEQUENTIAL LOGICAL NETWORKS

In previous sections, particularly Sections 2.6 and 3.2 of Volume I, we described rules for interconnecting decision elements to obtain logical diagrams or networks, noting that some logical networks having feedback are

---

* This timing may be rather critical.  More complex arrangements are possible, using several flip-flops and clock pulses for state variables, in which time duration of the clock pulses is not critical.

not combinational. Noncombinational networks can be considered to be sequential networks, if appropriate definitions are made to specify the synchronization and internal reaction times of the decision elements. In this section, we shall discuss further several models of synchronization for networks and the implications of these assumptions.

For the first model, we generalize the definition of a decision element as follows.

**Definition 6.3.1**  A *synchronized decision element* has $m$ inputs, $i_1, i_2, \ldots,$ $i_m$, one output $f$ such that the output at time $t + \Delta$, denoted by $f'$, is a complete switching function of the inputs $i_1, i_2, \ldots, i_m$, and the output $f$ at time $t$.

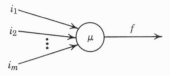

Figure 6.3.1   A synchronized decision element.

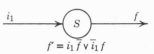

$$f' = i_1 \bar{f} \vee \bar{i_1} f$$

Figure 6.3.2   An example of a synchronized decision element.

Thus we have $f' = \mu(i_1, i_2, \ldots, i_m, f)$, where $\mu$ represents the complete switching function. We represent the synchronized decision element as shown in Figure 6.3.1. Physically, one may think of the delay time of $\Delta$ for each synchronized element as the interval of time between successive clock pulses, where the clock pulse is an input (not shown) to each synchronized decision element. Here each clock pulse can be considered as a reading time (and the only reading time) for inputs and outputs of the elements. Note that the synchronized decision element is a generalization of the decision element described in Section 2.6, in that both a time delay of $\Delta$ has been introduced into the element and the output at $t + \Delta$ may depend on the output as well as the inputs at time $t$. This dependence of a synchronized decision element on $f$ provides a simple mechanism for describing elements with "memory."

Consider, for example, element $S$ shown in Figure 6.3.2. Given that $S$ has a starting output of 0, the output remains 0 until a signal $i_1 = 1$ is applied; at time $\Delta$ later $f$ changes to a 1 and remains 1 until another input of $i_1 = 1$ is applied, then changing back to $f = 0$ after a delay of $\Delta$. Thus $S$ is a memory device having a "trigger" input and is similar to an electronic flip-flop circuit called a *Schmidt trigger*.

**Definition 6.3.2**  A *synchronized logical network* is an interconnection of synchronized decision elements satisfying the following rules.

1. An output of a synchronized decision element can be attached to one or more inputs of synchronized decision elements.

2. The constant values 0 and 1 may be assigned to inputs of the synchronized decision elements.

3. No two outputs of synchronized decision elements are interconnected.

As in logical networks the branches are called input, output, and internal branches.

A synchronized logical network is a synchronous sequential network. Let the synchronized logical network have $n$ input branches labeled $x_1, x_2, \ldots, x_n$, $m$ output branches labeled $z_1, z_2, \ldots, z_m$, and $k$ internal branches, labeled $v_1, v_2, \ldots, v_k$; then the states of the network are the $(m + k)$-tuples of values of $z_1, z_2, \ldots, z_m, v_1, v_2, \ldots, v_k$. The inputs are the $n$-tuples of values of $x_1, x_2, \ldots, x_n$, and the outputs are the $m$-tuples of values of $z_1, z_2, \ldots, z_m$. The output equations and next state equations respectively are

$$\text{Output Equations} \begin{cases} z_1 = z_1 \\ z_2 = z_2 \\ \cdot \\ \cdot \\ \cdot \\ z_m = z_m. \end{cases}$$

$$\text{Next State Equations} \begin{cases} z_1' = z_1'(x_1, x_2, \ldots, x_n, z_1, z_2, \ldots, z_m, v_1, v_2, \ldots, v_k) \\ z_2' = z_2'(x_1, x_2, \ldots, x_n, z_1, z_2, \ldots, z_m, v_1, v_2, \ldots, v_k) \\ \cdot \\ \cdot \\ \cdot \\ z_m' = z_m'(x_1, x_2, \ldots, x_n, z_1, z_2, \ldots, z_m, v_1, v_2, \ldots, v_k) \\ v_1' = v_1'(x_1, x_2, \ldots, x_n, z_1, z_2, \ldots, z_m, v_1, v_2, \ldots, v_k) \\ v_2' = v_2'(x_1, x_2, \ldots, x_n, z_1, z_2, \ldots, z_m, v_1, v_2, \ldots, v_k) \\ \cdot \\ \cdot \\ \cdot \\ v_k' = v_k'(x_1, x_2, \ldots, x_n, z_1, z_2, \ldots, z_m, v_1, v_2, \ldots, v_k). \end{cases}$$

Thus, in this case, the output equations are trivial, being simply the values on a particular set of branches of the network. The next state equations are simply those for the respective synchronized decision elements, where the $i_1, i_2, \ldots, i_m$ input variables to the element are some subset of $(x_1, x_2, \ldots, x_n, z_1, z_2, \ldots, z_m, v_1, v_2, \ldots, v_k)$.

With some minor changes one can also define synchronized decision elements and logical networks so that the elements do not all have the same delay time $\Delta$; rather each element may have a specified delay of $k\Delta$, where $k$ is some positive finite integer (see Exercise 4).

For actual switching elements, usually the reaction time of the switching element cannot be specified because of various tolerances of the components used in the element, aging effects, etc. For synchronous networks, these difficulties are circumvented by having an external clock control the

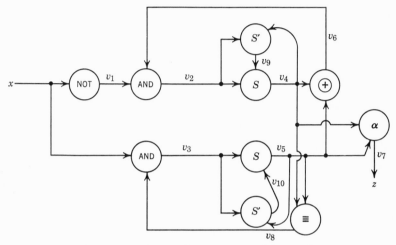

Figure 6.3.3    An asynchronous sequential network.

passing of signals to various parts of the network and by extending the period between clock pulses sufficiently so that the elements have enough time to react.

For the second model, we assume that the reaction time of the elements is not infinite, but it is also not precisely known. An asynchronous network is formed by interconnecting these decision elements where the interconnection rules are identical to those of Definition 6.3.2. For asynchronous networks, although the exact reaction times of elements are not known, correct operation is attained by suitably arranging the elements so that the input sequence behavior and output sequence behavior are the same even under certain timing variations. Consider the network shown in Figure 6.3.3. This network has one input $x$ and one output $z$; we assume that the reaction times of the elements are not precisely known, but that all elements have approximately the same reaction time and that the input changes occur only after sufficient time for all elements to react. As done previously, we shall assume "level-type" signals. The outputs of the elements are labeled $v_1$ through $v_{10}$ and are described by the following equations.

$$v_1' = \bar{x}$$
$$v_2' = v_1 v_6,$$
$$v_3' = x v_8,$$
$$v_4' = \bar{v}_2 v_4 \lor v_2 v_9,$$
$$v_5' = \bar{v}_3 v_5 \lor v_3 v_{10},$$
$$v_6' = v_4 \bar{v}_5 \lor \bar{v}_4 v_5,$$
$$v_7' = v_4 \bar{v}_5,$$
$$v_8' = v_4 v_5 \lor \bar{v}_4 \bar{v}_5,$$
$$v_9' = \bar{v}_2 \bar{v}_4 \lor v_2 v_9,$$
$$v_{10}' = \bar{v}_3 \bar{v}_5 \lor v_3 v_{10}.$$

Let us assume that this network has

$$x = 0,\ v_1 = 1,\ v_2 = 0,\ v_3 = 0,\ v_4 = 0,\ v_5 = 0,\ v_6 = 0,$$
$$z = v_7 = 0,\ v_8 = 1,\ v_9 = 1,\ \text{and}\ v_{10} = 1$$

as a starting condition. From the previous equations the $v_1'$ through $v_{10}'$ values can be computed. They are equal to the respective $v_i$ values so that no element in the network will tend to change. This is therefore called a *stable state* of the network. When $x$ changes from 0 to 1, $v_1$ will tend to change from 1 to 0 since $v_1' = 0$; also $v_3' = 1$, so $v_3$ is tending to change from 0 to 1. No other elements are tending to change, as can be checked by the reader. Now since we do not know the exact reaction times of the elements, either $v_1$ or $v_3$ may change first or else both $v_1$ and $v_3$ may change simultaneously. If $v_1$ changes first, then no other element will tend to change and eventually $v_3$ will change from 0 to 1. If $v_3$ changes first, then $v_5$ will tend to change, but no other elements will be affected. Since all elements are assumed to react in approximately the same time, we shall assume that $v_1$ changes to 0 before $v_5$ changes from 0 to 1. Thus no matter whether $v_1$ or $v_3$ changes first we shall arrive at the condition

$$x = 1,\ v_1 = 0,\ v_2 = 0,\ v_3 = 1,\ v_4 = 0,\ v_5 = 1,\ v_6 = 0,$$
$$v_7 = 0,\ v_8 = 1,\ v_9 = 1,\ v_{10} = 1.$$

The condition of $v_1$ and $v_3$ both tending to change at the same time is called a *race condition* in the asynchronous network. As will be seen later, race conditions require careful analysis in asynchronous networks to be sure that undesired network operation cannot occur because of the race condition. With the conditions on $v_1$ through $v_{10}$ given previously, the only elements tending to change are $v_6$ and $v_8$. If $v_6$ changes first, it does not cause $v_2$ to tend to change; thus $v_8$, the only remaining element to change, will eventually change. If $v_8$ changes first, from 1 to 0, $v_3$ tends to change from 1 to 0, and if $v_3$ does change, $v_{10}$ tends to change from 1 to 0, but then no further changes can occur. Thus, in either case, we arrive at the stable state

$$x = 1, v_1 = 0, v_2 = 0, v_3 = 0, v_4 = 0, v_5 = 1, v_6 = 1,$$

$$v_7 = 0, v_8 = 0, v_9 = 1, v_{10} = 0.$$

Continuing the analysis, when input $x$ changes back from 1 to 0, only $v_1$ tends to change from 0 to 1. After several signal changes the network will stop at the stable state

$$x = 0, v_1 = 1, v_2 = 0, v_3 = 0, v_4 = 1, v_5 = 1, v_6 = 0,$$

$$v_7 = 0, v_8 = 1, v_9 = 0, v_{10} = 0.$$

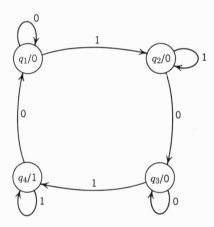

Figure 6.3.4   State diagram for network of Figure 6.3.3.

This analysis can be completed and the action of the network depicted by the state diagram in Figure 6.3.4. The states of this diagram correspond to the following stable states of the network.

| State Label | Network Stable State | | | | | | | | | | |
|---|---|---|---|---|---|---|---|---|---|---|---|
| | $x$ | $v_1$ | $v_2$ | $v_3$ | $v_4$ | $v_5$ | $v_6$ | $v_7$ | $v_8$ | $v_9$ | $v_{10}$ |
| $q_1$ | 0 | 1 | 0 | 0 | 0 | 0 | 0 | 0 | 1 | 1 | 1 |
| $q_2$ | 1 | 0 | 0 | 0 | 0 | 1 | 1 | 0 | 0 | 1 | 0 |
| $q_3$ | 0 | 1 | 0 | 0 | 1 | 1 | 0 | 0 | 1 | 0 | 0 |
| $q_4$ | 1 | 0 | 0 | 0 | 1 | 0 | 1 | 1 | 0 | 0 | 1 |

The output $z = v_7$ is shown in the circle for the state, and the input $x$ is shown on the transitions between states.

From the state diagram the network behavior can be described as follows. The output remains 0 until the sequence of inputs contains a 1 followed by one or more zeros followed by a 1; then the output becomes a 1. Another 0 on the input resets the output to 0, and the output becomes 1 only after another similar input sequence occurs.

From the analysis given we saw that the circuit operation is fairly independent of the reaction time of each element. However, we must assume that the NOT-element $v_1$ changes from 1 to 0 when starting from the original starting condition before the following sequence of changes occur; $v_3$ from 0 to 1 followed by $v_5$ from 0 to 1 followed by $v_6$ from 0 to 1. For, indeed, if $v_6$ becomes 1 before $v_1$ changes from 1 to 0, then $v_2$ would tend to change from 0 to 1 and this could create erroneous operation of the network.

## 6.4 MODELS FOR SEQUENTIAL MACHINES

In the previous sections the concept of state for a sequential network has been introduced and several examples of a model for sequential machines, called a state diagram, have been given in Figures 6.1.1, 6.2.5, and 6.3.4. In this section we present a formal definition of a sequential machine, show how this definition corresponds to various models for sequential machines, and give two matrix representations for sequential machines.

**Definition 6.4.1** A *sequential machine* $\mathcal{M}$ consists of the following.

1. A finite set $Q$ of internal states.
2. A finite set $I$ of inputs.
3. A finite set $W$ of outputs.
4. A mapping $\tau$ (called the *transition map* of $\mathcal{M}$) of a subset $D_\tau$ of $Q \times I$ onto a subset of $Q$.
5. A mapping $\omega$ (called the output map of $\mathcal{M}$) of a subset $D_\omega$ of $Q \times I$ onto $W$.

We denote $\mathcal{M}$ by the ordered 5-tuple $\mathcal{M} = (Q, I, W, \tau, \omega)$. A machine $\mathcal{M}$ is called *transition complete* if $D_\tau = Q \times I$, $\mathcal{M}$ is called *complete* if $D_\tau = D_\omega = Q \times I$. If $\mathcal{M}$ is not complete, it is called *incomplete* or *incompletely specified*.

For a given state $q \in Q$ and input $i \in I$, the map $\tau$ is said to define a *next state* $\tau(q, i) \in Q$ if $(q, i) \in D_\tau$ and $\omega$ is said to define an *output* $\omega(q, i) \in W$ if $(q, i) \in D_\omega$.

A sequential machine may be shown graphically in a *state diagram* by representing each state in $Q$ by a circle in which the state symbol appears and by drawing directed lines from one state to another to correspond to the map $\tau$; thus if $\tau(q_j, i_k) = q_m$, a line is drawn from $q_j$ to $q_m$, with an arrowhead at $q_m$, and on the line we place input $i_k$. For map $\omega$ we also assign outputs to arrows; for example, if $\omega(q_j, i_k) = w_n$, then with the $i_k$ assignment to the line we also assign $w_n$ as $i_k/w_n$.

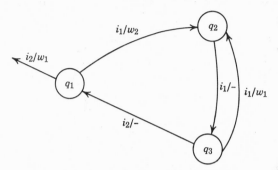

Figure 6.4.1 A Mealy model state diagram.

Given the sequential machine,

$$Q = \{q_1, q_2, q_3\},$$
$$I = \{i_1, i_2\},$$
$$W = \{w_1, w_2\},$$

$$\begin{pmatrix} \tau(q_1, i_1) = q_2 \\ \tau(q_2, i_1) = q_3 \\ \tau(q_3, i_1) = q_2 \\ \tau(q_3, i_2) = q_1 \end{pmatrix},$$

$$\begin{pmatrix} \omega(q_1, i_1) = w_2 \\ \omega(q_1, i_2) = w_1 \\ \omega(q_3, i_1) = w_1 \end{pmatrix},$$

we can represent this machine as a state diagram as shown in Figure 6.4.1. This type of state diagram is called a *Mealy model*. Another type of representation for a sequential machine is called a *Moore model*. For a Moore model a new map $\omega^*$ replaces $\omega$, where $\omega^*$ maps a subset of $Q$ into the set $W$. In this model the outputs are directly dependent on only the states rather than the states and inputs. In the state diagram, then, the outputs may be given in the circles rather than on the directed lines between states. If in the preceding example, $\omega$ were replaced with a $\omega^*$ defined by

$$\begin{cases} \omega^*(q_1) = w_2, \\ \omega^*(q_3) = w_1, \end{cases}$$

then the state diagram of Figure 6.4.2 is obtained.

Here the Moore and Mealy models have been slightly generalized in that the models were originally developed for completely specified sequential

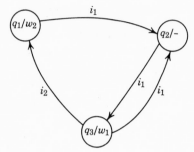

Figure 6.4.2    A Moore model state diagram.

machines and we have defined the models to include the incompletely specified case.*

A tabular form, called the *Huffman flow table*, can also be used to represent a sequential machine. Let rows of a table represent states and columns represent inputs; we can then place the next states and outputs as entries $q/w$ in the table to represent completely a sequential machine. The examples for the Mealy and Moore models are shown as Huffman flow tables in Figure 6.4.3*a* and *b*, respectively. Those next state entries and output entries which contain dashes correspond to the unspecified $Q \times I$ mappings in $\tau$ and $\omega$, respectively. For the output being associated with a state, as in the Moore model, we obtain a Huffman flow table that has the same output for all entries of a row.

A connection matrix, which may also be used to represent a sequential machine, is defined as

$$C = [c_{ij}],$$

where the matrix has one row and one column for each state, and the entry $c_{ij}$ is the union of all input-output pairs from state $q_i$ to state $q_j$.

---

* One might also consider another type of incomplete specification, in either model, in which an arrow (a *transition*) existed between states, but the input associated with this transition was not specified. We assume that this transition will not conflict with the deterministic behavior of the machine. This type of incomplete specification could then be treated by allowing the sets of inputs to include an element that would be interpreted as an unspecified input.

| States | Inputs | |
|:---:|:---:|:---:|
| | $i_1$ | $i_2$ |
| $q_1$ | $q_2/w_2$ | $-/w_1$ |
| $q_2$ | $q_3/-$ | $-/-$ |
| $q_3$ | $q_2/w_1$ | $q_1/-$ |

(a)

| States | Inputs | |
|:---:|:---:|:---:|
| | $i_1$ | $i_2$ |
| $q_1$ | $q_2/w_2$ | $-/w_2$ |
| $q_2$ | $q_3/-$ | $-/-$ |
| $q_3$ | $q_2/w_1$ | $q_1/w_1$ |

(b)

Figure 6.4.3 Huffman flow tables.

In Figure 6.4.4 we give two examples of state diagrams and their corresponding connection matrices. For a Moore model, the entry $c_{ij}$ is the union of all inputs from state $q_i$ to $q_j$, and for the outputs we construct an output vector $W_0$.

$$W_0 = \begin{bmatrix} w_1 \\ w_2 \\ \cdot \\ \cdot \\ \cdot \\ w_n \end{bmatrix},$$

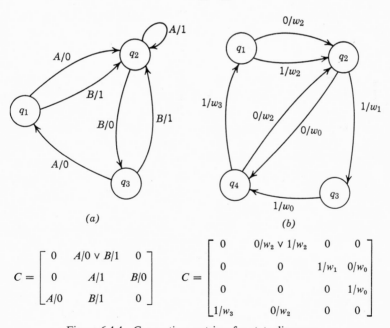

(a)

(b)

$$C = \begin{bmatrix} 0 & A/0 \vee B/1 & 0 \\ 0 & A/1 & B/0 \\ A/0 & B/1 & 0 \end{bmatrix}$$

$$C = \begin{bmatrix} 0 & 0/w_2 \vee 1/w_2 & 0 & 0 \\ 0 & 0 & 1/w_1 & 0/w_0 \\ 0 & 0 & 0 & 1/w_0 \\ 1/w_3 & 0/w_2 & 0 & 0 \end{bmatrix}$$

Figure 6.4.4 Connection matrices for state diagrams.

where there is a row for each state, and the row entry $w_i$ is the output for state $q_i$. For example, the connection matrix and output vector for the state diagram of Figure 6.4.2 are

$$
\begin{array}{c}
\phantom{C = } 1\ 2\ 3 \\
C = \begin{array}{c} 1 \\ 2 \\ 3 \end{array}\!\!
\begin{bmatrix}
0 & i_1 & 0 \\
0 & 0 & i_1 \\
i_2 & i_1 & 0
\end{bmatrix}
\qquad
W_0 =
\begin{bmatrix}
w_2 \\
- \\
w_1
\end{bmatrix}.
\end{array}
$$

Another matrix representation for sequential machines is by *transition matrices*. Here the distribution of transitions for any given input is described. We associate with each input $i$ a transition matrix $T^i$ defined as

$$
T^i = [t_{jk}{}^i],
$$

where there is one row and one column for each state, and where $t_{jk}{}^i = 1$ if input $i$ takes state $q_j$ into $q_k$, $t_{jk}{}^i = 0$ if input $i$ takes $q_j$ to a state $q_p$, $p \neq k$, and $t_{jk}{}^i$ is a dash if $\tau(q_j, i)$ is undefined.* We also define a state vector $Q_0$ by

$$
Q_0 =
\begin{bmatrix}
q_1 \\
q_2 \\
\cdot \\
\cdot \\
\cdot \\
q_n
\end{bmatrix}
$$

and a set of output vectors $W_{0i}$

$$
W_{0i} =
\begin{bmatrix}
w_{1i} \\
w_{2i} \\
\cdot \\
\cdot \\
\cdot \\
w_{ni}
\end{bmatrix},
$$

one $W_{0i}$ for each input $i$, where $w_{ki}$ is the output associated with the transition leaving state $q_k$ for input $i$, except $w_{ki}$ is a dash if no such output is

* If $\tau(q_j, i)$ is undefined, the $j$th row of $T^i$ is a row of dashes, and we call the row *blank*.

specified. Thus for the state diagram of Figure 6.4.4a we obtain the transition matrix representation

$$
T^A = \begin{bmatrix} 0 & 1 & 0 \\ 0 & 1 & 0 \\ 1 & 0 & 0 \end{bmatrix}
\qquad
T^B = \begin{bmatrix} 0 & 1 & 0 \\ 0 & 0 & 1 \\ 0 & 1 & 0 \end{bmatrix}.
$$

$$
Q_0 = \begin{bmatrix} q_1 \\ q_2 \\ q_3 \end{bmatrix}
\qquad
W_{0A} = \begin{bmatrix} 0 \\ 1 \\ 0 \end{bmatrix}
\qquad
W_{0B} = \begin{bmatrix} 1 \\ 0 \\ 1 \end{bmatrix}.
$$

and for Figure 6.4.4b we obtain

$$
T^0 = \left[\begin{array}{cccc} 0 & 1 & 0 & 0 \\ 0 & 0 & 0 & 1 \\ - & - & - & - \\ 0 & 1 & 0 & 0 \end{array}\right]
\qquad
T^1 = \begin{bmatrix} 0 & 1 & 0 & 0 \\ 0 & 0 & 1 & 0 \\ 0 & 0 & 0 & 1 \\ 1 & 0 & 0 & 0 \end{bmatrix}
$$

$$
Q_0 = \begin{bmatrix} q_1 \\ q_2 \\ q_3 \\ q_4 \end{bmatrix}
\qquad
W_{00} = \begin{bmatrix} w_2 \\ w_0 \\ - \\ w_2 \end{bmatrix}
\qquad
W_{01} = \begin{bmatrix} w_2 \\ w_1 \\ w_0 \\ w_3 \end{bmatrix}.
$$

For the Moore model we need only define a single output vector $w_0$

$$
W_0 = \begin{bmatrix} w_1 \\ w_2 \\ \cdot \\ \cdot \\ \cdot \\ w_n \end{bmatrix},
$$

where $w_k$ is the output associated with state $q_k$. Thus for the Moore model of Figure 6.4.2 we obtain

$$
T^{i_1} = \begin{bmatrix} 0 & 1 & 0 \\ 0 & 0 & 1 \\ 0 & 1 & 0 \end{bmatrix}
\qquad
T^{i_2} = \begin{bmatrix} - & - & - \\ - & - & - \\ 1 & 0 & 0 \end{bmatrix}
$$

$$
Q_0 = \begin{bmatrix} q_1 \\ q_2 \\ q_3 \end{bmatrix}
\qquad
W_0 = \begin{bmatrix} w_2 \\ - \\ w_1 \end{bmatrix}.
$$

The serial binary adder is a simple example of a sequential machine found in digital computers. The inputs to the machine are the addend and augend bits; there are two states to the machine, one representing a carry bit equal to 0 and the other a carry bit of 1. The output is the sum bit. A Mealy model state diagram for the serial binary adder is shown in Figure 6.4.5, where $q_0$ corresponds to the carry bit equal to 0 and $q_1$ to the carry bit equal to 1.

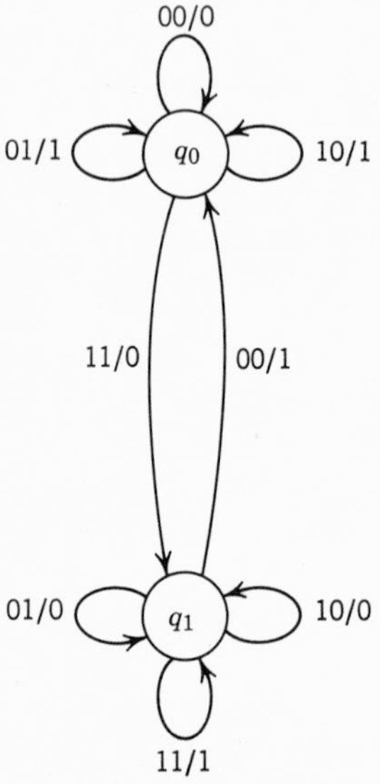

Some special definitions for machines are of interest.

**Definition 6.4.2**    A state $q_j$ of a machine $\mathscr{M}$ is called a *stable state* if for any input $i \in I$ such that

$$\tau(q_k, i) = q_j$$

it follows that

$$\tau(q_j, i) = q_j.$$

**Definition 6.4.3**    A machine $\mathscr{M}$ is called *asynchronous* if each state $q_j \in Q$ is a stable state. However, $\mathscr{M}$ is called *synchronous* if it is not asynchronous.

Intuitively, the definition of an asynchronous machine means that it will change state only on changes of input. For example, an input sequence $i_j, i_k, i_k, i_m$ with $i_j, i_k,$ and $i_m \in I$ of an asynchronous machine will produce the same changes of outputs as the sequence $i_j, i_k, i_m,$ if the machine is assumed to start in the same state for each of these sequences. Note that the state diagram of Figure 6.3.4 for the asynchronous logical network shown in Figure 6.3.3 satisfies this definition for an asynchronous machine. There are many different definitions for "asynchronous circuit" and "asynchronous machine," however, and thus one must be careful when encountering these terms.

Figure 6.4.5    State diagram for a serial binary adder.

## 6.5  SOME ELEMENTARY PROPERTIES

In this section we study some elementary properties of the matrix models for sequential machines. We shall be interested in describing the behavior of sequential machines for given sequences of inputs. We shall see that we can obtain answers to certain questions regarding this behavior by algebraic manipulations of the matrix models. We use the Moore model in this section, but usually the results carry over to the Mealy model with only minor modifications.

The transition matrices and the connection matrix for a machine $\mathcal{M}$ are interrelated by the equation

$$C = \bigvee_i u_i T^i,$$

where $u_i$ stands for the $i$th input, $i$ ranges over all inputs $i \in I$, and blank entries in $T^i$ are treated as zeros.

**Theorem 6.5.1** Every nonblank row of a transition matrix $T^i$ contains exactly one 1.

This theorem follows directly from the definition of a transition matrix and the fact that the transition map $\tau$ has at most one image for any state, input pair $(q_j, i_k)$. Since $\tau(q_j, i_k)$ has at most one image for the transition map, these machines are also often referred to as "deterministic" sequential machines.

**Theorem 6.5.2** The property of Theorem 6.5.1 is invariant under multiplication of transition matrices, where multiplication is performed as usual, and $0 + 1 = 1 + 0 = 1$, $0 + 0 = 0$, $1 \cdot 0 = 0 \cdot 1 = 0 \cdot 0 = 0$, $1 \cdot 1 = 1$, and where blank entries are treated like zeros, and any row of zeros is then converted to a blank row.

PROOF. If $T^i$ and $T^j$ are transition matrices, we need to show that each nonblank row of $T^i T^j$ contains exactly one 1. Since the rows of $T^i$ contain only one 1, or are blank, the rows of $T^i T^j$ are either chosen from the rows of $T^j$ or are blank. The rows of $T^j$ satisfy the condition, however, and thus so do the rows of $T^i T^j$. The result extends inductively to the product of any finite number of transition matrices.

If we are interested in tracing the sequential machine transitions, given some starting state $q_k$ and some input sequence $i_1, i_2, \ldots, i_p$, we can easily follow the next states and outputs of the machine directly on the state diagram and obtain a sequence of states that the machine passes through and also a sequence of outputs produced by the machine. Of course, if we arrive at some state $q_j$ and have some input $i_m$ for which no transition from $q_j$ is specified, then the next states and outputs can be said only to be unspecified from $i_m$ through $i_p$. That is, the states following $q_j$ and the outputs following due to $q_j$ and $i_m$ are unknown. We may also be interested only in the final state and output, which is given by the machine. The following theorems show how transition matrices can be used to obtain this information.

**Theorem 6.5.3** If $\mathcal{M}$ is in state $q_k$ and input $i$ is applied, the next state and the next output when defined are given by the $k$th rows of $T^i Q_0$ and $T^i W_0$, respectively, where $T^i$ is the transition matrix for $\mathcal{M}$ for input $i \in I$.

This theorem follows directly from the definition of transition matrices. Note that if the next state and next outputs are undefined for state $q_k$ under input $i$, then $T^i$ has blanks in row $i$ so that $T^i Q_0$ and $T^i W_0$ have blanks in row $k$ under obvious interpretation of multiplication and addition with the blanks.

**Theorem 6.5.4**   If the sequence $i_1$, $i_2$ (that is, $i_1$ followed by $i_2$) is applied to $\mathcal{M}$ in state $q_k$, the state and output after sequence $i_1$, $i_2$, if defined, are given by the $k$th rows of $T^{i_1} T^{i_2} Q_0$ and $T^{i_1} T^{i_2} W_0$, respectively.

PROOF.   Let $\tau(q_k, i_1) = q_r$ and let $\tau(q_r, i_2) = q_p$. Then by the definition of a transition matrix, the $k$th row of $T^{i_1}$ contains a 1 in column $r$ and the $r$th row of $T^{i_2}$ contains a 1 in column $p$. Therefore the $k$th row of $T^{i_1} T^{i_2}$ is merely the $r$th row of $T^{i_2}$. Thus the $k$th row of $(T^{i_1} T^{i_2}) Q_0$ is $q_p$ and the $k$th row of $(T^{i_1} T^{i_2}) W_0$ is $w_p$.

By induction this result may be extended to yield the following theorem.

**Theorem 6.5.5**   If the input sequence $i_1$, $i_2$, ..., $i_p$ is applied to $\mathcal{M}$ in state $q_k$, the final state and output, if defined, are given by the $k$th rows of $T^{i_1} T^{i_2} \cdots T^{i_p} Q_0$ and $T^{i_1} T^{i_2} \cdots T^{i_p} W_0$, respectively.

We obtain more information in the matrix products than just the final state and output caused by the input sequence when the machine starts in state $q_k$. In fact, we have columns of results giving the final state and output for the machine starting in any state at all by looking at the appropriate row of the result, where blanks will indicate undefined states or outputs.

The connection matrix representation is especially useful in answering the following question about sequential machines. Starting in state $q_i$ what input sequences of length $r$ produce a final state $q_j$? Let us define a multiplication of connection matrices $A$ and $B$ as

$$A = [a_{ik}] \qquad B = [b_{kj}]$$

$$AB = \left[ \overset{n}{\underset{k=1}{\mathsf{V}}} \, a_{ik} b_{kj} \right],$$

where $A$ and $B$ have $n$ rows and columns and the $ij$ entry for $AB$ is shown above.

**Theorem 6.5.6**   If $C$ is the connection matrix for a machine $\mathcal{M}$, the $ij$ entry of $C^r$ gives all input-output sequences of length $r$ which take $\mathcal{M}$ from state $q_i$ to state $q_j$.

This theorem follows directly from the definition of connection matrices and their multiplication. The reader should note the similarity of this

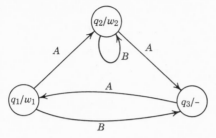

Figure 6.5.1   An example machine.

result with Theorem 5.6.3 and associated remarks for connection matrices of bilateral switching networks.

As an example of these theorems, consider $\mathcal{M}$ shown in Figure 6.5.1. The transition matrix representation for $\mathcal{M}$ is

$$T^A = \begin{array}{c} \\ 1 \\ 2 \\ 3 \end{array}\begin{array}{ccc} 1 & 2 & 3 \\ \left[\begin{array}{ccc} 0 & 1 & 0 \\ 0 & 0 & 1 \\ 1 & 0 & 0 \end{array}\right]\end{array} \qquad T^B = \begin{array}{c} \\ 1 \\ 2 \\ 3 \end{array}\begin{array}{ccc} 1 & 2 & 3 \\ \left[\begin{array}{ccc} 0 & 0 & 1 \\ 0 & 1 & 0 \\ - & - & - \end{array}\right]\end{array}$$

$$Q_0 = \begin{bmatrix} q_1 \\ q_2 \\ q_3 \end{bmatrix} \qquad W_0 = \begin{bmatrix} w_1 \\ w_2 \\ - \end{bmatrix}$$

Thus the connection matrix $C = \bigvee_i u_i T^i$ is

$$C = AT^A \vee BT^B$$

$$= \begin{bmatrix} 0 & A & 0 \\ 0 & 0 & A \\ A & 0 & 0 \end{bmatrix} \vee \begin{bmatrix} 0 & 0 & B \\ 0 & B & 0 \\ - & - & - \end{bmatrix}$$

$$= \begin{bmatrix} 0 & A & B \\ 0 & B & A \\ A & 0 & 0 \end{bmatrix}.$$

Applying Theorem 6.5.5 for input sequence $A, B, A$, we compute

$$T^A T^B T^A Q_0$$

and

$$T^A T^B T^A W_0.$$

$$T^A T^B = \begin{bmatrix} 0 & 1 & 0 \\ 0 & 0 & 1 \\ 1 & 0 & 0 \end{bmatrix} \begin{bmatrix} 0 & 0 & 1 \\ 0 & 1 & 0 \\ - & - & - \end{bmatrix} = \begin{bmatrix} 0 & 1 & 0 \\ - & - & - \\ 0 & 0 & 1 \end{bmatrix}$$

$$(T^A T^B) T^A = \begin{bmatrix} 0 & 1 & 0 \\ - & - & - \\ 0 & 0 & 1 \end{bmatrix} \begin{bmatrix} 0 & 1 & 0 \\ 0 & 0 & 1 \\ 1 & 0 & 0 \end{bmatrix} = \begin{bmatrix} 0 & 0 & 1 \\ - & - & - \\ 1 & 0 & 0 \end{bmatrix}$$

$$T^A T^B T^A Q_0 = \begin{bmatrix} 0 & 0 & 1 \\ - & - & - \\ 1 & 0 & 0 \end{bmatrix} \begin{bmatrix} q_1 \\ q_2 \\ q_3 \end{bmatrix} = \begin{bmatrix} q_3 \\ - \\ q_1 \end{bmatrix}$$

$$T^A T^B T^A W_0 = \begin{bmatrix} 0 & 0 & 1 \\ - & - & - \\ 1 & 0 & 0 \end{bmatrix} \begin{bmatrix} w_1 \\ w_2 \\ - \end{bmatrix} = \begin{bmatrix} - \\ - \\ w_1 \end{bmatrix}.$$

Thus with input sequence $A$, $B$, $A$, and $\mathcal{M}$ in state $q_1$ we have a final state of $q_3$ and an undefined output. Starting in state $q_2$ for the same input sequence gives both an undefined final state and output, and finally if $\mathcal{M}$ is started in state $q_3$, for this input sequence, the final state and output are $q_1$ and $w_1$ respectively.

To determine all paths of length two for $\mathcal{M}$ we form $C^2$

$$C^2 = \begin{bmatrix} 0 & A & B \\ 0 & B & A \\ A & 0 & 0 \end{bmatrix} \cdot \begin{bmatrix} 0 & A & B \\ 0 & B & A \\ A & 0 & 0 \end{bmatrix} =$$

$$\begin{array}{c} \\ 1 \\ = 2 \\ 3 \end{array} \begin{array}{c} \begin{array}{ccc} 1 & 2 & 3 \end{array} \\ \begin{bmatrix} BA & AB & AA \\ AA & BB & BA \\ 0 & AA & AB \end{bmatrix} \end{array}.$$

And for all paths of length three for $\mathcal{M}$ we form $C^3$.

$$C^3 = C^2 C = \begin{array}{c} \\ 1 \\ 2 \\ 3 \end{array} \begin{array}{c} \begin{array}{ccc} 1 \qquad\quad 2 \qquad\qquad\quad 3 \end{array} \\ \begin{bmatrix} AAA & BAA \vee ABB & BAB \vee ABA \\ BAA & AAA \vee BBB & AAB \vee BBA \\ ABA & AAB & AAA \end{bmatrix} \end{array}.$$

Thus the input sequence of length three with the machine starting in state $q_1$ and ending in state $q_2$ are $BAA$ and $ABB$ as designated by the 1,2-entry of $C^3$. Note that, in general, the entries in the matrix products $C^2$ and $C^3$ are not commutative; that is, sequence $ABB$ in entry 1, 2 of $C^3$ is not the same as sequence $BBA$.

## 6.6 TRANSFORMATIONS BETWEEN MEALY AND MOORE MODELS

The Moore model for a machine has an output mapping $\omega^*$ that maps a subset of the set $Q$ of states of the machine onto the output set $W$. For a Mealy model the output mapping $\omega$ maps a subset of $Q \times I$ onto the set $W$. Since all other parts of the definitions for Mealy and Moore model machines are identical, it may appear that the Mealy model is "more general" than the Moore model; for example, one might imagine there are Mealy model machines which, roughly speaking, if started in some designated state, could produce input-output pairs of sequences not possible by any Moore model machine. We show that this is not true, however, by describing a transformation that can be used to transform any Mealy model machine into a Moore model machine, and also one that can transform any Moore model machine into a Mealy model machine. In both of these transformations we shall see how the two different models can produce the same input-output pairs of sequences, and thus in this sense are equivalent. The notion of the models having the "same input-output sequences" will be made more precise subsequently.

Because the simpler transformation is from a Moore model to a Mealy model, we consider this one first. Assume we have some Moore model machine

$$\mathcal{M}^* = (Q^*, I^*, W^*, \tau^*, \omega^*),$$

where     $Q^*$ is a finite set of states,
           $I^*$ is a finite set of inputs,
           $W^*$ is a finite set of outputs,
           $\tau^*$ is a map of a subset $D_\tau^*$ of $Q^* \times I^*$ into $Q^*$,
and     $\omega^*$ is a map of a subset of $Q^*$ onto $W^*$.

We shall assume that $\mathcal{M}^*$ has the following additional property. If there exists a $q^* \in Q^*$ such that no $\tau^*(q', i) = q^*$ is defined for any $q' \in Q^*$ and $i \in I^*$, then $\omega^*(q^*)$ is also undefined. This restriction is a rather trivial one since if such a $q^*$ existed, no input sequence could cause $\mathcal{M}^*$ to arrive at $q^*$ to give a defined output $\omega^*(q^*)$ except, of course, the null sequence of inputs with $\mathcal{M}^*$ starting in state $q^*$. We construct a Mealy model machine $\mathcal{M} = (Q, I, W, \tau, \omega)$ as follows.

Set
$$Q = Q^* = (q_1, q_2, \ldots, q_n),$$
$$I = I^* = (i_1, i_2, \ldots, i_m),$$
$$W = W^* = (w_1, w_2, \ldots, w_p),$$
and
$$\tau = \tau^*.$$

Now for $\omega$ we wish to map a subset of $Q \times I$ onto $W$. We define $\omega$ as follows:
$$\omega(q_j, i_k) = w_r,$$
if
$$\tau^*(q_j, i_k) = q_s$$
and
$$\omega^*(q_s) = w_r.$$

If either $\omega^*(q_s)$ is undefined when $\tau^*(q_j, i_k) = q_s$ or if $\tau^*(q_j, i_k)$ is undefined, then $\omega(q_j, i_k)$ is undefined.

From this construction $Q$, $I$, $W$, and $\tau$ immediately satisfy the definition of a (Mealy model) sequential machine. Finally, $\omega$ certainly maps a subset of $Q \times I$ into $W$, but from the restriction on $\mathcal{M}^*$ such that $\omega^*(q^*)$ is undefined if $\tau^*(q', i) = q^*$ is not defined for any $q' \in Q^*$ and $i \in I$, it also follows that $\omega$ maps a subset of $Q \times I$ onto $W$. Thus $\mathcal{M}$, as constructed, is a Mealy model sequential machine. Now suppose $q_j$ is some state of $\mathcal{M}^*$ and some input $i \in I^*$ applied to $\mathcal{M}^*$ in state $q_j$ has $\tau^*$ defined as $\tau^*(q_j, i) = q_s$. Then for $\mathcal{M}$, $\tau(q_j, i) = q_s$. Now, if we also have for $\mathcal{M}^*$, $\omega^*(q_s) = w_r$, then for $\mathcal{M}$, $\omega(q_j, i) = w_r$. In addition, if $\tau^*(q_j, i)$ is undefined for $\mathcal{M}^*$, then $\tau(q_j, i)$ is undefined for $\mathcal{M}$; and if $\tau^*(q_j, i) = q_s$, but $\omega^*(q_s)$ is undefined, then $\omega(q_j, i)$ is undefined for $\mathcal{M}$. Thus for input sequences of length one (single inputs), for any state $q_j \in Q^*$ and input $i \in I^*$ of $\mathcal{M}^*$, the state $q_j \in Q$ and input $i \in I$ of $\mathcal{M}$ create exactly the same output behavior. By induction, any finite length input sequence applied to $\mathcal{M}^*$ starting in some arbitrary state $q_j$ will give the same output sequence behavior as if the input sequence were applied to $\mathcal{M}$ in state $q_j$. Note also that the sequences of states are the same for both machines. Thus, in this sense, we say that $\mathcal{M}$ and $\mathcal{M}^*$ have the same input-output sequence behavior.

Now we describe the transformation from a Mealy model machine $\mathcal{M} = (Q, I, W, \tau, \omega)$ to a Moore model machine $\mathcal{M}^* = (Q^*, I^*, W^*, \tau^*, \omega^*)$. As in the previous transformation, we make a rather trivial restriction on the Mealy model machine. We assume that if $\omega(q_j, i_k)$ of $\mathcal{M}$ is defined, then $\tau(q_j, i_k)$ of $\mathcal{M}$ is also defined. This is easily accomplished for any

Mealy model by adding an extra state $q_{jk}$ to $Q$ for each case having $\omega(q_j, i_k)$ defined but $\tau(q_j, i_k)$ undefined, and then redefining $\tau(q_j, i_k) = q_{jk}$. For machine $\mathcal{M}^*$ we define

$$I^* = I = (i_1, i_2, \ldots, i_m),$$
$$W^* = W = (w_1, w_2, \ldots, w_p).$$

To define $Q^*$, $\omega^*$, and $\tau^*$ let $P_s$ be the set of all pairs $(q_j, i_k)$ of $\mathcal{M}$ such that both $\tau(q_j, i_k)$ and $\omega(q_j, i_k)$ are defined and $\tau(q_j, i_k) = q_s$. That is, $P_s$ is the set of all state-input pairs that have a transition "entering" state $q_s$ and have a defined output. Let $W_s = \{w_{1s}, w_{2s}, \ldots, w_{rs}\}$ be the subset of all outputs $\omega(q_j, i_k)$ where $(q_j, i_k) \in P_s$. If $P_s$ is empty for $q_s$ of $\mathcal{M}$, then let $q_{s0}^* \in Q^*$ and $\omega^*(q_{s0}^*)$ be undefined. If $P_s$ is not empty and $W_s$ is a set of only one element $w_{1s} \in W$, let $q_{s1}^* \in Q^*$ and $\omega^*(q_{s1}^*) = w_{1s}$, if there is no $(q_j, i_k)$ such that $\tau(q_j, i_k) = q_s$ and $\omega(q_j, i_k)$ is undefined; otherwise let $q_{s0}^* \in Q^*$ and $q_{s1}^* \in Q^*$ and $\omega^*(q_{s1}^*) = w_{1s}$ and $\omega^*(q_{s0}^*)$ be undefined. If $P_s$ is not empty and $W_s = \{w_{1s}, w_{2s}, \ldots, w_{rs}\}$, where $r > 1$, then let $q_{s1}^* \in Q^*$, $q_{s2}^* \in Q^*$, $\ldots, q_{sr}^* \in Q^*$ and $\omega^*(q_{st}^*) = w_{ts}$, where $1 \leq t \leq r$; also, if there exists some $\tau(q_j, i_k) = q_s$ and $\omega(q_j, i_k)$ is undefined, then let $q_{s0}^* \in Q^*$ and $\omega^*(q_{s0})$ be undefined. We let $Q^*$ be the set of all states $q_{sj}^*$ defined above. Since both $Q$ and $W$ are finite sets, it follows that $Q^*$ is a finite set. (Note that $Q^*$ may have more elements than $Q$.) We let $\omega^*$ be defined as above; note that $\omega^*$ maps a subset of $Q^*$ onto $W^* = W$ since $\omega$ of $\mathcal{M}$ maps a subset of $Q \times I$ onto $W$ and by our restriction on $\mathcal{M}$ if $\omega(q_j, i_k)$ is defined, $\tau(q_j, i_k)$ is also defined. Thus both $Q^*$ and $\omega^*$ satisfy the definition of a Moore model sequential machine. Finally, $\tau^*$ is defined as follows.

If $\tau(q_j, i_k)$ is undefined for any $i_k \in I$, $\tau^*(q_{jt}^*, i_k)$ is undefined for $i_k \in I^*$ and all $q_{jt}^* \in Q^*$.

If $\tau(q_j, i_k) = q_s$ and $\omega(q_j, i_k) = w_u$, $\tau^*(q_{jt}^*, i_k) = q_{su}^*$ for $i_k \in I^*$ and all $q_{jt}^* \in Q^*$.

If $\tau(q_j, i_k) = q_s$ and $\omega(q_j, i_k)$ is undefined, $\tau^*(q_{jt}^*, i_k) = q_{s0}^*$, for $q_{s0}^* \in Q^*$. Since $\tau^*$ is seen immediately to be a mapping of a subset of $Q^* \times I^*$ into $Q^*$, we conclude that $\mathcal{M}^*$ is a Moore model sequential machine.

If an input sequence $i_1, i_2, \ldots, i_r$ is applied to $\mathcal{M}$ starting in state $q_j$, next state and output sequences will be obtained, where possibly some undefined outputs or next states appear in the sequences. An identical output sequence and a similar state sequence are obtained if $i_1, i_2, \ldots, i_r$ is applied to $\mathcal{M}^*$ in $q_{jt}^* \in Q^*$. This can be proved by induction similar to the one for the previous transformation.

An example of the transformation from a Moore model to a Mealy model sequential machine is the machine $\mathcal{M}^*$ shown in Figure 6.6.1.

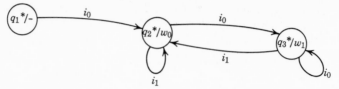

Figure 6.6.1     A Moore model example $\mathcal{M}^*$.

Note that state $q_1^* \in Q^*$ is such that no $\tau^*(q', i_j)$ is defined for any $q' \in Q^*$ and $i_j \in I^* = \{i_0, i_1\}$. However, $\omega^*(q_1^*)$ is undefined, thus satisfying the restriction required in the transformation. Applying the transformation to $\mathcal{M}^*$, we obtain the Mealy model $\mathcal{M}$ shown in Figure 6.6.2, as can be checked easily by the reader.

Machines $\mathcal{M}^*$ and $\mathcal{M}$ realize the same input-output sequences as stated in the transformation procedure. For example, if we start $\mathcal{M}^*$ in

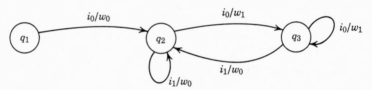

Figure 6.6.2     Mealy model $\mathcal{M}$ by transforming Figure 6.6.1.

state $q_1^*$ and give the input sequence $i_0, i_0, i_1$, we obtain the next state sequence $q_2^*, q_3^*, q_2^*$ and the output sequence $w_0, w_1, w_0$. Similarly, starting $\mathcal{M}$ in state $q_1$ and applying input sequence $i_0, i_0, i_1$, we obtain $q_2, q_3, q_2$ as the next state sequence and $w_0, w_1, w_0$ as the sequence of outputs.

As an example of the Mealy model to Moore model transformation consider the Mealy model machine $\mathcal{M}_1$ shown in Figure 6.6.3. Note that this machine is identical to that shown in Figure 6.4.1, except that state

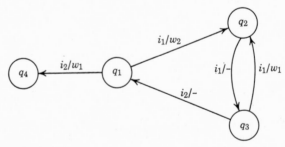

Figure 6.6.3     A Mealy model example $\mathcal{M}_1$.

$q_4$ has been added to $\mathcal{M}_1$ so that $\mathcal{M}_1$ will satisfy the restriction mentioned in the description of the transformation.

From this machine we wish to obtain a Moore model machine $\mathcal{M}_1^* = (Q^*, I^*, W^*, \tau^*, \omega^*)$. Using the transformation rules, we obtain

$$I^* = I = \{i_1, i_2\},$$
$$W^* = W = \{w_1, w_2\},$$
$$P_1 = \phi,$$
$$P_2 = \{(q_1, i_1), (q_3, i_1)\}.$$

Thus

$$W_2 = \{w_1, w_2\},$$

since

$$\omega(q_1, i_1) = w_2$$

and

$$\omega(q_3, i_1) = w_1.$$
$$P_3 = \phi,$$
$$P_4 = \{(q_1, i_2)\} \quad \text{and} \quad W_4 = \{w_1\},$$

since

$$\omega(q_1, i_2) = w_1.$$

Thus

$$Q^* = \{q_{10}^*, q_{21}^*, q_{22}^*, q_{30}^*, q_{41}^*\},$$

$\omega^*$ is defined as

$$\begin{cases} \omega^*(q_{10}^*) \quad \text{undefined} \\ \omega^*(q_{21}^*) = w_1 \\ \omega^*(q_{22}^*) = w_2 \\ \omega^*(q_{30}^*) \quad \text{undefined} \\ \omega^*(q_{41}^*) = w_1 \end{cases}$$

and $\tau^*$ is defined as

$$\begin{cases} \tau^*(q_{10}^*, i_1) = q_{22}^* \\ \tau^*(q_{10}^*, i_2) = q_{41}^* \\ \tau^*(q_{21}^*, i_1) = q_{30}^* \\ \tau^*(q_{21}^*, i_2) \quad \text{undefined} \\ \tau^*(q_{22}^*, i_1) = q_{30}^* \\ \tau^*(q_{22}^*, i_2) \quad \text{undefined} \\ \tau^*(q_{30}^*, i_1) = q_{21}^* \\ \tau^*(q_{30}^*, i_2) = q_{10}^* \\ \tau^*(q_{41}^*, i_1) \quad \text{undefined} \\ \tau^*(q_{41}^*, i_2) \quad \text{undefined}. \end{cases}$$

This machine is shown in Figure 6.6.4. Note that $\mathcal{M}_1{}^*$ has one more state than $\mathcal{M}_1$, and thus, if $\mathcal{M}_1{}^*$ were transformed back to a Mealy model $\mathcal{M}_2$, $\mathcal{M}_2$ would have five states rather than four states as $\mathcal{M}_1$ of Figure 6.6.3. Since $\mathcal{M}_2$ and $\mathcal{M}_1$ do not each have the same number of states, it is not clear that they each have the same input-output sequence behavior. In Chapter 7 we shall see more clearly how $\mathcal{M}_2$ and $\mathcal{M}_1$ can be considered to be "equivalent" machines.

This section simply serves the purpose of showing, by constructing transformations, that the Mealy and Moore models are equally powerful

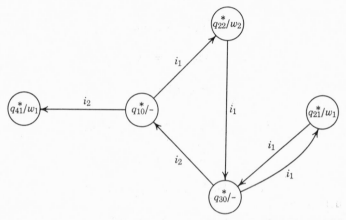

Figure 6.6.4   Moore model $\mathcal{M}_1{}^*$ by transformation of $\mathcal{M}_1$ of Figure 6.6.3.

in modeling input-output sequence behavior. Furthermore, since transformations were constructed, one can now change from one model to the other if this transformation would prove desirable for some purpose; for example, one of the models may be more applicable in some type of circuitry than the other model.

## 6.7   REGULAR EXPRESSIONS AND SEQUENTIAL MACHINES

A natural question pertaining to sequential machines is: how can we characterize the input sequences that give certain outputs for some machine $\mathcal{M}$ starting in a state $q$? Also, for what sets of input sequences can a machine be obtained so that the output is always some specific output for an input sequence in the set but is a different output for input sequences not in the set? In this section we give such a characterization of input sequences for complete Moore model sequential machines, denoted here by $\mathcal{M} = (Q, I, W, \tau, \omega)$. We present the case for the output set $W$ having exactly two elements, calling these outputs 0 and 1, respectively.

We say that $\mathcal{M}$ starting in some state $q_1 \in Q$ *accepts* an input sequence $i_1, i_2, \ldots, i_p$ if $\tau(q_j, i_j) = q_{j+1}, 1 \leq j \leq p$, and $\omega(q_{p+1}) = 1$. If $\omega(q_{p+1}) = 0$, we say that $\mathcal{M}$ *rejects* the input sequence. We are interested in characterizing the set of finite input sequences that can be accepted by $\mathcal{M}$ in $q_1$. A set of finite input sequences is called an *event*. Certain events, called *regular events*, are described by *regular expressions;* Kleene was the first to show that regular expressions categorize the events that can be accepted by a sequential machine.

Given a finite set of inputs $I = \{i_1, i_2, \ldots, i_m\}$, a regular expression is defined recursively as follows.

**Definition 6.7.1** Given a finite set $I$, symbols $\phi$ and $\Lambda$, operators $\cup$, $\cdot$, and *, and the use of parentheses; an expression is a *regular expression* if and only if it can be formed by a finite number of applications of the following.

1. It is a string (input sequence) consisting of a single input symbol $i_j$, $1 \leq j \leq m$, a single $\phi$, or a single $\Lambda$.

2. If $\beta_1$ and $\beta_2$ are regular expressions, then so are $\beta_1^*$, $(\beta_1 \cup \beta_2)$, and $(\beta_1 \cdot \beta_2)$; where the $\cup$ and $\cdot$ operations also satisfy the distributive laws $\beta_1 \cdot (\beta_2 \cup \beta_3) = \beta_1 \cdot \beta_2 \cup \beta_1 \cdot \beta_3$ and $(\beta_2 \cup \beta_3) \cdot \beta_1 = \beta_2 \cdot \beta_1 \cup \beta_3 \cdot \beta_1$.

We interpret the symbols $\phi$ and $\Lambda$, and the operations $\cup$, $\cdot$, and * as follows.

(*a*) The symbol $\phi$ is the null string (input sequence of length 0).

(*b*) The symbol $\Lambda$ is the empty set of strings.

(*c*) The set $\beta_1 \cup \beta_2$ is the set union of sets $\beta_1$ and $\beta_2$.

(*d*) The set $\beta_1 \cdot \beta_2$ (usually we omit the dot and simply write $\beta_1\beta_2$) is the *concatenation* of $\beta_1$ and $\beta_2$, that is, it is the set of strings consisting of taking any string of $\beta_1$ and following it with any string from $\beta_2$. (Note that in general $\beta_1\beta_2 \neq \beta_2\beta_1$.)

(*e*) The set $\beta_1^*$ is the union of sets denoted by $\phi$, $\beta_1$, $\beta_1\beta_1$, $\beta_1\beta_1\beta_1$, ..., and is called the *iterate* of $\beta_1$.

A set of sequences of inputs from $I$ is called a *regular set* if and only if it is denoted by a regular expression, and similarly an event is called a *regular event* if and only if it is denoted by a regular expression.

As an example, consider the set of input sequences $(i_1i_2 \cup i_3) \cdot (i_3 \cup i_2i_4)$. This is obviously a regular expression following from 1 and 2 of Definition 6.7.1. This denotes the set of input sequences: $(i_1i_2 \cup i_3)(i_3 \cup i_2i_4) = i_1i_2i_3 \cup i_1i_2i_2i_4 \cup i_3i_3 \cup i_3i_2i_4$. As a second example, consider the regular expression $(i_1i_1 \cup i_2i_2)^*$. This expression denotes the infinite set

$$\phi, i_1i_1, i_2i_2, i_1i_1i_1i_1, i_1i_1i_2i_2, i_2i_2i_1i_1, i_2i_2i_2i_2, i_1i_1i_1i_1i_1i_1, \ldots.$$

It should be mentioned that not all events are regular events. For example, the following set of sequences is not regular: the set of sequences of $I = \{i_1, i_2\}$, where the sequence $i_1i_1 \cdots i_1i_2$ of length $l$ is an element of the set if and only if $l$ is prime.

Although there is no complete algebraic procedure to test whether two regular expressions are equivalent, certain identities are evident from Definition 6.7.1 and its interpretation. Some of these are

$$(\beta_1\beta_2) \cup (\beta_1\beta_3) = \beta_1(\beta_2 \cup \beta_3),$$
$$\phi^* = \phi,$$
$$\phi \cup \beta_1^* = \beta_1^*,$$
$$\phi\beta_1 = \beta_1\phi = \beta_1,$$
$$(\beta_1 \cup \beta_2)^* = (\beta_1^* \cup \beta_2^*)^* = (\beta_1^*\beta_2^*)^*,$$
$$\beta_1 \cup \beta_2 = \beta_2 \cup \beta_1,$$
$$\Lambda^* = \phi,$$
$$\beta_1\Lambda = \Lambda\beta_1 = \Lambda,$$
$$\beta_1 \cup \Lambda = \Lambda \cup \beta_1 = \beta_1.$$

To show that the set of input sequences accepted by any machine $\mathscr{M}$ starting in some designated state is a regular set, we describe an algorithm of McNaughton and Yamada which obtains the regular expression for $\mathscr{M}$.

Let         $\mathscr{M} = \{Q, I, W, \tau, \omega)$ be a complete machine.
$$Q = \{q_1, q_2, \ldots, q_n\},$$
$$I = \{i_1, i_2, \ldots, i_m\},$$
$$W = \{0, 1\},$$
and let
$$q_{u_1}, q_{u_2}, \ldots, q_{u_p}$$
be the states for which
$$\omega(q_{u_i}) = 1.$$

The algorithm consists of inductively constructing auxiliary regular expressions as follows.

1. Let $\alpha_{ij}{}^0$ be the union of input symbols that have direct transitions from state $q_i$ to state $q_j$, and $\alpha_{ij}{}^0 = \Lambda$ if there are no transitions from $q_i$ to $q_j$. That is, $\alpha_{ij}{}^0$ is the $ij$ entry of the connection matrix for $\mathscr{M}$, where $\Lambda$ replaces 0.

2. $\alpha_{ij}^{k} = \alpha_{ij}^{k-1} \cup \alpha_{ik}^{k-1}(\alpha_{kk}^{k-1})^*\alpha_{kj}^{k-1}$ for $1 \leq k \leq r$. Thus $\alpha_{ij}^{k}$ is a regular expression for the set of all input sequences which take $\mathcal{M}$ from state $q_i$ to state $q_j$ without going "through" any state $q_r$, $r > k$.

With these two rules, it follows that the regular expression for input sequences which are accepted by $\mathcal{M}$ starting in state $q_s$ is

$$\alpha_{su_1}^{n} \cup \alpha_{su_2}^{n} \cup \cdots \cup \alpha_{su_p}^{n}$$

where $n$ is the number of states in $\mathcal{M}$.

The example shown in Figure 6.7.1 illustrates this algorithm. For this machine let $\mathcal{M}$ start in state $q_3$. To obtain the regular expression we calculate $\alpha_{31}^{3} \cup \alpha_{32}^{3}$.

$$\alpha_{11}^{0} = \Lambda \qquad \alpha_{21}^{0} = \Lambda \qquad \alpha_{31}^{0} = i_2,$$

$$\alpha_{12}^{0} = i_2 \qquad \alpha_{22}^{0} = i_1 \qquad \alpha_{32}^{0} = \Lambda,$$

$$\alpha_{13}^{0} = i_1 \qquad \alpha_{23}^{0} = i_2 \qquad \alpha_{33}^{0} = i_1,$$

$$\alpha_{21}^{1} = \Lambda,$$

$$\alpha_{22}^{1} = i_1 \cup \Lambda(\Lambda)^*i_2 = i_1,$$

$$\alpha_{23}^{1} = i_2 \cup \Lambda(\Lambda)^*i_1 = i_2,$$

$$\alpha_{31}^{1} = i_2 \cup i_2(\Lambda)^*\Lambda = i_2,$$

$$\alpha_{32}^{1} = \Lambda \cup i_2(\Lambda)^*i_2 = i_2 i_2,$$

$$\alpha_{33}^{1} = i_1 \cup i_2(\Lambda)^*i_1 = i_1 \cup i_2 i_1,$$

$$\alpha_{31}^{2} = \alpha_{31}^{1} \cup \alpha_{32}^{1}(\alpha_{22}^{1})^*\alpha_{21}^{1},$$

$$= i_2 \cup i_2 i_2(i_1)^*\Lambda = i_2,$$

$$\alpha_{32}^{2} = \alpha_{32}^{1} \cup \alpha_{32}^{1}(\alpha_{22}^{1})^*\alpha_{22}^{1},$$

$$= i_2 i_2 \cup i_2 i_2(i_1)^*i_1 = i_2 i_2(i_1)^*,$$

$$\alpha_{33}^{2} = \alpha_{33}^{1} \cup \alpha_{32}^{1}(\alpha_{22}^{1})^*\alpha_{23}^{1},$$

$$= (i_1 \cup i_2 i_1) \cup i_2 i_2(i_1)^*i_2,$$

$$\alpha_{31}^{3} = \alpha_{31}^{2} \cup \alpha_{33}^{2}(\alpha_{33}^{2})^*\alpha_{31}^{2},$$

$$\alpha_{32}^{3} = \alpha_{32}^{2} \cup \alpha_{33}^{2}(\alpha_{33}^{2})^*\alpha_{32}^{2},$$

Therefore

$$\alpha_{31}^{3} \cup \alpha_{32}^{3} = (\alpha_{31}^{2} \cup \alpha_{32}^{2}) \cup \alpha_{33}^{2}(\alpha_{33}^{2})^*(\alpha_{31}^{2} \cup \alpha_{32}^{2}),$$

$$= (\alpha_{33}^{2})^*(\alpha_{31}^{2} \cup \alpha_{32}^{2}),$$

$$= (i_1 \cup i_2 i_1 \cup i_2 i_2(i_1)^*i_2)^*[i_2 \cup i_2 i_2(i_1)^*].$$

Although this expression is rather complicated, it describes the set of all input sequences accepted by $\mathcal{M}$ starting in $q_3$.

By the inductive definition of $\alpha_{ij}{}^k$, it is readily seen that the form of the regular expression depends on the numbering of the states of $\mathcal{M}$. An equivalent, but considerably more complex, regular expression for this example machine is obtained if the numbering of states $q_2$ and $q_3$ are interchanged. This should be checked by the reader.

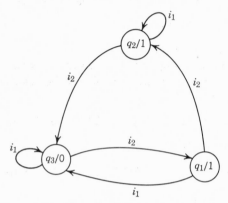

Figure 6.7.1   Example $\mathcal{M}$ for regular expression.

By this algorithm we obtain the following theorem.

**Theorem 6.7.1**   The set of input sequences accepted by any machine $\mathcal{M}$ is a regular expression.

The next algorithm, also due to McNaughton and Yamada, shows how to obtain a machine $\mathcal{M}$, with a designated starting state, which will accept the set of input sequences given by a regular expression.

With each occurrence of an input symbol in a regular expression $\beta$ we associate a *position* directly to the right of the symbol. Thus the positions of input $i_j$ are numbered $1, 2, \ldots$, from left to right as $i_j$ appears in the regular expression. A position is called an *initial position* if some input sequence contained in $\beta$ begins with the symbol associated with that position. Similarly, a position is called a *terminal position* if some sequence contained in $\beta$ ends with the symbol associated with the position. A *transition* is an ordered pair of positions $i$ and $j$, such that if an input sequence reaches the input symbol of the $i$th position, it can be followed by the input symbol of the $j$th position, and the input sequence so formed is an initial segment of an input sequence contained in $\beta$. An *allowable sequence of positions* is a finite sequence beginning with an initial position and ending in a terminal position such that any adjacent pair of positions of the sequence is a transition.

A machine $\mathcal{M}$ can be constructed for $\beta$ as follows. Assume $\beta$ has $p$ positions; then let $\mathcal{M}$ have an initial state plus one state for each set of positions, that is, $2^p + 1$ states for $\mathcal{M}$. An input $i_j$ applied to a state corresponding to a set $S$ of positions leads to the state corresponding to the set $S'$ of just those positions $P$ such that $i_j$ is the input symbol associated with $i_j$ and there is a transition from at least one position of $S$ to $P$. If there is no such position $P$, then $i_j$ leads to the state $\Lambda$ associated with the null set. Furthermore, any $i_j$ leaving the state $\Lambda$ associated with the null set is a self-loop returning to the state $\Lambda$. A state has an output 1 if at least one position of the corresponding set of positions is a terminal position; otherwise a state has an output 0.

By this second algorithm we obtain the following.

**Theorem 6.7.2** Given a regular expression $\beta$, a sequential machine $\mathcal{M}$ exists that accepts an input sequences if and only if it is an element of $\beta$.

We shall not prove here that this algorithm gives a machine realizing $\beta$, but rather we illustrate the algorithm with an example.

Let
$$\beta = (i_1 \cup i_2)^* i_2.$$

We assign positions as follows:

$$\beta = (i_1 \cup i_2)^* i_2$$
$$\text{positions } 1 \quad 2 \quad 3$$

The 8 sets of positions are

$$(\Lambda), (1), (2), (3), (1, 2), (1, 3), (2, 3), \quad \text{and} \quad (1, 2, 3),$$

where $(\Lambda)$ denotes the null set.

The initial positions are 1, 2, and 3, and the single terminal position is 3. The transitions for $\beta$ are

$$[1, 1], [1, 2], [1, 3], [2, 1], [2, 2], [2, 3].$$

We set up a correspondence between the 8 sets of positions and states of $\mathcal{M}$, and also add a starting state as follows:

$$q_0 = \text{starting state},$$
$$q_1 \leftarrow (1),$$
$$q_2 \leftarrow (2),$$
$$q_3 \leftarrow (3),$$
$$q_4 \leftarrow (1, 2),$$
$$q_5 \leftarrow (1, 3),$$
$$q_6 \leftarrow (2, 3),$$
$$q_7 \leftarrow (1, 2, 3),$$
$$q_8 \leftarrow (\Lambda).$$

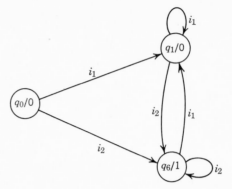

Figure 6.7.2    Machine $\mathcal{M}$ realizing the regular expression $\beta = (i_1 \cup i_2)^* i_2$.

The outputs are

$$\omega(q_3) = \omega(q_5) = \omega(q_6) = \omega(q_7) = 1$$

and all other outputs are 0, since position 3 is the only terminal position.

Starting in $q_0$, if input $i_1$ is applied, the only position associated with $i_1$ is 1. Thus

$$\tau(q_0, i_1) = q_1.$$

Starting in $q_0$ if input $i_2$ is applied, either position 2 or 3 is associated with $i_2$, so that

$$\tau(q_0, i_2) = q_6.$$

Now it is readily verified that

$$\tau(q_1, i_1) = q_1,$$
$$\tau(q_1, i_2) = q_6,$$
$$\tau(q_6, i_1) = q_1,$$

and

$$\tau(q_6, i_2) = q_6.$$

Thus states $q_2$, $q_3$, $q_4$, $q_5$, $q_7$, and $q_8$ are never reached when starting in $q_0$, and the resulting state diagram, realizing $\beta$, is shown in Figure 6.7.2.

From Theorems 6.7.1 and 6.7.2 we see that for every regular expression $\beta$ there is a sequential machine that recognizes $\beta$, and also that every sequential machine recognizes some regular expression. Thus regular expressions characterize precisely the terminal behavior of sequential machines.

As discussed earlier, for each complete sequential machine there is some corresponding sequential network, and thus regular expressions can also be used to represent sequential networks (sometimes called automata). Direct equivalences between various types of sequential networks and regular expressions have been worked out (see References [5, 6, 9, 20]), but we shall not discuss this here.

The regular expression representation has the advantages of being both precise and concise. Obviously, this representation can be extended to machines having more than two outputs by simply encoding the outputs into binary $p$-tuples and then representing the input-output behavior by a set of $p$ regular expressions, one for each binary output signal. This extension, although direct, can become quite involved. However, no better method is known.

**Exercises**

**1.** Given the sequential network having two delay units shown below:
  (a) Determine the set of output equations and the set of next state equations for the network.
  (b) Draw a Mealy model state diagram for the network.
  (c) Determine the stable states of the network.
  (d) What is the final state and output of this network if the initial state is $y_1 = y_2 = 0$ and the input sequence 0 0, 1 0, 0 0 is applied to the network?

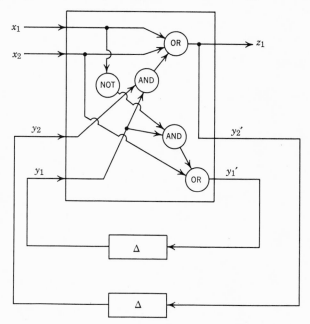

**2.** (a) Determine a Moore model state diagram for the following serial decoder. The network has a binary input $x = 0$ or 1, and a "reset" input $r = 0$ or 1, and an output representing numbers 0, 1, 2, 3, and 4. The network should "decode" the following sequences of input signals on the $x$ input to the outputs indicated, if $r = 0$. Whenever $r = 1$ the network should be "reset" so it may again receive a sequence of $x$ inputs for decoding.

| $x$ Input Sequence | | Required Output |
|---|---|---|
| 0, 0, 0 | $\rightarrow$ | 0 |
| 0, 0, 1 | $\rightarrow$ | 1 |
| 0, 1, 0 | $\rightarrow$ | 2 |
| 0, 1, 1 | $\rightarrow$ | 3 |
| 1, 0, 0 | $\rightarrow$ | 4 |

We also desire to have an "error" indication as an output whenever an input sequence of $x$'s of three values, other than those indicated, is given to the network with $r = 0$.

(b) From the state diagram, encode the states and design a sequential network of the form of the basic model. (*Hint:* You should not require more than four delay units.) Assume the following encoding for representing the outputs:

| | Encoded Output | | | | |
|---|---|---|---|---|---|
| Output | $z_1$ | $z_2$ | $z_3$ | $z_4$ | $z_5$ |
| 0 | 0 | 0 | 0 | 0 | 0 |
| 1 | 1 | 0 | 0 | 0 | 0 |
| 2 | 0 | 1 | 0 | 0 | 0 |
| 3 | 0 | 0 | 1 | 0 | 0 |
| 4 | 0 | 0 | 0 | 1 | 0 |
| Error | 0 | 0 | 0 | 0 | 1 |

3. Given a sequential machine $\mathscr{M} = (Q, I, W, \tau, \omega)$ described by

$$Q = \{q_1, q_2, q_3\},$$
$$I = \{\alpha, \beta, \gamma\},$$
$$W = \{a, b, c\},$$

$$\tau = \left\{\begin{array}{l} q_1 \times \alpha \rightarrow q_2 \\ q_2 \times \alpha \rightarrow q_3 \\ q_3 \times \alpha \rightarrow q_1 \\ q_1 \times \beta \rightarrow q_1 \\ q_1 \times \gamma \rightarrow q_3 \\ q_3 \times \gamma \rightarrow q_3 \end{array}\right\},$$

$$\omega = \left\{\begin{array}{l} q_1 \times \alpha = a \\ q_2 \times \alpha = b \\ q_3 \times \gamma = c \\ q_1 \times \beta = c \end{array}\right\}$$

(a) Give the Mealy model state diagram, the Huffman flow table, and the transition matrix representations for $\mathscr{M}$.

(b) If the machine is given a sequence of inputs $\alpha$, $\alpha$, $\gamma$, what are the final states and outputs when the machine is started in states $q_1$, $q_2$, and $q_3$, respectively? Are they defined?

(c) If the inputs $I$, outputs $W$, and states $Q$, are encoded as

$$I = \begin{matrix} & x_1 & x_2 \\ \begin{cases} \alpha = 0 & 0 \\ \beta = 0 & 1 \\ \gamma = 1 & 0 \end{cases} \end{matrix},$$

$$W = \begin{matrix} & z_1 & z_2 \\ \begin{cases} a = 1 & 1 \\ b = 1 & 0 \\ c = 0 & 1 \end{cases} \end{matrix},$$

$$Q = \begin{matrix} & y_1 & y_2 \\ \begin{cases} q_1 = 0 & 0 \\ q_2 = 0 & 1 \\ q_3 = 1 & 0 \end{cases} \end{matrix},$$

determine the basic model sequential network for $\mathcal{M}$.

4. Generalize the notion of synchronized logical networks of Section 6.3 such that the delay time of each element is some multiple $k\Delta$ of $\Delta$, where $k$ is a fixed positive integer for each element in the range $1 \le k \le p$. Make appropriate definitions for the elements and logical network and also show how such networks can be considered to be synchronous sequential networks.

5. State and prove the analogous theorem to Theorem 6.5.5 for Mealy model sequential machines.

6. In Figure 6.2.2 a basic model for sequential networks is shown which is obtained from Equations (6.2.1) and (6.2.2). Suppose, instead, the following model is used.

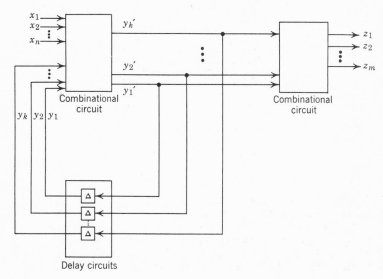

Delay circuits

Describe the next state and output equations which represent this model, and discuss the similarities and differences between this model and that of Figure 6.2.2. Also, give a proper representation of this model by variations (when or if variations are required) of the Moore model sequential machine, the Mealy model sequential machine, and the Huffman flow tables.

7. (*a*) Construct a Mealy model sequential machine to represent the following behavior of an elevator. States: $q_1, q_2, q_3$ to represent three floor positions of the elevator. Inputs: button $f_1$ to go to floor 1, $f_2$ to go to floor 2, $f_3$ to go to floor 3, and $n$ to indicate no button pushed. Outputs: $U$ for "up" signal; $D$ for "down" signal; and $H$ for "hold" signal. The elevator is to always return to floor 1 if no other directions are given. Also, assume that only one of the inputs $f_1, f_2, f_3$ is given, and no other input is given until the elevator reaches the correct floor.

   (*b*) Construct a similar model in which all possible occurrences of $f_1, f_2, f_3$ inputs should be remembered and executed by the elevator.

8. (*a*) Transform the following Mealy model sequential machine into a Moore model.

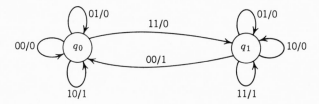

   (*b*) Transform the Moore model from (*a*) into a Mealy model.

9. Transform the following Moore model into a Mealy model machine.

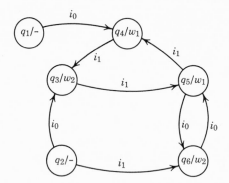

REFERENCE NOTATIONS

In Sections 6.2 and 6.3 a brief discussion of several types of sequential networks was given. Other, and more detailed, treatments appear in previous books; for example, see [2, 8, 12, 18, 21, 22, 30]. In [12] Gill discusses synchronous machines. In [23] McCluskey discusses the similarities and differences between two commonly distinguished sequential circuits: pulse-type (also called pulse mode) and level-type (also called fundamental mode) circuits. In [7] Cadden also discusses several types of sequential circuits and gives transformations between these circuits, similar to those of Section 6.6. Equivalence of machine models is also considered in [4, 11].

The original development of complete sequential machine models can be found in Moore [28], Huffman [17], and Mealy [25]. The incomplete sequential machine models of Section 6.4 closely follows Miller [26, 27] and Beatty and Miller [3, 4]; also see Ginsburg [14, 15], Paull and Unger [29], and Elgot and Rutledge [10] for treatments of the state minimization problem to be discussed in the next chapter. The transition matrix formulation for sequential machines follows Seshu, Miller, and Metze [32]. Other matrix formulations appear in [1, 12, 16]. Experiments on machines to determine their structure was considered by Moore [28], and has since been extensively studied; for example, see Gill [12], Chapters 4 and 5, and Ginsburg [15], Chapter 1.

Regular expressions and their equivalence with sequential machines were first shown by Kleene [20]. Brozozowski [5, 6] has studied relations between regular expressions and sequential machines in some detail, and the material of Section 6.7 follows this work as well as the transformations described by McNaughton and Yamada in [24]. Further references on sequential machines appear in Chapters 7 through 10.

**REFERENCES**

1. Aufenkamp, D. D. and F. E. Hohn, "Analysis of Sequential Machines,"*Trans. IRE*, Vol. EC-6, pp. 276–285, December 1957.
2. Bartee, T. C., I. L. Lebow, and I. S. Reed, *Theory and Design of Digital Machines*, McGraw-Hill Book Co., New York, 1962, Chapter 7.
3. Beatty, J. C. and R. E. Miller. "Some Theorems for Incompletely Specified Sequential Machines with Applications to State Minimization," *AIEE Proceedings of the Third Annual Symposium on Switching Circuit Theory and Logical Design*, S-141, pp. 123–136, September 1962.
4. Beatty, J. C. and R. E. Miller, "An Approach to State Minimization for Incompletely Specified Sequential Machines," *IBM Research Report*, RC-1055, September 1963.
5. Brozozowski, J. A., "A Survey of Regular Expressions and Their Applications," *IRE Transactions on Electronic Computers*, Vol. EC-11, No. 2, pp. 324–335, June 1962.
6. Brozozowski, J. A., "Properties of Regular Expressions and State Diagrams," Princeton University, Dept. of Electrical Engineering, Digital Systems Laboratory, Technical Report No. 15, March 1962.
7. Cadden, W. J., "Equivalent Sequential Circuits," *Trans. IRE*, Vol. CT-6, pp. 30–34, March 1959.
8. Caldwell, S. H., *Switching Circuits and Logical Design*, John Wiley and Sons, New York, 1958, Chapters 12, 13, and 14.
9. Copi, I. M., C. C. Elgot, and J. B. Wright, "Realization of Events by Logical Nets," *Journal of the Association for Computing Machinery*, Vol. 5, No. 2, pp. 181–196, April 1958.
10. Elgot, C. C. and J. D. Rutledge, "Machine Properties Preserved under State Minimization," *AIEE Proceedings of the Third Annual Symposium on Switching Circuit Theory and Logical Design*, S-141, pp. 61–70, September 1962.
11. Gill, Arthur, "Comparison of Finite-State Models," *IRE Transitions on Circuit Theory*, Vol. CT-7, No. 2, pp. 178–179, June 1960.

12. Gill, Arthur, *Introduction to the Theory of Finite-State Machines*, McGraw-Hill Book Co., New York, 1962.
13. Gillespie, R. G. and D. D. Aufenkamp, "On the Analysis of Sequential Machines," *Trans. IRE*, Vol. EC-7, pp. 119–122, June 1958.
14. Ginsburg, S., "A Synthesis Technique for Minimal State Sequential Machines," *IRE Transactions on Electronic Computers*, Vol. EC-8, No. 1, pp. 13–24, March 1959.
15. Ginsburg, S., *An Introduction to Mathematical Machine Theory*, Addison-Wesley Publishing Co., Reading, Mass., 1962.
16. Hohn, F. E., S. Seshu, and D. D. Aufenkamp, "The Theory of Nets," IRE Transactions on Electronic Computers, Vol. EC-6, No. 3, pp. 154–161, September 1957.
17. Huffman, D. A., "The Synthesis of Sequential Switching Circuits," *Journal of the Franklin Institute*, Vol. 257, Nos. 3 and 4, pp. 161–190 and 275–303, March and April 1954.
18. Humphrey, W. S., Jr., *Switching Circuits with Computer Applications*, McGraw-Hill Book Co., New York, 1958, Chapter 10.
19. Kautz, W. H., "State-Logic Relations in Autonomous Sequential Networks," *Proceedings of the Eastern Joint Computer Conference*, December 3–5, 1958.
20. Kleene, S. C., "Representation of Events in Nerve Nets and Finite Automata," *Automata Studies, Annals of Mathematics Studies* No. 34, pp. 3–41, Princeton University Press, New Jersey, 1956.
21. Marcus, M. P., *Switching Circuits for Engineers*, Prentice-Hall, Englewood Cliffs, New Jersey, 1962, Chapters 13–20.
22. McCluskey, E. J., Jr., and T. C. Bartee, editors, *A Survey of Switching Circuit Theory*, McGraw-Hill Book Co., New York, 1962, Chapters 7–11,
23. McCluskey, E. J., Jr., "Fundamental Mode and Pulse Mode Sequential Circuits," *Proceedings of the IFIP Congress*, 1962, Information Processing, Munich, Germany, North-Holland Publishing Co., Amsterdam, pp. 725–730.
24. McNaughton, R. F. and H. Yamada, "Regular Expressions and State Graphs for Automata," *IRE Transactions on Electronic Computers*, Vol. EC-9, No. 1, pp. 39–47, March 1960.
25. Mealy, G. H., "A Method for Synthesizing Sequential Circuits," *BSTJ*, Vol. 34, pp. 1045–1079, September 1955.
26. Miller, R. E., "State Reduction for Sequential Machines," *IBM Research Report*, RC-121, June 15, 1959.
27. Miller, R. E., "Switching Theory and Logical Design of Automatic Digital Computer Circuits," *IBM Research Report*, RC-473, June 1961, Chapter 2.
28. Moore, E. F., "Gedanken-Experiments on Sequential Machines," *Automata Studies, Annals of Mathematics Studies* No. 34, pp. 129–153, Princeton University Press, New Jersey, 1956.
29. Paull, M. C. and S. H. Unger, "Minimizing the Number of States in Incompletely Specified Sequential Switching Functions," *Trans. IRE*, Vol. EC-8, No. 3, pp. 356–367.
30. Phister, M., Jr., *Logical Design of Digital Computers*, John Wiley and Sons, New York, 1958, Chapters 5 and 6.
31. "Sequential Transducer Issue," *Trans. IRE*, Vol. CT-6, March 1959.
32. Seshu, S., R. E. Miller, and G. Metze, "Transition Matrices of Sequential Machines," *Trans. IRE*, Vol. CT-6, pp. 5–12, March 1959.

# 7

# Sequential Machine Compatibility, Equivalence, and State Minimization

## 7.1 INTRODUCTION

In Chapter 6 we discussed various models for sequential machines. Here we consider state minimization for sequential machines. That is, given some sequential machine $\mathcal{M}$ we wish to find another sequential machine $\mathcal{M}'$ which "does as much and possibly more than $\mathcal{M}$" such that $\mathcal{M}'$ also has the minimum number of states for any machine so related to $\mathcal{M}$. We need to describe precisely what is meant by "does as much and possibly more"; thus we define relations in Sections 7.2 and 7.3 between states of $\mathcal{M}$ and also between pairs of machines. Throughout this chapter we use the sequential machine model of Definition 6.4.1, an incomplete Mealy model.

State minimization is of theoretical interest since the number of states of a machine is an important parameter; it is also useful in designing sequential networks. If we realize the states of the machine by binary storage devices, for an $n$ state machine we need at least $s$ storage devices, where $s$ equals the smallest integer greater than or equal to $\log_2 n$.* By reducing $n$, we may reduce $s$, and thus use fewer storage devices in a circuit realization. The number of logical equations in the set of next state equations (6.2.2) and the number of variables for the next state equations and output equations will also be reduced as $s$ is reduced.

Do these reductions reduce the total cost of a sequential circuit? If storage elements are very expensive as compared to logical elements, then a minimum state machine would probably cost a minimum amount since it requires the fewest number of storage elements. Although the number of next state equations decrease and the number of variables in the sets of equations decrease with state reduction, we are not assured, however, that the total cost of a sequential circuit will be minimal by using a

* We use the symbol $\lceil x \rceil$ to designate the smallest integer greater than or equal to $x$, and thus $s = \lceil \log_2 n \rceil$.

minimum state machine. This difficulty results because the cost of realizing the sets of output equations and next state equations may be larger for the minimum state machine than for some nonminimum state machine. Also, it may at times be desirable to use a nonminimum number of memory elements to design a sequential network.

In this chapter both the inclusion relation between machines and the state minimization theorems are considered. Other properties of sequential machines giving further insight into the design problem are discussed in Chapter 8.

In Sections 7.4 and 7.5 we discuss various theorems leading to state minimization procedures, and in Section 7.6 we find that for complete sequential machines the process of state minimization becomes particularly simple; in this case we see that a unique minimum state machine exists for any complete sequential machine.

## 7.2  APPLICABLE INPUT SEQUENCES AND STATE COMPATIBILITY

As we saw in Chapter 6, certain input sequences applied to an incomplete sequential machine $\mathcal{M}$ in some state $q_1$ give a defined final output, whereas other input sequences have an undefined final output. If the machine is viewed simply as an input-output device, we can restrict our attention to input sequences that give a defined final output, since an undefined final output implies that for some reason we do not require any given specific output when that input sequence is applied to $\mathcal{M}$ in state $q_1$.

**Definition 7.2.1**    A sequence $i_1, i_2, \ldots, i_p$ of inputs with $i_j \in I$ for $1 \leq j \leq p$ is said to be *applicable* to $\mathcal{M}$ in a state $q_1$ if there is a sequence of states $q_1, q_2, \ldots, q_p$ with $q_j \in Q$ for $1 \leq j \leq p$ such that for $1 \leq j \leq p - 1$ $(q_j, i_j) \in D_r$, where $\tau(q_j, i_j) = q_{j+1}$, and $(q_p, i_p) \in D_\omega$.

The sequence of states $q_1, q_2, \ldots, q_p$ is called the *state sequence produced*, and the output $\omega(q_p, i_p)$ is called the *final output produced* by $\mathcal{M}$ in state $q_1$ under the input sequence $i_1, i_2, \ldots, i_p$.

Note that for an input sequence to be applicable to $\mathcal{M}$ in $q_1$, we need both a state sequence and a final output to be produced by the input sequence. Since $\mathcal{M}$ is, in general, an incompletely defined machine, some of the outputs $\omega(q_j, i_j)$ for $1 \leq j < p$ may be undefined, since we require only that $\omega(q_p, i_p)$ be defined. Thus, in general, certain initial segments of an applicable input sequence to $\mathcal{M}$ in $q_1$ may not be applicable input sequences to $\mathcal{M}$ in $q_1$. This definition is justified, however, if we consider that only those input sequences producing outputs are actually of interest.

Certainly, if no outputs for any $(q_j, i_j)$, $1 \leq j \leq p$ are defined, we would not consider $\mathscr{M}$ viewed as an input-output device to be "doing anything" for that input sequence. By Definition 7.2.1, when no outputs are defined, $i_1, i_2, \ldots, i_p$, or any of its initial segments, would not be called applicable, even though a state sequence may be produced by $i_1, i_2, \ldots, i_p$.

From Definition 7.2.1 for each state $q_1$ of $\mathscr{M}$ we can associate that set of input sequences that are applicable to $\mathscr{M}$ in state $q_1$. Then we may define the following binary relation between pairs of states of $\mathscr{M}$.

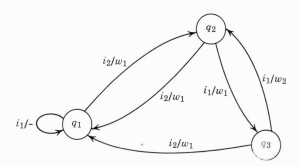

Figure 7.2.1.   Compatibility of states example.

**Definition 7.2.2**   States $p_1$ and $q_1$ of a machine $\mathscr{M} = (Q, I, W, \tau, \omega)$ are *incompatible* if there exists some input sequence $i_1, i_2, \ldots, i_p$ which is applicable both to $\mathscr{M}$ in state $p_1$ and $\mathscr{M}$ in state $q_1$ such that the output produced by $\mathscr{M}$ in $p_1$ is not equal to the output produced by $\mathscr{M}$ in $q_1$ under the input sequence $i_1, i_2, \ldots, i_p$. We denote this incompatibility relation between $p_1$ and $q_1$ by $p_1 \sim q_1$.

States $p_1$ and $q_1$ of $\mathscr{M}$ are *compatible* if they are not incompatible. We denote compatible states by $p_1 \sim q_1$.

Clearly, $p_1 \sim p_1$ for any state $p_1 \in Q$. Also, if $p_1 \sim q_1$, then $q_1 \sim p_1$. Thus the compatibility relation is reflexive and symmetric. In general, however, the compatibility relation is not transitive, and thus compatibility is not an equivalence relation. We shall show in Section 7.6 that for the special case of complete machines the compatibility relation is an equivalence relation; and it is this reduction to an equivalence relation which simplifies materially state minimization for complete machines.

We illustrate Definitions 7.2.1 and 7.2.2 by the sequential machine in Figure 7.2.1. This machine is transition complete and has only one output undefined, that for the pair $(q_1, i_1)$. Thus any input sequence in the set of input sequences denoted by the regular expression $i_1(i_1)^*$ is not an applicable input sequence for $\mathscr{M}$ in $q_1$, since the final output is undefined in each case. Similarly, any input sequence in the set denoted by $(i_2 \cup i_1 i_2) i_1 (i_1)^*$ is not applicable for $\mathcal{M}$ in $q_3$. What other input sequences are not applicable for $\mathcal{M}$ in $q_1, q_2$, and $q_3$, respectively?

The single input $i_1$ is an input sequence applicable to both $q_2$ and $q_3$. Since $\omega(q_2, i_1) = w_1$ and $\omega(q_3, i_1) = w_2$, and $w_1 \neq w_2$, by Definition 7.2.2 $q_2 \sim q_3$. Although it is not obvious at this point in the discussion, $q_1 \sim q_2$ and $q_1 \sim q_3$. The reader may convince himself of this by trying to find an input sequence applicable to both $q_1$ and $q_2$ (or $q_1$ and $q_3$) that produces different final outputs. We shall presently consider better methods for determining the compatibility of states of $\mathcal{M}$. If compatibility were a transitive relation, then $q_2 \sim q_1$ and $q_1 \sim q_3$ would imply that $q_2 \sim q_3$, but as we readily see from this example, $q_2 \sim q_3$.

The compatibility relation defines subsets of $Q$ as follows.

**Definition 7.2.3**  A set $S$ of states of $\mathcal{M}$ ($S \subseteq Q$) is *compatible* if all pairs of states contained in $S$ are compatible. $S$ is a *maximum compatible set* if $S$ is not a proper subset of any compatible set.

In our example, the maximum compatible sets are $\{q_1, q_2\}$ and $\{q_1, q_3\}$. In Section 7.4 we shall see how compatible sets play an important role in state minimization. For this reason we now give an algorithm for computing the set of all maximum compatible sets of a given machine. The maximum compatible sets of $\mathcal{M}$ characterize all compatible sets of $\mathcal{M}$ since any compatible set of $\mathcal{M}$ must be a subset of some maximum compatible set.

**Definition 7.2.4**  The class of all maximum compatible sets of states of a machine $\mathcal{M}$ is called the *final class* of $\mathcal{M}$.

An algorithm to obtain the final class is as follows.

### Final Class Algorithm

STEP 1.  Let $S_0 = Q$ be the set of all the states of $\mathcal{M}$. For an input $i$, let $W_i$ be the set of outputs $\omega(q, i)$ for each $q \in S_0$ where $(q, i) \in D_\omega$. If $W_i$ is empty or has only one element (equal outputs when defined), $S_0$ is not altered for input $i$. If, however, there exists a pair of states $q_j$ and $q_k$ belonging to $S_0$ with $(q_j, i) \in D_\omega$ and $(q_k, i) \in D_\omega$, but $\omega(q_j, i) \neq \omega(q_k, i)$ then $S_0$ is replaced by the two sets $S_{0j}$ and $S_{0k}$, where $S_{0j}$ contains all the states of $S_0$ except $q_j$, and $S_{0k}$ contains all the states of $S_0$ except $q_k$. Using $S_{0j}, S_{0k}$ as a class of sets of states, this step is repeated on all pairs of states having unequal outputs for input $i$ in all sets in the class and for each input $i \in I$. Thus through successive splittings for each input, we obtain a class of sets of states of $\mathcal{M}$ where no set has conflicting outputs for any input.

STEP 2.  Let $S_m$ be a set of states of a class $Z$ (where $Z$ is obtained from Step 1 or a previous application of Step 2). Let $T_{mi}$ be the set of next states of the states of $S_m$ under input $i$, that is, $q \in T_{mi}$ if and only if $q' \in S_m$ and $\tau(q', i) = q$. If $T_{mi}$ is included in some set of the class of sets of states $Z$, then $S_m$ is not altered.  If $T_{mi}$ is not included in some set of the class $Z$, then $S_m$ is to be replaced by a pair of new sets as follows.  In this case there exists a pair of states $q_j$ and $q_k$ of $S_m$ such that $(q_j, i) \in D_\tau$ and $(q_k, i) \in D_\tau$, and the pair of states $[\tau(q_j, i), \tau(q_k, i)]$ is not included in any set of the class $Z$. Then $S_m$ is replaced by the two sets $\{S_m - q_j\}$ and $\{S_m - q_k\}$, forming a new class $Z'$.

STEP 3.  Repeat Step 2 for each class $Z'$, each set $S_m$ in each class $Z'$, and for each input $i$ until no new class can be formed by Step 2.  As each class $Z'$ is formed, eliminate any duplication of sets of the class and any set properly contained in another set.

We shall show that the final class algorithm gives the final class for any machine $\mathcal{M}$. It is readily verified that the algorithm terminates in a finite number of steps because both $I$ and $Q$ are finite sets. For clarity of definition, only pairs of states are used for finding new sets; however, for practical purposes, larger sets of states (rather than just pairs of states) can be used both in Steps 1 and 2 for finding new classes of sets of states. We demonstrate this in subsequent examples.

Let $\Sigma$ denote the class obtained at the termination of the algorithm. To show that we obtain the final class by this algorithm we show first that no incompatible pair of states is included in any set of $\Sigma$. Assume that $S \in \Sigma$ and $\{q, q'\} \subseteq S$ but $q \sim q'$. From the definition of incompatibility if $q \sim q'$ there exists some input sequence $i_1, i_2, \ldots, i_p$, which is applicable to $\mathcal{M}$ in $q$ and also to $\mathcal{M}$ in $q'$. If $q, q_2, \ldots, q_p$ and $q', q_2', \ldots, q_p'$ are the respective state sequences produced by $i_1, i_2, \ldots, i_p$, then $\omega(q_p, i_p) \neq \omega(q_p', i_p)$. Since $\{q, q'\} \subseteq S$, then by Step 2 we must have $\{q_2, q_2'\}$ included in some set of $\Sigma$; otherwise Step 2 would have split $S$ into two sets $S - q$ and $S - q'$. Now assume $\{q_j, q_j'\}$ are together in some set of $\Sigma$; then $\{q_{j+1}, q_{j+1}'\}$ must also be included in some set of $\Sigma$, for $1 \leq j \leq p$, by a similar reason as for $\{q_2, q_2'\}$. Thus by induction $\{q_p, q_p'\}$ must be included in some set of $\Sigma$. But this is impossible since Step 1 splits any set into two sets if the outputs under some input are both defined and different, and by hypothesis $\omega(q_p, i_p) \neq \omega(q_p', i_p)$. Thus each set of $\Sigma$ is a compatible set for $\mathcal{M}$. Let us now suppose $S$ is a maximum compatible set for $\mathcal{M}$, but $S$ is not an element of $\Sigma$. Certainly, $S$ is not properly contained in any set of $\Sigma$ since each set of $\Sigma$ is a compatible and $S$ is a maximum compatible. Since $S$ is a subset of $Q$ and $S \notin \Sigma$, this means that at some step in the algorithm a pair of states $\{q_j, q_k\} \subseteq S$ were split to form a pair of new sets. This implies that $q_j \sim q_k$, where some sequence of inputs was found applicable to both $q_j$ and $q_k$, which lead to a pair of states split by Step 1. Since $\{q_j, q_k\} \subseteq S$ and $S$ is assumed to be a maximum compatible set, this contradiction proves that each maximum compatible is an element of $\Sigma$. Now since Step 3 eliminates any properly contained sets, it follows that $\Sigma$ is the final class for $\mathcal{M}$.

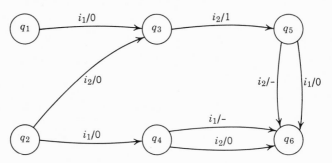

Figure 7.2.2.   A machine having several unspecified outputs and next states.

Several examples may help to illustrate the method of obtaining the final class.  First, reconsider the machine of Figure 7.2.1.

$$S_0 = Q = \{q_1, q_2, q_3\}.$$

By Step 1 we have $\omega(q_2, i_1) = w_1$ and $\omega(q_3, i_1) = w_2$; therefore we split $S_0$ into the two sets $S_3$ and $S_2$

$$S_0 = \{q_1, q_2, q_3\}$$

$$S_3 = \{q_1, q_2\} \qquad\qquad S_2 = \{q_1, q_3\}$$

Now the output for each state under input $i_2$ is equal to $w_1$ and the output of $q_1$ under input $i_1$ is undefined, so Step 1 is completed.  We must compute $T_{2,i_1}$, $T_{2,i_2}$, $T_{3,i_1}$, and $T_{3,i_2}$ for the class $Z = \{S_2, S_3\}$.  $T_{2,i_1} = \{q_1, q_2\}$ since $\tau(q_1, i_1) = q_1$ and $\tau(q_3, i_1) = q_2$.  Similarly,

$$T_{2,i_2} = \{q_1, q_2\},$$
$$T_{3,i_1} = \{q_1, q_3\},$$
$$T_{3,i_2} = \{q_1, q_2\}.$$

Since each $T_{k,i_j}$ is included in a set of the class $\{S_2, S_3\}$, no further changes are possible by Steps 2 and 3 and thus $\{S_2, S_3\}$ is the final class for the machine.

We now illustrate by diagrams rather than description how the algorithm is applied to the machine of Figure 7.2.2. The sets of states are denoted simply by sets of state indices, the $q$'s being omitted.

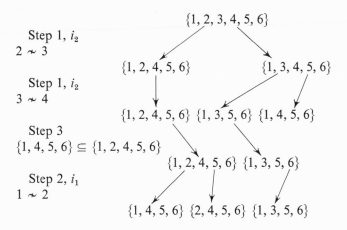

Step 1, $i_2$
2 ~ 3

Step 1, $i_2$
3 ~ 4

Step 3
$\{1, 4, 5, 6\} \subseteq \{1, 2, 4, 5, 6\}$

Step 2, $i_1$
1 ~ 2

Since no further separation occurs, the final class is $\{\{1, 4, 5, 6\}, \{2, 4, 5, 6\}, \{1, 3, 5, 6\}\}$.

As a final example consider the simple decoder shown in Figure 7.2.3. This machine is called a decoder because if it is assumed started in state $q_1$, the binary input sequences of length two can be interpreted as giving certain desired outputs. Here one might interpret input sequence 0, 1 as being decoded as output $w_1$ (or the binary equivalent to the number 1); input sequence 1, 0 as being decoded as output $w_2$ (or the binary equivalent of the number 2); and 1, 1 as being decoded as output $e$, which could

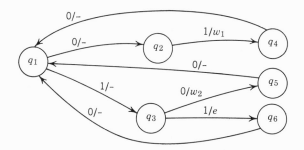

Figure 7.2.3.   A simple decoding machine.

mean an error. After each such sequence of length two, an input of 0 returns the machine to state $q_1$ so that it may again accept and decode length two input sequences. The final class calculation gives

$$\{1, 2, 3, 4, 5, 6\}$$

Step 1, input 1
2 ~ 3

$$\{1, 2, 4, 5, 6\} \qquad \{1, 3, 4, 5, 6\}$$

No further separation occurs and the final class is $Z = \{\{1, 2, 4, 5, 6\}, \{1, 3, 4, 5, 6\}\}$.

**Table 7.2.1**  Maximum Number of Sets $N$ in the Final Class for a Machine $\mathscr{M}$ with $n$ States

| $n$ | $N$ |
|---|---|
| 4 | 4 |
| 5 | 6 |
| 6 | 9 |
| 7 | 12 |
| 8 | 18 |
| 9 | 27 |
| 10 | 36 |
| 11 | 54 |
| 12 | 81 |
| 15 | 243 |
| 18 | 729 |
| 21 | 2187 |
| 27 | 6561 |

The compatibility relation for states of a sequential machine is very similar to that for decomposition discussed in Section 4.5, and the reader will also note the similarity of the respective algorithms for obtaining compatible sets.

In the three examples described so far the final class contains a relatively small number of compatible sets. Unfortunately, the final class may contain a very large number of sets, thus increasing both the complexity of the final class calculation and subsequent calculations. The maximum number of sets possible has been calculated as a function of the number of states in the original machine $\mathscr{M}$. Since a rather involved graph theoretical approach was used to solve this problem, we shall not give the proofs here; however, the following results are obtained.

Let $N$ = the maximum number of sets in the final class

and $n$ = the number of states in $\mathcal{M}$.

Then $N = 3^k$ for $n = 3k$,

$\qquad N = 2 \cdot 3^{k-1}$ for $n = 3k - 1$,

and $\qquad N = 4 \cdot 3^{k-1}$ for $n = 3k + 1$,

where $k = 1, 2, 3, \ldots$.

Several values of $n$ and $N$ are tabulated in Table 7.2.1 to illustrate the rather rapid growth of $N$ with increasing $n$.

An example of this effect is the machine shown in Figure. 7.2.4 which has six states and produces a final class containing nine sets.

Calculating the final class, using several shortcuts, we obtain

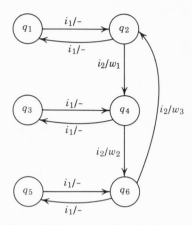

Figure 7.2.4. A machine which produces a final class with nine compatibles.

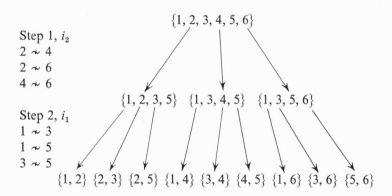

Step 1, $i_2$
2 ~ 4
2 ~ 6
4 ~ 6

Step 2, $i_1$
1 ~ 3
1 ~ 5
3 ~ 5

It is rather easy to see how this machine can be expanded into a machine with $n = 3k$ states for any positive integer $k$, where the maximum number $N$ is obtained for the number of sets in the final class.

The following sections show how the final class is related to obtaining a minimum state machine.

## 7.3 MACHINE INCLUSION AND EQUIVALENCE

With the definition of applicability of an input sequence to a machine starting in some state, we can compare the input-output properties of machines and thus give precision to the two earlier statements that "$\mathcal{M}'$

does as much and possibly more than $\mathcal{M}$" and that of finding a "minimum state machine for $\mathcal{M}$."

**Definition 7.3.1**  Let $\mathcal{M} = (Q, I, W, \tau, \omega)$ and $\mathcal{M}' = (Q', I', W', \tau', \omega')$, where $q_1 \in Q$ and $q_1' \in Q'$. We say that $\mathcal{M}'$ *in state* $q_1'$ *includes* $\mathcal{M}$ in state $q_1$ if for every input sequence $i_1, i_2, \ldots, i_p$ which is applicable to $\mathcal{M}$ in $q_1$ the following conditions hold:

1. $i_j \in I'$ for $1 \leq j \leq p$.
2. $i_1, i_2, \ldots, i_p$ is applicable to $\mathcal{M}'$ in $q_1'$.
3. Let $q_1, q_2, \ldots, q_p$ be the state sequence produced by $\mathcal{M}$ in $q_1$ and $q_1', q_2', \ldots, q_p'$ be the state sequence produced by $\mathcal{M}'$ in $q_1'$ under $i_1, i_2, \ldots, i_p$; then $\omega(q_p, i_p) \in W'$ and $\omega'(q_p', i_p) = \omega(q_p, i_p)$.

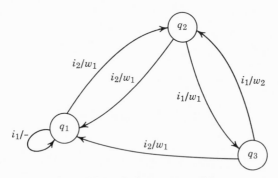

Figure 7.3.1.   A three state machine.

When and only when this definition holds would we say that "$\mathcal{M}'$ starting in state $q_1$ does as much and possibly more than $\mathcal{M}$ starting in state $q_1$." We also extend this to a relation between machines where we do not specify the starting state of each machine.

**Definition 7.3.2**  A machine $\mathcal{M}' = (Q', I', W', \tau', \omega')$ is said to *include* a machine $\mathcal{M} = (Q, I, W, \tau, \omega)$ if for every state $q \in Q$ there exists a $q' \in Q'$ such that $\mathcal{M}'$ in state $q'$ includes $\mathcal{M}$ in state $q$. We denote this relation by $\mathcal{M}' \supseteq \mathcal{M}$.

In Definition 7.3.1, consider the special case in which machine $\mathcal{M}'$ is the same machine as $\mathcal{M}$. In this case, it is readily verified that if $\mathcal{M}$ in state $q_i$ includes $\mathcal{M}$ in state $q_j$, then $q_i \sim q_j$. The converse, however, is not, in general, true. For example, reconsider the machine of Figure 7.2.1, shown again in Figure 7.3.1. We saw earlier that $q_1 \sim q_3$. Here input sequence $i_2, i_1$ is applicable to $\mathcal{M}$ in $q_1$, but it is not applicable to $\mathcal{M}$ in $q_3$; thus $\mathcal{M}$ in state $q_3$ does not include $\mathcal{M}$ in state $q_1$. Similarly, input sequence $i_2$, $i_2$, $i_1$ is applicable to $\mathscr{M}$ in $q_3$, but is not applicable to $\mathscr{M}$ in $q_1$; thus $\mathscr{M}$ in state $q_1$ does not include $\mathscr{M}$ in state $q_3$.

An example of machine inclusion between two different machines are machines $\mathscr{M}$ and $\mathscr{M}'$ of Figure 7.3.2. For $\mathscr{M}$ and $\mathscr{M}'$ we have that $\mathscr{M}'$ in state $q_1'$ includes $\mathscr{M}$ in state $q_1$. This can be shown by induction on the length of the input sequence. Certainly, $\mathscr{M}'$ in state $q_1'$ includes $\mathscr{M}$ in state $q_1$ for all input sequences of length 1 since $i_j$ is applicable to $\mathscr{M}$ in $q_1$ and also $\mathscr{M}'$ in $q_1'$ and $\omega(q_1, i_j) = \omega'(q_1', i_j)$, for $j = 1, 2$. Now suppose Definition 7.3.1 holds for all sequences of length $p - 1$. Starting in state

Machine $\mathscr{M}$

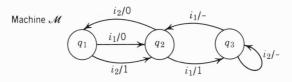

Machine $\mathscr{M}'$

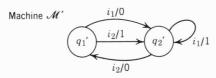

Figure 7.3.2. Inclusion between pairs of machines.

$q_1$ of $\mathscr{M}$, the last state of $\mathscr{M}$ after an input sequence of length $p - 1$ will be $q_1$, $q_2$, or $q_3$. If the last state is $q_3$, then concatenating another input onto the input sequence of length $p - 1$ gives a sequence of length $p$, but since $\omega(q_3, i_j)$ is undefined for either $j = 1$ or 2, the sequence is not applicable to $\mathscr{M}$ in $q_1$. Thus Definition 7.3.1 also holds. Now suppose the last state in $\mathscr{M}$ were $q_1$ after an input sequence of length $p - 1$. In this case the last input in the sequence must have been $i_2$ with output 0 since this is the only transition into $q_1$. But now since $\mathscr{M}'$ in $q_1'$ includes $\mathscr{M}$ in $q_1$ for this sequence of length $p - 1$, it follows that $\mathscr{M}'$ must have a last state of $q_1'$ for this sequence. Then, of course, concatenating a $p$th input onto the sequence simply takes $\mathscr{M}$ to $q_2$ and $\mathscr{M}'$ to $q_2'$, and the outputs are equal. Thus Definition 7.3.1 also holds in this case. A similar argument for $\mathscr{M}$ ending in state $q_2$ shows that $\mathscr{M}'$ must end in $q_2'$, from which it is easily checked that Definition 7.3.1 is again satisfied for any input sequence of length $p$. This proves the result that $\mathscr{M}'$ in state $q_1'$ includes $\mathscr{M}$ in state $q_1$.

It can also be shown that $\mathscr{M}'$ in state $q_2'$ includes $\mathscr{M}$ in state $q_2$, and $\mathscr{M}'$ in either state $q_1'$ or $q_2'$ includes $\mathscr{M}$ in state $q_3$. By applying Definition 7.3.2 directly we see that $\mathscr{M}' \supseteq \mathscr{M}$.

The inclusion relation for machines is reflexive; that is, $\mathcal{M} \supseteq \mathcal{M}$ for any machine $\mathcal{M}$. This follows directly from Definitions 7.3.2 and 7.3.1 if $\mathcal{M}'$ is identical to $\mathcal{M}$ and if $q'$ of Definition 7.3.2 is taken as state $q$ of $\mathcal{M}$. Furthermore, it follows immediately that the inclusion relation is transitive: if $\mathcal{M} \supseteq \mathcal{M}'$ and $\mathcal{M}' \supseteq \mathcal{M}''$, then $\mathcal{M} \supseteq \mathcal{M}''$. In general, the inclusion relation is not symmetric—$\mathcal{M} \supseteq \mathcal{M}'$ does not imply that $\mathcal{M}' \supseteq \mathcal{M}$. For example, if $\mathcal{M}$ is again considered to be the machine of Figure 7.3.1, and $\mathcal{M}'$ is exactly the same machine, except that the output $\omega'(q_1', i_1)$ is defined [say, $\omega'(q_1', i_1) = w_2$], certainly $\mathcal{M}' \supseteq \mathcal{M}$, but it is not true that $\mathcal{M} \supseteq \mathcal{M}'$. This can be shown as follows.

Input sequence $i_1$ is applicable to $\mathcal{M}'$ in state $q_1'$, but is not applicable to $\mathcal{M}$ in state $q_1$; thus $\mathcal{M}$ in state $q_1$ does not include $\mathcal{M}'$ in state $q_1'$. For state $q_1'$ of $\mathcal{M}'$, however, does either state $q_2$ or $q_3$ of $\mathcal{M}$ give the desired inclusion relation? Obviously, $q_2$ of $\mathcal{M}$ does not work since $\omega(q_2, i_1) = w_1$, but $\omega'(q_1', i_1) = w_2$. Similarly, $\mathcal{M}$ in state $q_3$ does not include $\mathcal{M}'$ in state $q_1'$ since input sequence $i_2, i_1$ is not applicable to $\mathcal{M}$ in $q_3$, but is applicable to $\mathcal{M}'$ in $q_1'$. For $\mathcal{M}$ and $\mathcal{M}'$ of Figure 7.3.2 it can also be shown that $\mathcal{M} \not\supseteq \mathcal{M}'$. How would this be shown? Since the inclusion relation between machines is not, in general, symmetric, it is not, in general, an equivalence relation. In particular cases, however, it may be symmetric, for which we say

**Definition 7.3.3**  If both $\mathcal{M} \supseteq \mathcal{M}'$ and $\mathcal{M}' \supseteq \mathcal{M}$, then we call $\mathcal{M}'$ *equivalent* to $\mathcal{M}$.

In Section 7.6 we show that for complete machines the inclusion relation between machines reduces automatically to an equivalence relation.

It should be noted that for any given machine $\mathcal{M}$, the inclusion relation defines a class of machines where each member $\mathcal{M}'$ is related to $\mathcal{M}$ by $\mathcal{M}' \supseteq \mathcal{M}$. This concept of the class of machines which includes $\mathcal{M}$ is useful in several ways. For example, if we wish to design a sequential network for $\mathcal{M}$, we may realize any member of the class of machines that includes $\mathcal{M}$ rather than $\mathcal{M}$ itself, thus possibly giving a better design than one obtained directly from $\mathcal{M}$. In general, the class of machines which includes a given machine $\mathcal{M}$ is infinite. Furthermore, given two machines $\mathcal{M}$ and $\mathcal{M}'$ it is not immediately evident how one determines whether the inclusion relation $\mathcal{M}' \supseteq \mathcal{M}$ holds between the two machines. Rather than concern ourselves with this problem, in the next sections we shall concentrate on generating a class of machines which includes some given machine $\mathcal{M}$, where this class also includes those machines which contain a minimum number of states. In particular, we shall be interested in giving a procedure for obtaining machines from this class which contain a minimum number of states.

## 7.4 COMPATIBLE SETS FOR STATE MINIMIZATION

We now show that compatible sets of states and machine inclusion are very closely related to the problem of determining a minimum state machine for a given machine. First, we define precisely the concept of a minimum state machine, and then discuss two minimization problems.

**Definition 7.4.1** A machine $\mathcal{M}' = (Q', I, W, \tau', \omega')$ is called *a reduction of* $\mathcal{M} = (Q, I, W, \tau, \omega)$ if $\mathcal{M}' \supseteq \mathcal{M}$ and $|Q'| \leq |Q|$.* $\mathcal{M}'$ is called a *minimum state machine for* $\mathcal{M}$ if for any machine $\mathcal{M}'' = (Q'', I, W, \tau'', \omega'')$ with $\mathcal{M}'' \supseteq \mathcal{M}$ it also follows that $|Q''| \geq |Q'|$. If $\mathcal{M}'$ is a minimum state machine for $\mathcal{M}$, we denote this by $\mathcal{M}' \overset{\text{min}}{\supseteq} \mathcal{M}$.

Given a machine $\mathcal{M}$ there may be more than one machine $\mathcal{M}'$ where $\mathcal{M}' \overset{\text{min}}{\supseteq} \mathcal{M}$ in the class of machines that are reductions of $\mathcal{M}$. Thus various types of machine minimization problems can be considered. For example, we might be interested in obtaining (1) all minimum state machines for $\mathcal{M}$ or (2) one minimum state machine for $\mathcal{M}$. Both these problems are considered here. Certain similarities and differences of these two minimization problems will become evident through some of the theorems developed in this and the following section.

Since sets of states of $\mathcal{M}$, having certain properties, are required for describing the class of machines that include the minimum state machines for $\mathcal{M}$, the following definitions are given.

**Definition 7.4.2** For a machine $\mathcal{M} = (Q, I, W, \tau, \omega)$ a set $T \subseteq Q$ of states is said to *follow* a set $S \subseteq Q$ under some input $i \in I$ when $t \in T$ if and only if there is a state $s \in S$ such that $(s, i) \in D_\tau$ and $\tau(s, i) = t$. We denote this relation by $S \xrightarrow{(\mathcal{M}, i)} T$.

For the machine of Figure 7.3.1 the set $\{q_1, q_2\}$ is seen to follow set $\{q_1, q_3\}$ under input $i_2$; thus $\{q_1, q_3\} \xrightarrow{(\mathcal{M}, i_2)} \{q_1, q_2\}$.

**Definition 7.4.3** Let $\mathcal{M} = (Q, I, W, \tau, \omega)$ be a machine and $\Sigma = \{S_1, \ldots, S_p\}$ be a class of sets of states of $\mathcal{M}$; that is, $S_j \subseteq Q$ for $1 \leq j \leq p$. For each $S_j \in \Sigma$ and each input $i \in I$, we define a subclass $\Sigma_{j,i}$ of $\Sigma$ as follows: $S \in \Sigma_{j,i}$ if and only if $S \in \Sigma$ and $S_j \xrightarrow{(\mathcal{M}, i)} T$ implies that $T \subseteq S$. The $\Sigma_{j,i}$ are called the *image subclasses* of $\Sigma$, since in each case the elements of $\Sigma_{j,i}$ are sets of $\Sigma$ that include the set $T$ which follows $S_j$ under input $i$.

---

* In this definitition and throughout the chapter, we use the notation $|Q|$ to denote the number of elements in the set $Q$; that is, the cardinality of $Q$.

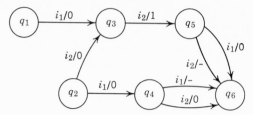

Figure 7.4.1.   Machine of Figure 7.2.2 redrawn.

In the special case that there is no state $q \in S_j$ such that $(q, i) \in D_r$; then $T$ is the empty set, and since the empty set is included in every set of $\Sigma$, $\Sigma_{j,i} = \Sigma$.

As an example of this definition, let $\Sigma$ be the final class for the machine shown in Figure 7.2.2. For clarity this figure is redrawn in Figure 7.4.1. Here $\Sigma = \{S_1, S_2, S_3\}$, where

$$S_1 = \{q_1, q_4, q_5, q_6\},$$
$$S_2 = \{q_2, q_4, q_5, q_6\},$$
$$S_3 = \{q_1, q_3, q_5, q_6\}.$$

For $S_2$, we have

$$S_2 \xrightarrow{(\mathcal{M}, i_1)} \{q_4, q_6\},$$

and since $\{q_4, q_6\}$ is included both in $S_1$ and $S_2$, we have that the image subclass

$$\Sigma_{2,i_1} = \{S_1, S_2\}.$$

Similarly, $S_1 \xrightarrow{(\mathcal{M}, i_1)} \{q_3, q_6\}$ so that $\Sigma_{1,i_1} = \{S_3\}$ since $S_3$ is the only set of $\Sigma$ which includes $\{q_3, q_6\}$.

The complete set of image subclasses for this machine and $\Sigma$, which may be checked by the reader, is

$$\Sigma_{1,i_1} = \{S_3\},$$
$$\Sigma_{1,i_2} = \{S_1, S_2, S_3\},$$
$$\Sigma_{2,i_1} = \{S_1, S_2\},$$
$$\Sigma_{2,i_2} = \{S_3\},$$
$$\Sigma_{3,i_1} = \{S_3\},$$
$$\Sigma_{3,i_2} = \{S_1, S_2, S_3\}.$$

For this same machine let us consider another class of sets of states $\Sigma' = \{S_1', S_2', S_3'\}$, where

$$S_1' = \{q_1, q_6\},$$
$$S_2' = \{q_2, q_3\},$$
$$S_3' = \{q_4, q_5\}.$$

Note that each state of the machine appears in exactly one $S_i'$. In this case, however, $\{q_2, q_3\} \xrightarrow{(\mathcal{M}, i_2)} \{q_3, q_5\}$ and $\{q_3, q_5\}$ is not included in any set of $\Sigma'$. Thus $\Sigma'_{2, i_2}$ is empty. Also, $\{q_1, q_6\} \xrightarrow{(\mathcal{M}, i_2)} \phi$ which displays the special case mentioned earlier in which $\Sigma'_{1, i_2} = \Sigma'$. The reader may check the following results.

$$
\begin{aligned}
\Sigma'_{1, i_1} &= \{S_2'\} & \Sigma'_{2, i_2} &= \phi, \\
\Sigma'_{1, i_2} &= \Sigma' & \Sigma'_{3, i_1} &= \{S_1'\}, \\
\Sigma'_{2, i_1} &= \{S_3'\} & \Sigma'_{3, i_2} &= \{S_1'\}.
\end{aligned}
$$

**Definition 7.4.4** Let $\mathcal{M} = (Q, I, W, \tau, \omega)$, let $\Sigma = \{S_1, \ldots, S_p\}$ with $S_j \subseteq Q$ for $1 \leq j \leq p$, and let $\Sigma_{j, i}$ be the image subclasses of $\Sigma$. The class $\Sigma$ is said to be *closed* if for every $i$ and $j$ ($1 \leq j \leq p$ and $i \in I$) it follows that $\Sigma_{j, i} \neq \phi$.

In other words, $\Sigma$ is closed if and only if for every $i \in I$ and $j$ such that $S_j \in \Sigma$, where $S_j \xrightarrow{(\mathcal{M}, i)} T$ it follows that $T \subseteq S_k$ for some $S_k \in \Sigma$.

The final class $\Sigma = \{S_1, S_2, S_3\}$ considered previously can be seen to be closed. However, $\Sigma'$ is not closed since $\Sigma'_{2, i_2} = \phi$. Similarly, if $\Sigma''$ is taken as

$$\Sigma'' = \{S_1'', S_2'', S_3''\},$$

where

$$
\begin{aligned}
S_1'' &= \{q_1, q_4, q_5, q_6\}, \\
S_2'' &= \{q_2, q_4, q_5, q_6\}, \\
S_3'' &= \{q_1, q_3, q_5\}.
\end{aligned}
$$

Then

$$S_1'' \xrightarrow{(\mathcal{M}, i_1)} \{q_3, q_6\},$$

and since $\{q_3, q_6\}$ is not included in any $S_j''$, $\Sigma''_{1, i_1} = \phi$ and $\Sigma''$ is not closed.

**Definition 7.4.5** If $\Delta$ and $\Pi$ are two classes of sets of states of $\mathcal{M}$, we say that $\Delta$ is *covered by* $\Pi$, or $\Pi$ *covers* $\Delta$, if for each set $D \in \Delta$ there exists a set $P \in \Pi$ such that $D \subseteq P$. We denote this relation by $\Delta \mathbin{C} \Pi$.

In particular, if $\Delta$ is the class of sets of states of $\mathcal{M}$ where $D \in \Delta$ if and only if $D = q \in Q$ (that is, each state is a set of $\Delta$), then we say that "all the states of $\mathcal{M}$ are covered by $\Pi$," meaning that each state of $\mathcal{M}$ is included in at least one set of $\Pi$.

As in the inclusion relation between machines, the covering relation between classes is transitive and reflexive but not necessarily symmetric.

For the machine of Figure 7.4.1 and the classes $\Sigma$, $\Sigma'$ and $\Sigma''$ defined previously, we have that $\Sigma'' \mathbin{C} \Sigma$, and certainly $\Sigma$ is not covered by $\Sigma''$.

Also, all states of $\mathcal{M}$ are covered by $\Sigma$, $\Sigma'$, or $\Sigma''$. Finally, we see that $\Sigma$ and $\Sigma'$ are not related by the covering relation. That is, $\Sigma \not\subset \Sigma'$ and $\Sigma' \not\subset \Sigma$.

**Definition 7.4.6**   A class $\Sigma$ of sets of states of a machine $\mathcal{M}$ is called a *C-class for $\mathcal{M}$* if

1. Every element of $\Sigma$ is a compatible.
2. $\Sigma$ is closed.
3. Every state of $\mathcal{M}$ is covered by $\Sigma$.
4. The empty set $\phi$ is not an element of $\Sigma$.

A *C*-class $\Sigma$ for $\mathcal{M}$ is called a *minimum C-class for $\mathcal{M}$* if every *C*-class $\Sigma'$ for $\mathcal{M}$ has $|\Sigma| \leq |\Sigma'|$.

Consider the class $\Sigma = \{S_1, S_2, S_3\}$ defined previously for the machine $\mathcal{M}$ of Figure 7.4.1. Since $\Sigma$ is the final class for $\mathcal{M}$, every element of $\Sigma$ (that is, every set) is a compatible set; thus condition (1) of Definition 7.4.6 is satisfied for $\Sigma$. Also, $\Sigma$ is closed as stated earlier, thus satisfying condition (2). Since every state of $\mathcal{M}$ appears in some set of $\Sigma$, condition (3) is also satisfied, and obviously condition (4) is satisfied. Thus $\Sigma$ is a *C*-class for $\mathcal{M}$.

The class $\Sigma' = \{S_1', S_2', S_3'\}$ fails to be a *C*-class for $\mathcal{M}$ since $S_2' = \{q_2, q_3\}$ is not a compatible and also since $\Sigma'$ is not closed. It may be checked, however, that the class $\{\{q_1, q_2\}, \{q_3, q_4\}, \{q_5, q_6\}\}$ fails to be a *C*-class for $\mathcal{M}$ only by condition (1), Definition 7.4.6. Similarly, $\Sigma''$ defined earlier fails to be a *C*-class for $\mathcal{M}$ only by condition (2) of the definition.

If we consider the class $\{\{q_2, q_4, q_6\}, \{q_1, q_3, q_5, q_6\}\}$, however, we shall find that this class is another *C*-class for $\mathcal{M}$, and since no single element *C*-class for $\mathcal{M}$ is possible, this class is a minimum *C*-class for $\mathcal{M}$.

As we shall see subsequently, from any *C*-class for a machine $\mathcal{M}$, we can define one or more machines, where each such machine $\mathcal{M}'$ is related to $\mathcal{M}$ by $\mathcal{M}' \supseteq \mathcal{M}$. Also, the minimum *C*-class will provide minimum state machines for $\mathcal{M}$. Before defining machines from *C*-classes, however, we present some further properties of *C*-classes.

**Definition 7.4.7**   A class $\Sigma$ of sets of states of a machine $\mathcal{M}$ is called *normal* when no set of $\Sigma$ is included in any other set of $\Sigma$. If $\Sigma$ is arbitrary, we call $\Sigma'$ the *normalization* of $\Sigma$ if

1. $\Sigma' \subseteq \Sigma$.
2. $\Sigma'$ is normal.
3. $\Sigma \complement \Sigma'$.

The normalization of any class $\Sigma$ gives a unique class $\Sigma'$.

In the following theorem, we see that condition (1) of Definition 7.4.6 for a $C$-class for $\mathcal{M}$ may be replaced by the condition (1a) given in the theorem.

**Theorem 7.4.1** A class $\Sigma = \{S_1, \ldots, S_p\}$ of $\mathcal{M} = (Q, I, W, \tau, \omega)$, which satisfies

(1a) For each $j$, $1 \leq j \leq p$, and each $i \in I$, if $q \in S_j$ and $q' \in S_j$, where $(q, i) \in D_\omega$ and $(q', i) \in D_\omega$ then $\omega(q, i) = \omega(q', i)$,

and also satisfies conditions (2), (3), and (4) of the $C$-class definition, is a $C$-class for $\mathcal{M}$. Conversely, a $C$-class for $\mathcal{M}$ satisfies condition (1a).

PROOF. If $\Sigma$ is a $C$-class for $\mathcal{M}$, then any set $S_j \in \Sigma$ is compatible by condition (1); thus for any pair of states $q$ and $q'$ which belong to $S_j$ and have $(q, i) \in D_\omega$ and $(q', i) \in D_\omega$, it follows directly from the definition of compatibility that $\omega(q, i) = \omega(q', i)$, since $i$ is an input sequence applicable to both $\mathcal{M}$ in $q$ and to $\mathcal{M}$ in $q'$. Thus condition (1a) is satisfied and the second part of the theorem is proved. To prove the first part of the theorem, let $p_1 \in S$, $q_1 \in S$, and $S \in \Sigma$. Assume that $p_1 \sim q_1$. Thus there exists some input sequence $i_1, i_2, \ldots, i_k$ which is applicable to both $\mathcal{M}$ in $p_1$ and $\mathcal{M}$ in $q_1$, which produces state sequences $p_1, p_2, \ldots, p_k$ and $q_1, q_2, \ldots, q_k$, respectively, where $(p_k, i_k) \in D_\omega$ and $(q_k, i_k) \in D_\omega$ and $\omega(p_k, i_k) \neq \omega(q_k, i_k)$. From condition (2) of Definition 7.4.6, $\Sigma$ is closed and thus $(p_j, q_j)$ is included in some set of $\Sigma$ for each $j$, $1 \leq j \leq k$. Then, however, $(p_k, q_k)$ violates condition (1a), and this contradiction proves that each set of $\Sigma$ is a compatible set, thus proving the theorem.

We now refer back to the class $\{\{q_1, q_2\}, \{q_3, q_4\}, \{q_5, q_6\}\}$ for the machine of Figure 7.4.1, which earlier was claimed to fail from being a $C$-class only by condition (1) of the $C$-class definition. By considering set $\{q_3, q_4\}$ we see that $\omega(q_3, i_2) = 1$ and $\omega(q_4, i_2) = 0$, thus showing that the class also fails condition (1a) of Theorem 7.4.1.

**Theorem 7.4.2** Let $\mathcal{M} = (Q, I, W, \tau, \omega)$, $S \subseteq Q$ and $i \in I$. If $S$ is compatible, and $S \xrightarrow{(\mathcal{M}, i)} T$, then $T$ is compatible.

PROOF. Let $p_1 \in T$ and $q_1 \in T$. Assume $p_1 \sim q_1$. Then there exists an input sequence $i_1, i_2, \ldots, i_k$ which is applicable to both $\mathcal{M}$ in $p_1$ and $\mathcal{M}$ in $q_1$, where if we let $p_1, p_2, \ldots, p_k$ and $q_1, q_2, \ldots, q_k$ be the state sequences produced by $\mathcal{M}$ in $p_1$ and $q_1$, respectively, under $i_1, i_2, \ldots, i_k$, it follows that $\omega(p_k, i_k) \neq \omega(q_k, i_k)$. By Definition 7.4.2, however, under input $i$, there exists two states $p_0$ and $q_0$, both elements of $S$ such that $\tau(p_0, i) = p_1$ and $\tau(q_0, i) = q_1$. Then $i, i_1, \ldots, i_k$ is applicable to both

$\mathcal{M}$ in $p_0$ and $q_0$, and since $\omega(p_k, i_k) \neq \omega(q_k, i_k)$, $p_0 \sim q_0$, thus contradicting the hypothesis that $S$ is compatible. This contradiction proves that $T$ is compatible.

**Corollary 7.4.2.1**    The final class of a machine $\mathcal{M}$ is a $C$-class for $\mathcal{M}$.

PROOF.    Let $\Phi$ be the final class of $\mathcal{M}$ and let $F \in \Phi$. Then $F$ is compatible and if $F \xrightarrow{(\mathcal{M}, i)} G$ for some $i \in I$, then by Theorem 7.4.2, $G$ is compatible and therefore $G$ is contained in some set of $\Phi$, since $\Phi$ is the class of all maximum compatibles for $\mathcal{M}$. This proves that $\Phi$ is closed. Thus conditions (1) and (2) of Definition 7.4.6 are satisfied. Obviously, conditions (3) and (4) of the definition are also satisfied, and thus, $\Phi$ is a $C$-class for $\mathcal{M}$.

This corollary thus corroborates our earlier conclusion that the final class for the machine of Figure 7.4.1 is a $C$-class for the machine. Another corollary gives further insight into the final class for a machine.

**Corollary 7.4.2.2**    Let $\mathcal{M}$ be a machine and $\Phi$ be a class of sets of states of $\mathcal{M}$. $\Phi$ is the final class for $\mathcal{M}$ if and only if $\Phi$ is a normal $C$-class for $\mathcal{M}$ and $\Phi$ covers every $C$-class for $\mathcal{M}$.

PROOF.    If $\Phi$ is the final class for $\mathcal{M}$, then from Corollary 7.4.2.1, $\Phi$ is a $C$-class for $\mathcal{M}$. By the definition of final class, $\Phi$ must be normal, and also $\Phi$ must cover every $C$-class for $\mathcal{M}$ since every set of a $C$-class must be a compatible, and each compatible is covered by some set in $\Phi$. Conversely assume that $\Psi$ is the final class for $\mathcal{M}$; then by hypothesis $\Psi C \Phi$ since $\Psi$ is a $C$ class for $\mathcal{M}$. Thus every set $K$ of $\Psi$ is included in a set $F \in \Phi$, $K \subseteq F$. Since $\Phi$ is a $C$-class by assumption, $F$ is compatible, and since $K$ is a maximum compatible, it follows that $K = F$. Thus every maximum compatible is an element of $\Phi$. Now since $\Phi$ is also normal by hypothesis, $\Phi$ contains only maximum compatibles, and thus $\Phi = \Psi$.

**Definition 7.4.8**    Let $\mathcal{M} = (Q, I, W, \tau, \omega)$, let $\Sigma = \{S_1, \ldots, S_p\}$ be a $C$-class for $\mathcal{M}$ with image subclasses $\Sigma_{j,i}$ and let $\mathcal{M}' = (Q', I, W, \tau', \omega')$, where $Q' = \{s_1, \ldots, s_p\}$. $\Sigma$ is said to *represent* $\mathcal{M}'$ if for each $j$ and $i$ with $1 \leq j \leq p$ and $i \in I$, the following conditions hold.

1. If there exists a state of $q \in S_j$ with $(q, i) \in D_\omega$, then $(s_j, i) \in D_{\omega'}$, and $\omega'(s_j, i) = \omega(q, i)$.
2. If there is a state $q \in S_j$ with $(q, i) \in D_\tau$, then $(s_j, i) \in D_{\tau'}$.
3. If $\tau'(s_j, i) = s_k$, then $S_k \in \Sigma_{j,i}$.

Note that this definition implies a one-to-one mapping of $\Sigma$ onto $Q'$; in particular, $S_j \to s_j$ for $1 \leq j \leq p$.

Machine $\mathcal{M}'$ is called *optimal for* $\Sigma$ if $\omega'$ and $\tau'$ are undefined except where required in (1), (2), and (3).

To illustrate this definition, consider the final class $\Sigma = \{S_1, S_2\}$ for the machine of Figure 7.3.1, where $S_1 = \{q_1, q_2\}$ and $S_2 = \{q_1, q_3\}$. Since $\Sigma$ is a $C$-class, we let $\{s_1, s_2\} = Q'$ be the set of states of the machine $\mathcal{M}'$ shown in Figure 7.4.2.

We shall verify that $\Sigma$ represents $\mathcal{M}'$ by checking that conditions (1), (2), and (3) are satisfied. For $q_1 \in S_1$, $(q_1, i_2) \in D_\omega$, and $\omega(q_1, i_2) = w_1$. Thus, for $\mathcal{M}'$, $(s_1, i_2) \in D_\omega$ and $\omega'(s_1, i_2) = w_1$. Since $(q_1, i_1) \notin D_\omega$, there is no requirement under condition (1) for this state input pair on the state input pair $(s_1, i_1)$ of $\mathcal{M}'$.

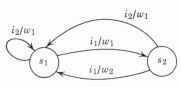

For $q_2 \in S_1$, both $(q_2, i_1) \in D_\omega$ and $(q_2, i_2) \in D_\omega$. We already have $(s_1, i_2) \in D_\omega$ and $\omega'(s_1, i_2) = w_1$, but since $\omega(q_2, i_2) = w_1$, this satisfies (1). $\omega(q_2, i_1) = w_1$ and also $\omega'(s_1, i_1) = w_1$. Thus condition (1) is satisfied for set $S_1$.

Figure 7.4.2. A machine $\mathcal{M}'$ represented by $\Sigma$ for $\mathcal{M}$ of Figure 7.3.1.

Similarly for $S_2$,

$$(q_1, i_1) \notin D_\omega,$$

$$\omega(q_1, i_2) = w_1,$$

$$\omega(q_3, i_1) = w_2,$$

$$\omega(q_3, i_2) = w_1,$$

$$\omega'(s_2, i_1) = w_2,$$

and

$$\omega'(s_2, i_2) = w_1,$$

so that (1) is satisfied for $S_2$.

We check conditions (2) and (3) as follows.

For

$$S_1 = \{q_1, q_2\},$$

$$\left.\begin{array}{l} \tau(q_1, i_1) = q_1 \\ \tau(q_2, i_1) = q_3 \end{array}\right] \Rightarrow \Sigma_{1, i_1} = \{S_2\},$$

$$\left.\begin{array}{l} \tau(q_1, i_2) = q_2 \\ \tau(q_2, i_2) = q_1 \end{array}\right] \Rightarrow \Sigma_{1, i_2} = \{S_1\},$$

and for $s_1$

$$\tau'(s_1, i_1) = s_2,$$

$$\tau'(s_1, i_2) = s_1,$$

so that (2) and (3) are satisfied for $S_1$.

For $$S_2 = \{q_1, q_3\},$$

$$\left.\begin{array}{l} \tau(q_1, i_1) = q_1 \\ \tau(q_3, i_1) = q_2 \end{array}\right] \Rightarrow \Sigma_{2, i_1} = \{S_1\},$$

$$\left.\begin{array}{l} \tau(q_1, i_2) = q_2 \\ \tau(q_3, i_2) = q_1 \end{array}\right] \Rightarrow \Sigma_{2, i_2} = \{S_1\},$$

and for $s_2$

$$\tau'(s_2, i_1) = s_1,$$
$$\tau'(s_2, i_2) = s_1.$$

Thus (2) and (3) are also satisfied for $S_2$, and $\Sigma$ represents $\mathcal{M}'$. Also, since $\omega'$ and $\tau'$ are defined only where required by the conditions of Definition 7.4.8, we see that $\mathcal{M}'$ is optimal for $\Sigma$.

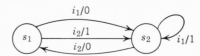

Figure 7.4.3.    Machine represented by final class for machine $\mathcal{M}$ of Figure 7.3.2.

As another example consider $\mathcal{M}$ of Figure 7.3.2. The final class for this machine is $\{\{q_1, q_3\}, \{q_2, q_3\}\}$. Letting $S_1 = \{q_1, q_3\}$ and $S_2 = \{q_2, q_3\}$ the following $\Sigma_{j, i}$ can be obtained.

$$\Sigma_{1, i_1} = \{S_2\},$$
$$\Sigma_{1, i_2} = \{S_2\},$$
$$\Sigma_{2, i_1} = \{S_2\},$$
$$\Sigma_{2, i_2} = \{S_1\}.$$

By applying Definition 7.4.8 to this $C$-class we obtain the machine shown in Figure 7.4.3. By referring to machine $\mathcal{M}'$ of Figure 7.3.2 we see that the machine of Figure 7.4.3 is identical to $\mathcal{M}'$, where $s_1 \equiv q_1'$ and $s_2 \equiv q_2'$ We also know that $\mathcal{M}' \supseteq \mathcal{M}$. This machine inclusion property is a general property of machines represented by $C$-classes, as we shall prove in Theorem 7.4.3.

**Definition 7.4.9**    A state $q$ of a machine $\mathcal{M}$ is called *degenerate* if no input sequence is applicable to $\mathcal{M}$ in $q$. $\mathcal{M}$ is called *degenerate* if $\mathcal{M}$ has at least one degenerate state; and $\mathcal{M}$ is called *nondegenerate* otherwise.

Given any machine $\mathcal{M}$, we may form a nondegenerate machine $\mathcal{M}'$ which is equivalent to $\mathcal{M}$ simply by deleting the degenerate states from

$\mathcal{M}$ and also deleting all transitions leading to or away from the degenerate states. Since this deletion does not affect any applicable input sequences, or the outputs produced by the applicable input sequences, it is obvious that the nondegenerate machine so produced is equivalent to $\mathcal{M}$.

The next theorem provides the basis for studying the $C$-classes of $\mathcal{M}$ when we are concerned with obtaining minimum state machines for $\mathcal{M}$. It is the basic theorem for state reduction of sequential machines.

A variant of this theorem was first proved by Paull and Unger [22], although their concept of applicability was slightly different from that used here. Some connections and variations of these concepts are discussed by Beatty and Miller in [2, 3].

**Theorem 7.4.3** If $\Sigma$ is a $C$-class for $\mathcal{M}$, then there exists a machine $\mathcal{M}'$ represented by $\Sigma$, and if $\Sigma$ represents $\mathcal{M}'$, then $\mathcal{M}' \supseteq \mathcal{M}$. If $\mathcal{M}$ is non-degenerate and $\mathcal{M}' \overset{\min}{\supseteq} \mathcal{M}$, then there exists a minimum $C$-class for $\mathcal{M}$ which represents $\mathcal{M}'$.

PROOF. Suppose $\Sigma = \{S_1, S_2, \ldots, S_p\}$ is a $C$-class for $\mathcal{M}$. Then an $\mathcal{M}' = (Q', I, W, \tau', \omega')$ represented by $\Sigma$ can be defined as follows. Let $Q' = \{s_1, s_2, \ldots, s_p\}$ where there is a one-to-one correspondence between $S_j$ and $s_j$, $1 \leq j \leq p$. By assumption, sets $I$ and $W$ of $\mathcal{M}'$ are equal to $I$ and $W$ of $\mathcal{M}$.

Let $\Sigma_{j,i}$ be the image subclass of $S_j$ under input $i$; then, since $\Sigma$ is a $C$-class for $\mathcal{M}$, $\Sigma_{j,i}$ is not empty for any $j$ or $i$. We define $\tau'(s_j, i) = s_k$, where $S_k$ is an arbitrary element of $\Sigma_{j,i}$. This defines $\tau'$ for $\mathcal{M}'$, giving a transition complete machine. Finally, we define $\omega'(s_j, i)$ as follows. If there exists a $q \in S_j$ such that $(q, i) \in D_\omega$, then let $\omega'(s_j, i) = \omega(q, i)$; otherwise let $(s_j, i) \notin D_{\omega'}$. From Theorem 7.4.1, it follows that $\omega'(s_j, i)$, if defined, must be unique. With this definition for $\mathcal{M}'$, it follows directly that $\mathcal{M}'$ satisfies Definition 7.4.8 so that $\Sigma$ represents $\mathcal{M}'$.

Now suppose that $\Sigma = \{S_1, S_2, \ldots, S_p\}$ is a $C$-class for $\mathcal{M}$ and $\Sigma$ represents $\mathcal{M}' = (Q', I, W, \tau', \omega')$; then $Q' = \{s_1, s_2, \ldots, s_p\}$ by Definition 7.4.8. To prove that $\mathcal{M}' \supseteq \mathcal{M}$, we must show that for any state $q$ of $\mathcal{M}$ there exists a state of $q'$ of $\mathcal{M}'$ such that $\mathcal{M}'$ in $q'$ includes $\mathcal{M}$ in $q$. For state $q$ of $\mathcal{M}$, if $q$ is degenerate, then no input sequences are applicable to $\mathcal{M}$ in $q$, so any state $s_j$ of $\mathcal{M}'$ has the property that $\mathcal{M}'$ in $s_j$ includes $\mathcal{M}$ in $q$; thus, we need only consider nondegenerate states of $\mathcal{M}$.

Let $q$ be a nondegenerate state of $\mathcal{M}$. Since $\Sigma$ is a $C$-class for $\mathcal{M}$, $q$ is an element of some set in $\Sigma$, let $q \in S_j$. We wish to show that $\mathcal{M}'$ in $s_j$ includes $\mathcal{M}$ in $q$. Let $i_1, i_2, \ldots, i_k$ be an input sequence which is applicable to $\mathcal{M}$ in $q$; let $q, q_2, \ldots, q_k$ be the state sequence produced, and let $\omega(q_k, i_k)$ be the final output produced by $\mathcal{M}$ in $q$ under this input sequence. Now $(s_j, i_1) \in D_{\tau'}$ for $\mathcal{M}'$ by condition (2) of Definition 7.4.8, since $\Sigma$ represents

$\mathcal{M}'$ and $(q, i_1) \in D_r$. Let $\tau'(s_j, i_1) = s_{j,2}$, where $s_{j,2}$ is some state of $\mathcal{M}'$. Let $S_{j,2}$ denote the set of $\Sigma$ defined by the one-to-one mapping of $\Sigma$ onto $Q'$. Then by condition (3) of Definition 7.4.8, it follows that $S_{j,2} \in \Sigma_{j,i_1}$, and in particular, $q_2 \in S_{j,2}$. Extending this notation, assume that $\tau'(s_{j,r}, i_r) = s_{j,r+1}$, $S_{j,r} \in \Sigma_{j,i_{r-1}}$, and $q_r \in S_{j,r}$ for $1 \leq r \leq k$. Then by induction, it follows that $S_{j,r+1} \in \Sigma_{j,i_r}$. In particular, $S_{j,k} \in \Sigma_{j,i_{k-1}}$ and $q_k \in S_{j,k}$. The state sequence produced by $\mathcal{M}'$ in $s_j$ under input sequence $i_1, i_2, \ldots, i_k$ is then $s_j, s_{j,2}, \ldots, s_{j,k}$. Now by condition (1) of Definition 7.4.8, since $(q_k, i_k) \in D_\omega$, and $\omega(q_k, i_k) = \omega'(s_{j,k}, i_k)$, it follows that $\mathcal{M}'$ in $s_j$ includes $\mathcal{M}$ in $q$. Now since $q$ of $\mathcal{M}$ is an arbitrary state of $\mathcal{M}$, the first part of the theorem is proved, namely, $\mathcal{M}' \supseteq \mathcal{M}$.

We now prove the second part of the theorem. Assume $\mathcal{M}$ is non-degenerate and $\mathcal{M}' \overset{\text{min}}{\supseteq} \mathcal{M}$. Since $\mathcal{M}$ is nondegenerate, each state $q$ of $\mathcal{M}$ has at least one input sequence (call it $i, i_2, \ldots, i_k$) which is applicable to $\mathcal{M}$ in $q$. Thus, for each state $q$ of $\mathcal{M}$, there exists a state $q'$ of $\mathcal{M}'$ such that $\mathcal{M}'$ in $q'$ includes $\mathcal{M}$ in $q$. Let $Q' = \{q_1', q_2', \ldots, q_n'\}$ of $\mathcal{M}'$. Let the class $\Sigma = \{S_1, S_2, \ldots, S_n\}$ of sets of states of $\mathcal{M}$ be defined as follows: $q \in S_j$ if and only if $\mathcal{M}'$ in $q_j'$ includes $\mathcal{M}$ in $q$. Since $\mathcal{M}$ is nondegenerate, it follows that each state $q$ of $\mathcal{M}$ appears in at least one $S_j \in \Sigma$. Thus every state of $\mathcal{M}$ is covered by $\Sigma$, so that $\Sigma$ satisfies condition (3) of the definition for a $C$-class. Assume that $q$ and $p$, both states of $\mathcal{M}$, are contained in some set $S_j \in \Sigma$ and for some input $i \in I$, $(q, i) \in D_\omega$, and $(p, i) \in D_\omega$ but $\omega(q, i) \neq \omega(p, i)$. By the definition of $\Sigma$, states $p$ and $q$, being elements of $S_j$, means that $\mathcal{M}'$ in $q_j'$ includes $\mathcal{M}$ in $p$ and $\mathcal{M}'$ in $q_j'$ includes $\mathcal{M}$ in $q$. By assumption, the input sequence consisting of the single input $i$ is applicable to $\mathcal{M}$ in $p$ and thus the input sequence $i$ is also applicable to $\mathcal{M}'$ in $q_j'$ and thus $\omega'(q_j', i) = \omega(p, i)$. Similarly, $\omega'(q_j', i) = \omega(q, i)$, but this is impossible since $\omega(p, i) \neq \omega(q, i)$ by assumption. Thus it follows that $\Sigma$ satisfies condition (1a) of Theorem 7.4.1 for a $C$-class of $\mathcal{M}$.

If conditions (2) and (4) can now be shown to be satisfied by $\Sigma$, then $\Sigma$ will be proved to be a $C$-class for $\mathcal{M}$. Assume that $\Sigma$ is not closed. Then there exists some $S_j \in \Sigma$ and $i \in I$ such that $S_j \xrightarrow{(\mathcal{M}, i)} T$ and $T \nsubseteq S_k$ for any $S_k \in \Sigma$. Thus for each $S_k \in \Sigma$, there exists a pair of states $\{p(k), q(k)\} \subseteq T$ such that $\{p(k), q(k)\} \nsubseteq S_k$. Let $p_0$ and $q_0$ be elements of $S_j$ such that $\tau(p_0, i) = p(k)$ and $\tau(q_0, i) = q(k)$. Now, $\mathcal{M}'$ in $q_k'$ does not include both $\mathcal{M}$ in $p(k)$ and $\mathcal{M}$ in $q(k)$, since $\{p(k), q(k)\} \nsubseteq S_k$; thus there exists some input sequence $i_1, i_2, \ldots, i_p$ which is applicable to both $\mathcal{M}$ in $p(k)$ and $\mathcal{M}$ in $q(k)$ where this input sequence produces different outputs. Then the input sequence $i, i_1, \ldots, i_p$ is applicable to both $\mathcal{M}$ in $p_0$ and $\mathcal{M}$ in $q_0$, again producing different outputs. This implies that $p_0$ and $q_0$ are not included in any $S \in \Sigma$, which contradicts the assumption and proves that $\Sigma$ is closed.

Finally, assume that some sets of $\Sigma$ are empty. Form $\Sigma''$ by deleting all empty sets of $\Sigma'$, then $\Sigma''$ is a *C*-class for $\mathcal{M}$. From the first part of the theorem, $\Sigma''$ represents a machine $\mathcal{M}''$, where $\mathcal{M}'' \supseteq \mathcal{M}$, and $\mathcal{M}''$ has fewer states than $\mathcal{M}'$. This contradicts the hypothesis that $\mathcal{M}' \overset{min}{\supseteq} \mathcal{M}$. Thus $\Sigma$ is a *C*-class for $\mathcal{M}$, and since any other *C*-class for $\mathcal{M}$ with fewer sets than $\Sigma$ would give a machine that includes $\mathcal{M}$ of fewer states than $\mathcal{M}'$, it follows that $\Sigma$ is a minimum *C*-class for $\mathcal{M}$, and the theorem is proved.

Having proved Theorem 7.4.3 we can see immediately that $\mathcal{M}'$ and $\mathcal{M}$ of Figure 7.3.2 are related by $\mathcal{M}' \supseteq \mathcal{M}$. This follows from the fact that $\mathcal{M}'$ is a machine that is represented by a *C*-class for $\mathcal{M}$, as shown in the discussion for Figure 7.4.3, and thus the inclusion relation automatically holds by Theorem 7.4.3. Thus the inductive proof given in Section 7.3 is unnecessary. By this theorem also, the machine $\mathcal{M}'$ of Figure 7.4.2 is seen to be related by $\mathcal{M}' \supseteq \mathcal{M}$ for $\mathcal{M}$ of Figure 7.3.1.

Since we are particularly interested in obtaining machines $\mathcal{M}'$ such that $\mathcal{M}' \overset{min}{\supseteq} \mathcal{M}$, we state the following corollary of Theorem 7.4.3.

**Corollary 7.4.3.1** Let $\Sigma$ be a minimum *C*-class for $\mathcal{M}$. Then $\Sigma$ represents some minimum state machine for $\mathcal{M}$. Also if $\Sigma$ represents $\mathcal{M}'$, then $\mathcal{M}' \overset{min}{\supseteq} \mathcal{M}$.

PROOF. This follows directly from Theorem 7.4.3, for if $\Sigma$ is a minimum *C*-class for $\mathcal{M}$, there is a machine $\mathcal{M}'$ represented by $\Sigma$ and $\mathcal{M}' \supseteq \mathcal{M}$. Now, if $\mathcal{M}$ is nondegenerate and $\mathcal{M}* \overset{min}{\supseteq} \mathcal{M}$, there exists a minimum *C*-class $\Sigma*$ for $\mathcal{M}$ such that $\Sigma*$ represents $\mathcal{M}*$. However, $\Sigma$ must have the same number of sets as $\Sigma*$ since $\Sigma$ is also a minimum *C*-class for $\mathcal{M}$. Thus $\mathcal{M}'$ has the same number of states as $\mathcal{M}*$ so that $\mathcal{M}' \overset{min}{\supseteq} \mathcal{M}$.

Now, if $\mathcal{M}$ is degenerate, let $\mathcal{M}''$ be the nondegenerate machine equivalent to $\mathcal{M}$, and let $\mathcal{M}* \overset{min}{\supseteq} \mathcal{M}''$. Then there is a minimum *C*-class $\Sigma''$ for $\mathcal{M}''$ such that $\Sigma''$ represents $\mathcal{M}*$. Let $\Sigma*$ for $\mathcal{M}$ be formed by adding the degenerate states of $\mathcal{M}$ to each set of $\Sigma''$. Then $|\Sigma*| = |\Sigma''|$. It can be shown that $\Sigma*$ is a minimum *C*-class for $\mathcal{M}$, and thus, as before, we conclude that $\mathcal{M}' \overset{min}{\supseteq} \mathcal{M}$—proving the corollary.

Returning to the two examples just discussed, it is easily seen that the final class $\{\{q_1, q_3\}, \{q_2, q_3\}\}$ for $\mathcal{M}$ of Figure 7.3.2 is a minimum *C*-class for $\mathcal{M}$. (The only possible class of states with fewer sets in which every state of $\mathcal{M}$ is covered would be $\{\{q_1, q_2, q_3\}\}$, and the set $\{q_1, q_2, q_3\}$ is not compatible.) Thus $\mathcal{M}'$ of Figure 7.4.3 is a minimum state machine for

$\mathcal{M}$ of Figure 7.3.2. By similar reasoning for $\mathcal{M}'$ of Figure 7.4.2 and $\mathcal{M}$ of Figure 7.3.1, we obtain $\mathcal{M}' \overset{\text{min}}{\supseteq} \mathcal{M}$.

The problem of finding one minimum state machine $\mathcal{M}'$ for $\mathcal{M}$ is thus reduced to finding a minimum $C$-class $\Sigma$ for $\mathcal{M}$, since $\Sigma$ represents a machine $\mathcal{M}'$ such that $\mathcal{M}' \overset{\text{min}}{\supseteq} \mathcal{M}$. Also from Theorem 7.4.3, each minimum state machine for a nondegenerate machine $\mathcal{M}$ is represented by some minimum $C$-class for $\mathcal{M}$. Since from Corollary 7.4.2.2, the final class covers every $C$-class for $\mathcal{M}$, the final class is useful in obtaining minimum $C$-classes.

Given the final class for $\mathcal{M}$, we now wish to consider the problem of obtaining a minimum $C$-class for $\mathcal{M}$. Although, in the previous two examples of this section, this was particularly simple, in general, there may be many possible classes of subsets of the sets of the final class to consider as possible minimum $C$-classes for $\mathcal{M}$, and it is necessary to explore them. For example, the final class for the machine of Figure 7.2.4 contained nine sets of states where each set contained two states. Thus there are numerous different classes in which each set of a class is a compatible. A search through all of them, testing each for satisfaction of the $C$-class properties, although finite, would indeed be rather tedious. In the next section we discuss various properties that reduce the search; first, however, we give some simple upper and lower bounds that limit the number of sets that are necessary to choose from for minimum $C$-classes for $\mathcal{M}$; then we show several examples of using these bounds to obtain minimum $C$-classes and minimum machines for $\mathcal{M}$.

Let

$p =$ the number of sets in a minimum $C$-class for $\mathcal{M}$,

$n = |Q|$,

$N =$ the number of sets in the final class,

$x =$ the minimum number of sets in any subclass $\Pi$ of the final class such that all the states of $\mathcal{M}$ are covered by $\Pi$.

Then

$$x \leq p \leq \min(n, N).$$

By condition (3) for a $C$-class for $\mathcal{M}$, it follows that $x \leq p$. Since $\mathcal{M} \supseteq \mathcal{M}$, it follows that $p \leq n$, and also since the final class is a $C$-class for $\mathcal{M}$, $p \leq N$. If $x = \min(n, N)$, the final class is a minimum $C$-class for $\mathcal{M}$; otherwise, searching of classes having between $x$ and $\min(n, N)$ sets is required to obtain a minimum $C$-class. Conditions (2) and (3) for a $C$-class are particularly useful in eliminating possible classes as minimum $C$-classes for $\mathcal{M}$. Also, as $C$-classes for $\mathcal{M}$ are found that have fewer than $\min(n, N)$ sets, the upper bound can be reduced to one less than the best

*C*-class so far attained, thus eliminating further inspection of classes of higher cardinality.

Let us reconsider the machine of Figure 7.4.1 which is shown again in Figure 7.4.4. The final class for this machine, as calculated previously, is

$$\{\{1, 4, 5, 6\}, \{2, 4, 5, 6\}, \{1, 3, 5, 6\}\}.$$

Calculating the bounds on $p$, we obtain $2 \leq p \leq 3$, since the cardinality of the subclass $\Sigma = \{\{2, 4, 5, 6\}, \{1, 3, 5, 6\}\}$ is two and this subclass of the

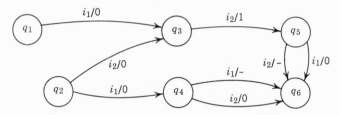

Figure 7.4.4.   Machine of Figure 7.2.2 and 7.4.1.

final class also covers the states of $\mathscr{M}$. Computing the sets that follow the sets of $\Sigma$, we obtain

$$\{2, 4, 5, 6\} \xrightarrow{(\mathscr{M}, i_1)} \{4, 6\},$$

$$\{2, 4, 5, 6\} \xrightarrow{(\mathscr{M}, i_2)} \{3, 6\},$$

$$\{1, 3, 5, 6\} \xrightarrow{(\mathscr{M}, i_1)} \{3, 6\},$$

$$\{1, 3, 5, 6\} \xrightarrow{(\mathscr{M}, i_2)} \{5, 6\}.$$

Thus $\Sigma$ is a minimum *C*-class for $\mathscr{M}$. We should also note that state $q_5$ is in both sets of $\Sigma$. In this example, if $q_5$ is eliminated from either of these sets, we would obtain another *C*-class, as can be checked by the reader. Thus

$$\Sigma' = \{\{2, 4, 6\}, \{1, 3, 5, 6\}\},$$

and

$$\Sigma' = \{\{2, 4, 5, 6\}, \{1, 3, 6\}\},$$

are also minimum *C*-classes for $\mathscr{M}$.

Note that in the previous example, where the class $\{\{q_1, q_2\}, \{q_1, q_3\}\}$ was found to be a minimum *C*-class for the machine of Figure 7.3.1, even though $q_1$ appears in both sets, it is not possible to eliminate $q_1$ from either set and still have a $C$-class. The reader can check this by showing that neither class $\{\{q_2\}, \{q_1, q_3\}\}$ nor class $\{\{q_1, q_2\}, \{q_3\}\}$ is closed.

Thus, as this example demonstrates, it is not always possible to obtain

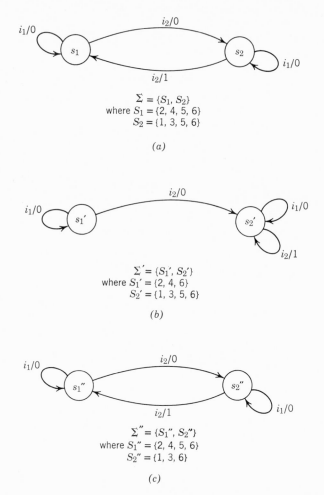

$$\Sigma = \{S_1, S_2\}$$
where $S_1 = \{2, 4, 5, 6\}$
$S_2 = \{1, 3, 5, 6\}$

(*a*)

$$\Sigma' = \{S_1', S_2'\}$$
where $S_1' = \{2, 4, 6\}$
$S_2' = \{1, 3, 5, 6\}$

(*b*)

$$\Sigma'' = \{S_1'', S_2''\}$$
where $S_1'' = \{2, 4, 5, 6\}$
$S_2'' = \{1, 3, 6\}$

(*c*)

Figure 7.4.5.   Several minimum state machines for the machine of Figure 7.4.4.

a minimum $C$-class which is simply a partition of the set of states of $\mathcal{M}$. This property adds an intriguing complexity to the problem of finding minimum $C$-classes for a given machine $\mathcal{M}$.

Minimum state machines represented by $\Sigma$, $\Sigma'$, and $\Sigma''$ for the machine of Figure 7.4.4 are shown in Figure 7.4.5*a*, *b*, and *c*, respectively.

The procedure to obtain a machine $\mathcal{M}'$ represented by $\Sigma$ (and, in fact,

| $\Sigma'$ | | $S_1$ (2, 4, 6) | $S_2$ (1, 3, 5, 6) |
|---|---|---|---|
| T Sets | $i_1$ | 4 6 – | 3 – 6 – |
| | $i_2$ | 3 6 – | – 5 6 – |
| Outputs | $i_1$ | 0 – – | 0 – 0 – |
| | $i_2$ | 0 0 – | – 1 – – |

Figure 7.4.6. Tabular form to find a machine represented by $\Sigma'$.

optimal for $\Sigma$) is straightforward. Given $\Sigma$, we compute the sets $T$ for each $S_j \in \Sigma$ and each $i \in I$. Then in $\mathcal{M}'$ we let $\tau'(s_j, i)$ be undefined if $T$ for $S_j \xrightarrow{(\mathcal{M}, i)} T$ is empty; otherwise we define $\tau'(s_j, i) = s_k$, where $S_k$ is any set of $\Sigma$ such that $T \subseteq S_k$. Since $\Sigma$ is closed, there must be at least one $S_k \in \Sigma$ which includes $T$ for each possible set $T$. Similarly, we define $\omega'(s_j, i)$ as follows. If there exists a $q \in S_j$ such that $(q, i) \in D_\omega$, then we let $\omega'(s_j, i) = \omega(q, i)$. If no such $q$ exists, then let $(s_j, i) \notin D_{\omega'}$. It immediately follows that the $\mathcal{M}'$ so defined is represented by $\Sigma$ and also is optimal for $\Sigma$.

This procedure can be illustrated by a tabular form, as shown in Figure 7.4.6, for $\Sigma'$ and the machine of Figure 7.4.4. By the procedure then $\tau'(s_1', i_1) = s_k$ must be defined since this $T = \{4, 6\}$. Since $\{4, 6\}$ is included in $S_1$, $\tau'(s_1', i_1) = s_1$. The other transitions and outputs can be checked by the reader.

The tabular form to find a machine represented by $\Sigma$ of Figure 7.4.5 is shown in Figure 7.4.7. In this case, we see that the $T$ set for $S_2$ under input $i_2$ is the set $\{5, 6\}$. Thus the transition from $s_2$ under input $i_2$ could be defined as either $\tau'(s_2, i_2) = s_1$ or $\tau'(s_2, i_2) = s_2$ since set $\{5, 6\}$ is included both in $S_1$ or $S_2$. Thus we see that more than one machine may be represented by a single $C$-class. For the machine shown in Figure 7.4.5a,

| $\Sigma$ | | $S_1$ (2, 4, 5, 6) | $S_2$ (1, 3, 5, 6) |
|---|---|---|---|
| T Sets | $i_1$ | 4 6 6 – | 3 – 6 – |
| | $i_2$ | 3 6 6 – | – 5 6 – |
| Outputs | $i_1$ | 0 – 0 – | 0 – 0 – |
| | $i_2$ | 0 0 – – | – 1 – – |

Figure 7.4.7. Tabular form to find a machine represented by $\Sigma$.

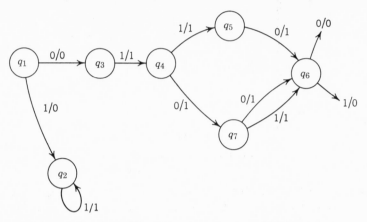

Figure 7.4.8   A machine with next states unspecified for state $q_6$.

we defined this transition as $\tau'(s_2, i_2) = s_1$, and this machine is identical to that represented by $\Sigma''$. If, however, $\tau'(s_2, i_2) = s_2$ were used, then a machine identical to that represented by $\Sigma'$ would have been obtained. For this example, it can be shown that $\Sigma$, $\Sigma'$, and $\Sigma''$ are the only minimum $C$-classes for $\mathcal{M}$, and it also follows that the machines of Figure 7.4.5$b$ and $c$ are the only possible minimum state machines for $\mathcal{M}$.

As our next example, we consider the machine shown in Figure 7.4.8 in which the next states under inputs 0 to 1 are unspecified for state $q_6$, but the outputs are specified as 0 for both inputs.  The final class calculation gives

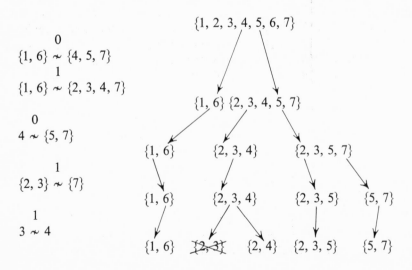

| Input \ Σ | $S_1$ | $S_2$ | $S_3$ | $S_4$ |
|---|---|---|---|---|
|  | 1, 6 | 2, 4 | 2, 3, 5 | 7 |
| 0 | 3/0 –/0 – | 7/1 – | – 6/1 | 6/1 |
| 1 | 2/0 –/0 | 2/1 5/1 | 2/1 4/1 – | 6/1 |
| States of $\mathscr{M}'$ | $s_1$ | $s_2$ | $s_3$ | $s_4$ |

Figure 7.4.9   Tabular form to find $\mathscr{M}'$.

Calculating the bounds on the minimum state machine, we obtain $4 \le p \le \min\{6, 4\} = 4$. Thus the final class is a minimum $C$-class; also eliminating 5 from set $\{5, 7\}$ we obtain

$$\Sigma = \{\{1, 6\}, \{2, 4\}, \{2, 3, 5\}, \{7\}\},$$

which is also a $C$-class for $\mathscr{M}$. Figure 7.4.9 shows a tabular form in which the next states and outputs are specified as done previously in flow charts. For the transition from $s_1$ under input 1, we have a choice of going to either $s_2$ or $s_3$ since $q_2$ of $\mathscr{M}$ appears in both $S_2$ and $S_3$. Two possible reduced machines thus exist for this set $\Sigma$. Figure 7.4.10 shows the machine when the choice $\omega'(s_1, 1) = s_2$ is made.

It is interesting to note that in the original machine of Figure 7.4.8, state $q_2$ has a self-loop with input/output 1/1, but in the reduced machine of Figure 7.4.10, this self-loop does not appear but has been replaced by two transitions of 1/1, one from $s_2$ to $s_3$ and the other from $s_3$ to $s_2$. This change arises from the fact that $q_2$ appears in the two compatibles $\{2, 4\}$ and $\{2, 3, 5\}$ and that it cannot be removed from either compatible without violating the closure requirement for a $C$-class.

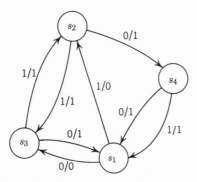

Figure 7.4.10   A minimum state machine for Figure 7.4.8.

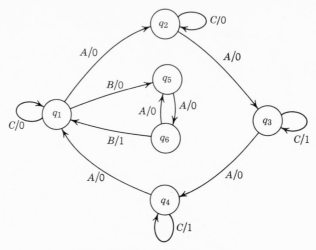

Figure 7.4.11    A six state machine.

In the next example, Figure 7.4.11, no reduction can be made if the unspecified transitions and outputs are completed on the machine before reduction is tried. This surprising fact was first discovered by Ginsburg, and is related to the fact that it may be necessary to have nondisjoint sets to obtain a minimum $C$-class. The machine can be reduced to the four state machine shown in Figure 7.4.12, however, since the final class is $\{\{1, 5\}, \{2, 6\}, \{3, 5\}, \{4, 6\}, \{5, 6\}\}$, and a minimum $C$-class is $\{\{1, 5\}, \{2, 6\}, \{3, 5\}, \{4, 6\}\}$.

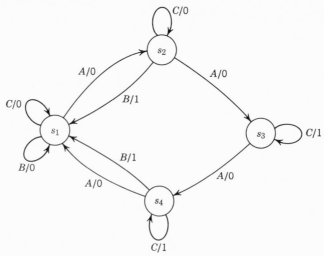

Figure 7.4.12    A minimum state machine for Figure 7.4.11.

## 7.5 ADDITIONAL PROPERTIES FOR SEQUENTIAL MACHINES WITH APPLICATIONS TO STATE MINIMIZATION

It has been established in Section 7.4 that a minimum state machine for any given machine $\mathcal{M}$ can be obtained by finding a minimum $C$-class for $\mathcal{M}$. Since the final class for $\mathcal{M}$ covers every $C$-class for $\mathcal{M}$ (Corollary 7.4.2.2), we can proceed to find a minimum $C$-class for $\mathcal{M}$ as follows. First, obtain the final class for $\mathcal{M}$ by the final class algorithm described in Section 7.2 or some other algorithm; second, calculate the bounds on the minimum $C$-class given in Section 7.4; third, search for a class of compatible sets (that is, each set being a subset of a set of the final class) which is a $C$-class and falls within the desired bounds; and last, continue searching for such a $C$-class until minimality can be proved.

This procedure for obtaining a minimum $C$-class is certainly finite, but in some instances it may require considerable searching. As was seen in Section 7.2, the final class for a machine $\mathcal{M}$ might contain a very large number of sets. This, combined with a large difference between the upper and lower bounds on the number of states in a minimum state machine for $\mathcal{M}$, could mean that many classes of sets of states for $\mathcal{M}$ may have to be searched before a minimum $C$-class for $\mathcal{M}$ is found. Thus in this section we seek properties of sequential machines that tend to reduce the number of classes which could possibly be $C$-classes for a given machine, thus reducing the search for minimum $C$-classes.

An example of a machine with many possible $C$-classes is the six-state machine of Figure 7.2.4 which has a final class containing nine maximum compatible sets. The bounds on $p$ (the number of sets in a minimum $C$-class for $\mathcal{M}$) are $3 \leq p \leq 6$. The class $\Sigma = \{\{1, 2\}, \{3, 4\}, \{5, 6\}\}$ can be shown to be a $C$-class for this machine, and since $|\Sigma| = 3$ from the lower bound we know that $\Sigma$ is a minimum $C$-class. In this case a minimum $C$-class was obtained readily.

Consider, however, the modified machine of Figure 7.2.4 as given in Figure 7.5.1. The final class for this machine is $\{\{1, 2\}, \{2, 3\}, \{2, 5\}, \{1, 4\}, \{3, 4\}, \{4, 5\}, \{1, 6\}, \{3, 6\}, \{5, 6\}\}$. As for the previous machine, the bounds on $p$ are again $3 \leq p \leq 6$. Here, however, the class $\Sigma = \{\{1, 2\}, \{3, 4\}, \{5, 6\}\}$ is not a $C$-class since $\Sigma$ is not closed.

Note that under input $i_3$ we have

$$\{1, 2\} \xrightarrow{(\mathcal{M}, i_3)} \{1, 6\},$$

$$\{3, 4\} \xrightarrow{(\mathcal{M}, i_3)} \{2, 3\},$$

and

$$\{5, 6\} \xrightarrow{(\mathcal{M}, i_3)} \{4, 5\}.$$

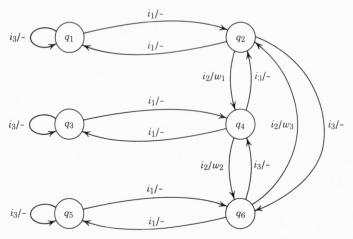

Figure 7.5.1    Modification of machine in Figure 7.2.4.

Now since we also obtain the following relations:

$$\{1, 6\} \xrightarrow{(\mathscr{M},i_3)} \{1, 4\},$$

$$\{1, 4\} \xrightarrow{(\mathscr{M},i_3)} \{1, 2\},$$

$$\{2, 3\} \xrightarrow{(\mathscr{M},i_3)} \{3, 6\},$$

$$\{3, 6\} \xrightarrow{(\mathscr{M},i_3)} \{3, 4\},$$

$$\{4, 5\} \xrightarrow{(\mathscr{M},i_3)} \{2, 5\},$$

and
$$\{2, 5\} \xrightarrow{(\mathscr{M},i_3)} \{5, 6\}$$

with some additional argument it can be shown that no three element class is a $C$-class for $\mathscr{M}$. After considerable searching, we find that no four element class is a $C$-class, and it can be shown that the class $\Sigma' = \{\{1, 2\}, \{1, 4\}, \{1, 6\}, \{3\}, \{5\}\}$ is a minimum $C$-class for $\mathscr{M}$. A resulting minimum machine is shown in Figure 7.5.2, where

$$s_1 \leftrightarrow \{1, 2\},$$

$$s_2 \leftrightarrow \{1, 4\},$$

$$s_3 \leftrightarrow \{1, 6\},$$

$$s_4 \leftrightarrow \{3\},$$

$$s_5 \leftrightarrow \{5\}.$$

The additional properties of sequential machines to be discussed in this section will help reduce the searching for a minimum $C$-class as well as provide further understanding of the two state minimization problems. Although the properties create substantial simplification for some machines, they do not, in general, eliminate completely the need for searching through possible classes of compatible sets for a minimum $C$-class.

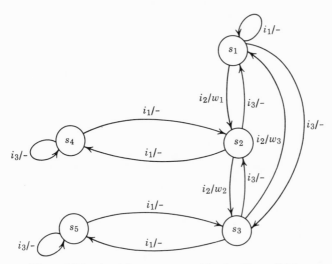

Figure 7.5.2   A minimum state machine for Figure 7.5.1.

**Definition 7.5.1**   The machine $\mathcal{M}^* = (Q^*, I, W, \tau^*, \omega^*)$ is called the *T-completion* of machine $\mathcal{M} = (Q, I, W, \tau, \omega)$ when

$$Q^* = Q \cup \{x\} \quad \text{and} \quad x \notin Q$$

and for all $i \in I$, and $q \in Q$

$$\tau^*(q, i) = \begin{cases} \tau(q, i), & \text{if} \quad (q, i) \in D_\tau \\ x, & \text{otherwise,} \end{cases}$$

$$\tau^*(x, i) = x.$$

$$\omega^*(q, i) = \begin{cases} \omega(q, i) & \text{if} \quad (q, i) \in D_\omega \\ \text{undefined otherwise.} \end{cases}$$

and

$$\omega^*(x, i) \text{ is undefined.}$$

For the remainder of this section, we shall use $\mathcal{M}^*$ to denote the *T-completion* of $\mathcal{M}$. Note that $\mathcal{M}^*$ is a transition complete machine, having one more state than $\mathcal{M}$, and $\mathcal{M}^*$ is equivalent to $\mathcal{M}$.

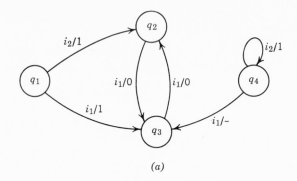

(a)

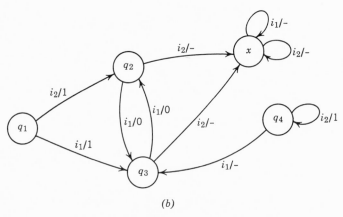

(b)

Figure 7.5.3. *T*-completion example. (*a*) Machine $\mathcal{M}$. (*b*) *T*-completion $\mathcal{M}^*$.

As an example of *T*-completion, let $\mathcal{M}$ be the machine of Figure 7.5.3*a*, then $\mathcal{M}^*$ is shown in Figure 7.5.3*b*.

**Theorem 7.5.1**   Let $\mathcal{M} = (Q, I, W, \tau, \omega)$ and let $\mathcal{M}^*$ be the *T*-completion of $\mathcal{M}$. If $\Sigma = \{S_1, \ldots, S_p\}$ is a *C*-class for $\mathcal{M}$, then $\Sigma^* = \{S_1^*, \ldots, S_p^*\}$ is a *C*-class for $\mathcal{M}^*$, where $S_j^* = S_j \cup \{x\}$ for $1 \leq j \leq p$. If $\Pi^* = \{P_1^*, \ldots, P_p^*\}$ is a *C*-class for $\mathcal{M}^*$, then $\Pi$ is a *C*-class for $\mathcal{M}$, where $\Pi = \{P_j \mid 1 \leq j \leq p \text{ and } P_j \neq \phi\}$ and $P_j = P_j^* - \{x\}$ for $1 \leq j \leq p$.

PROOF.   Let $\Sigma$ be a *C*-class for $\mathcal{M}$. Then by construction of $\Sigma^*$, and since $\Sigma$ covers all the states of $\mathcal{M}$, it follows that $\Sigma^*$ covers all the states of $\mathcal{M}^*$. For each $S_i \in \Sigma$, property (1*a*) of Theorem 7.4.1 is satisfied. Thus by the definition of $\omega^*(q, i)$ and since $\omega^*(x, i)$ is undefined for each $i \in I$, it follows that each $S_j^* \in \Sigma^*$ satisfies property (1*a*) relative to the $\omega^*$ mapping. Since $S_j^* = S_j \cup \{x\}$, each $S_j^*$ of $\Sigma^*$ is nonempty. It remains to show that $\Sigma^*$ is closed for $\Sigma^*$ to be a *C*-class for $\mathcal{M}^*$.

Suppose $S_j \xrightarrow{(\mathscr{M},i)} T$ and $T \subseteq S_k$. Some such $S_k$ exists since $\Sigma$ is closed. Then $S_j^* \xrightarrow{(\mathscr{M}^*,i)} T \cup \{x\}$ directly from the definition of $\tau^*$ and $S_j^*$. By definition, $S_k^* = S_k \cup \{x\}$. Therefore since $T \subseteq S_k$, it follows that $T \cup \{x\} \subseteq S_k^*$, thus proving that $\Sigma^*$ is closed. Since $\Sigma^*$ satisfies condition (1*a*) of Theorem 7.4.1 and conditions (2), (3), and (4) of the *C*-class definition, by Theorem 7.4.1 $\Sigma^*$ is a *C*-class for $\mathscr{M}^*$

For the $\Pi^*$, $\Pi$ part of the theorem, from the definition of $\Pi$, we see that $P_j$ is equal to $P_j^*$, with state $x$ deleted if it appears in $P_j^*$. In the special case that $P_j^* = \{x\}$, then $P_j = \phi$; but then $P_j$ is not defined as a set of $\Pi$. Thus the states of $\mathscr{M}$ are covered by $\Pi$, and no set of $\Pi$ is empty. We now show that property (1*a*) and closure are also satisfied by $\Pi$.

By Theorem 7.4.1, property (1*a*) is satisfied for $\Sigma^*$; thus directly from the definition of $\omega^*$ for $\mathscr{M}^*$, it also follows that (1*a*) is also satisfied for $\Pi$ for $\mathscr{M}$.

Suppose $P_j^* \xrightarrow{(\mathscr{M}^*,i)} R^*$. By closure of $\Pi^*$, $R^* \subseteq P_k^*$ for some $P_k^* \in \Pi^*$. If $P_j \xrightarrow{(\mathscr{M},i)} R$, then either $R = R^*$ and $x \notin R^*$ or $R = R^* - \{x\}$. In either case, $R \subseteq P_k$; however, if $P_k = \phi$, then $P_k \notin \Pi$; but then $R = \phi$ and $R \subseteq P$ for any $P \in \Pi$. Thus, in any case, $\Pi$ is closed, and $\Pi$ is a *C*-class for $\mathscr{M}$, which proves the theorem.

The following corollaries extend the connection between general incompletely specified machines and transition complete machines.

**Corollary 7.5.1.1** Let $\mathscr{M}$, $\mathscr{M}^*$, $\Sigma$, $\Sigma^*$, $\Pi$, and $\Pi^*$ be defined as in Theorem 7.5.1. If $\Sigma$ is a minimum *C*-class for $\mathscr{M}$, then $\Sigma^*$ is a minimum *C*-class for $\mathscr{M}^*$. If $\Pi^*$ is a minimum *C*-class for $\mathscr{M}^*$, then $\Pi$ is a minimum *C*-class for $\mathscr{M}$, and $|\Pi^*| = |\Pi|$.

PROOF. From the definition of $\Sigma^*$, $|\Sigma^*| = |\Sigma|$. If $\Sigma^*$ is not a minimum *C*-class for $\mathscr{M}^*$, there exists a *C*-class $\Sigma_1^*$ for $\mathscr{M}^*$, where $|\Sigma_1^*| < |\Sigma^*|$. By Theorem 7.5.1, there exists a *C*-class $\Sigma_1$ for $\mathscr{M}$, where $|\Sigma_1| \leq |\Sigma_1^*|$. Hence $|\Sigma_1| < |\Sigma^*|$, so $|\Sigma_1| < |\Sigma|$, contradicting the hypothesis that $\Sigma$ is a minimum *C*-class for $\mathscr{M}$ and proving that $\Sigma^*$ is a minimum *C*-class for $\mathscr{M}^*$. Similarly, $\Pi$ can be shown to be a minimum *C*-class for $\mathscr{M}$. Finally, $|\Pi| \leq |\Pi^*|$ by Theorem 7.5.1. If $|\Pi| < |\Pi^*|$, there exists a $\Pi_1^* = \{P_j \cup \{x\} \mid P_j \in \Pi\}$ where $\Pi_1^*$ is a *C*-class for $\mathscr{M}^*$, and $|\Pi_1^*| = |\Pi| < |\Pi^*|$, contradicting the minimality of $\Pi^*$ and proving that $|\Pi| = |\Pi^*|$.

The following corollaries of Theorem 7.5.1 are also readily proved. The reader should attempt to construct these proofs.

**Corollary 7.5.1.2** Let $\mathscr{M}$, $\mathscr{M}^*$, $\Sigma$, and $\Sigma^*$ be defined as in Theorem 7.5.1, and suppose $\mathscr{M}_1 = (Q_1, I, W, \tau_1, \omega_1)$ is represented by $\Sigma$. Then there exists a machine $\mathscr{M}_1^* = (Q_1, I, W, \tau_1^*, \omega_1)$ represented by $\Sigma^*$ such that $\tau_1^*$ is an extension of $\tau_1$.

**Corollary 7.5.1.3**  Let $\mathscr{M}$ and $\mathscr{M}^*$ be defined as in Theorem 7.5.1; then $\mathscr{M}' \overset{\text{min}}{\supseteq} \mathscr{M}^*$ if and only if $\mathscr{M}' \overset{\text{min}}{\supseteq} \mathscr{M}$.

**Corollary 7.5.1.4**  Let $\mathscr{M}$, $\mathscr{M}^*$, $\Pi$, and $\Pi^*$ be defined as in Theorem 7.5.1. Suppose $\mathscr{M}_1^* = (Q_1, I, W, \tau_1^*, \omega_1^*)$ is a minimum state machine for $\mathscr{M}^*$ and $\mathscr{M}_1^*$ is represented by $\Pi^*$, where $Q_1 = \{s_1, \ldots, s_p\}$. Then there exists a minimum state machine $\mathscr{M}_1 = (Q_1, I, W, \tau_1, \omega_1)$ for $\mathscr{M}$ represented by $\Pi$ and optimal for $\Pi$ such that $\tau_1^*$ is an extension of $\tau_1$ and $\omega_1^*$ is an extension of $\omega_1$.

Theorem 7.5.1 and its corollaries show that the problem of state minimization for $\mathscr{M}$ is essentially equivalent to the state minimization for the transition complete machine $\mathscr{M}^*$. In some of the following theorems, we discuss some properties of transition complete machines which are not, in general, true for nontransition complete machines. Using Theorem 7.5.1 and its corollaries, however, we see that these results may also be made to apply to nontransition complete machines.

**Definition 7.5.2**  Let $\mathscr{M} = (Q, I, W, \tau, \omega)$ and $S \subseteq Q$. We define the class $\Gamma'(S, \mathscr{M})$ as follows: $G \in \Gamma'(S, \mathscr{M})$ if and only if $G = S$ or there is some input sequence $i_1, \ldots, i_p$ and a set sequence $S_1, \ldots, S_p$ such that $S_p = G$ where $S \xrightarrow{(\mathscr{M}, i_1)} S_1$ and $S_j \xrightarrow{(\mathscr{M}, i_{j+1})} S_{j+1}$ for $1 \leq j < p$. We let $\Gamma(S, \mathscr{M})$ denote the normalization of $\Gamma'(S, \mathscr{M})$ less all sets of $\Gamma'(S, \mathscr{M})$ having only one element and call $\Gamma(S, \mathscr{M})$ the *generated class of S*.

**Theorem 7.5.2**  Let $\mathscr{M} = (Q, I, W, \tau, \omega)$ and let $\Sigma = \{S_1, \ldots, S_p\}$ be a class of sets of states of $\mathscr{M}$. Then $\Sigma$ is closed if and only if, for each $S_j \in \Sigma$, $\Gamma'(S_j, \mathscr{M}) \, \mathcal{C} \, \Sigma$.

The proof of this theorem is left to the reader; it follows almost directly from the definitions of $\Gamma'(S, \mathscr{M})$ and closure.

**Corollary 7.5.2.1**  If $\Sigma = \{S_1, \ldots, S_p\}$ is a closed class of sets of states for the machine $\mathscr{M}$, then for each $S_j \in \Sigma$, $\Gamma(S_j, \mathscr{M}) \, \mathcal{C} \, \Sigma$.

   PROOF.  $\Sigma$ is closed, so by Theorem 7.5.2 $\Gamma'(S_j, \mathscr{M}) \, \mathcal{C} \, \Sigma$. Now $\Gamma(S_j, \mathscr{M}) \subseteq \Gamma'(S_j, \mathscr{M})$, and thus, $\Gamma(S_j, \mathscr{M}) \, \mathcal{C} \, \Sigma$.

**Definition 7.5.3**  A class $\Sigma$ of sets of states of $\mathscr{M}$ is called *weakly closed* if $\Gamma(S, \mathscr{M})$ is covered by $\Sigma$ for each $S \in \Sigma$.

**Definition 7.5.4**  Given a subset $P \subseteq Q$, we call $\Sigma$ a *P-C-class for $\mathscr{M}$* if $\Sigma$ is a class of nonempty compatible subsets of $P$ which covers the states in $P$ and is weakly closed.

These two definitions are generalizations of those for closure and $C$-class for $\mathcal{M}$. In particular, if $P = Q$, then the $P$-$C$-class for $\mathcal{M}$ can be readily seen to be a $C$-class for $\mathcal{M}$.

**Definition 7.5.5**   A partition $\Lambda = \{P_1, \ldots, P_k\}$ of $Q$ into nonempty mutually disjoint sets is called a *decomposition for* $\mathcal{M}$ when for each compatible $S \subseteq Q$ and each $i \in I$, the following property holds. If $S \xrightarrow{(\mathcal{M},i)} T$ and $S \cap P_j \neq \phi$, then (1) $S \subseteq P_j$ and (2) either $|T| = 1$ or $T \subseteq P_j$.

Trivially, the class $\{Q\}$ for any machine $\mathcal{M}$, where $Q$ is the only set of the class, is a decomposition for $\mathcal{M}$. Some machines will be shown which have other less trivial decompositions. In this case, $C$-classes for $\mathcal{M}$ have a special structure as described in the next theorem.

**Theorem 7.5.3**   Let $\Lambda = \{P_1, \ldots, P_k\}$ be a decomposition for $\mathcal{M}$. Then every $C$-class $\Sigma$ for $\mathcal{M}$ is of the form $\Sigma_1 \cup \Sigma_2 \cup \cdots \cup \Sigma_k$, where $\Sigma_j$ is a $P_j$-$C$-class for $\mathcal{M}$, $1 \leq j \leq k$. Conversely, every $\Sigma = \Sigma_1 \cup \Sigma_2 \cup \cdots \cup \Sigma_k$ is a $C$-class for $\mathcal{M}$ when $\Sigma_j$ is a $P_j$-$C$-class for $\mathcal{M}$ for $1 \leq j \leq k$.

PROOF.   Suppose $\Lambda = \{P_1, \ldots, P_k\}$ is a decomposition for $\mathcal{M}$ and $\Sigma_j$ is a $P_j$-$C$-class for $\mathcal{M}$ for $1 \leq j \leq k$; then the class $\Sigma = \Sigma_1 \cup \Sigma_2 \cup \cdots \cup \Sigma_k$ is a class of compatible sets since each set of $\Sigma$ is a set of a $\Sigma_j$ and the sets of $\Sigma_j$ are compatibles. $\Sigma$ covers all the states of $\mathcal{M}$ since $\Lambda$ covers all states of $\mathcal{M}$ and each $\Sigma_j$ covers all states of each $P_j \in \Lambda$. Now since $\Sigma_j$ is weakly closed for each $j$ and $\Sigma$ covers all states of $\mathcal{M}$, it follows that $\Sigma$ is closed for $\mathcal{M}$. Finally, $\phi \notin \Sigma$ since $\phi \notin \Sigma_j$ for any $j$. Thus $\Sigma$ has been shown to satisfy all the conditions of the definition of a $C$-class for $\mathcal{M}$ and the second part of the theorem is proved.

Now assume that $\Sigma$ is a $C$-class for $\mathcal{M}$ and $\Lambda = \{P_1, \ldots, P_k\}$ is a decomposition for $\mathcal{M}$. Since each set $S \in \Sigma$ is a compatible, by definition of $\Lambda$ it is a subset of some $P_j$, $1 \leq j \leq k$. Thus $\Sigma = \Sigma_1 \cup \Sigma_2 \cup \cdots \cup \Sigma_k$ where $\Sigma_j = \{S \mid S \in \Sigma$ and $S \subseteq P_j\}$ for $1 \leq j \leq k$. Since $\Sigma$ is closed, and from the decomposition definition, if $S \xrightarrow{(\mathcal{M},i)} T$, then $|T| = 1$ or $T \subseteq P_j$, it follows that $\Sigma_j$ is weakly closed.

Now assume that $\Sigma_j$ does not cover some state $q \in P_j$; then $\Sigma$ would not cover $q \in P_j$ since the sets of $\Lambda$ are mutually disjoint and this contradicts condition (3) for a $C$-class. Finally, $\phi \notin \Sigma$ since each set of $\Sigma_j$ is a set of $\Sigma$ and $\phi \notin \Sigma$ by condition (4) for a $C$-class for $\mathcal{M}$. Thus $\Sigma_j$ is a $P_j$-$C$-class for $\mathcal{M}$ and the theorem is proved.

If a nontrivial decomposition exists for a machine $\mathcal{M}$ (that is, a $\Lambda = \{P_1, \ldots, P_k\}$, where $k > 1$), it follows from this theorem that minimum $C$-classes are of the form $\Sigma = \Sigma_1 \cup \Sigma_2 \cup \cdots \cup \Sigma_k$; thus it is possible to divide the problem of finding a minimum $C$-class into the $k$

smaller problems of finding the $\Sigma_j$ where $\Sigma_j$ is a minimum $P_j$-$C$-class for $\mathcal{M}$. Later we shall see how nontrivial decompositions for $\mathcal{M}$ can be obtained, if any exist.

The concept of decomposition is illustrated by the machine of Figure 7.5.4.

Consider the partition $\Lambda = \{\{q_1, q_2, q_3\}, \{q_4, q_5, q_6\}\}$ of nonempty disjoint sets of $\mathcal{M}$. We wish to show that $\Lambda$ is a decomposition for $\mathcal{M}$.

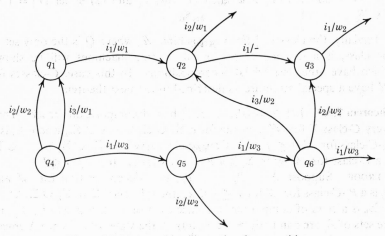

Figure 7.5.4    A machine illustrating decomposition.

The final class for $\mathcal{M}$, as can be checked by the reader, is $\{\{q_1, q_2\}, \{q_2, q_3\}, \{q_4, q_5\}, \{q_5, q_6\}\}$. Thus, to check for decomposition, we must test the sets $T$ for each compatible set $S$ of the final class, where $S \xrightarrow{(\mathcal{M},i)} T$. (Note that since single element sets $S$ automatically satisfy the conditions of Definition 7.5.5, these will not be tested.)

For $\hspace{3em} S = \{1, 2\},$

$$S \cap \{1, 2, 3\} \neq \phi.$$

However, $S \subseteq \{1, 2, 3\}$. Thus, (1) of Definition 7.5.5 is satisfied for this $S$. Now

$$\{1, 2\} \xrightarrow{(\mathcal{M},i_1)} \{2, 3\},$$

$$\{1, 2\} \xrightarrow{(\mathcal{M},i_2)} \phi,$$

$$\{1, 2\} \xrightarrow{(\mathcal{M},i_3)} \phi,$$

and thus, in this case, $S \xrightarrow{(\mathcal{M},i)} T$ is such that $T \subseteq P_j = \{1, 2, 3\}$.

For $S = \{4, 5\}$

$$S \cap \{4, 5, 6\} \neq \phi$$

However, $S \subseteq \{4, 5, 6\}$, satisfying (1) of Definition 7.5.5.

$$\{4, 5\} \xrightarrow{(\mathcal{M}, i_1)} \{5, 6\} = T_1,$$
$$\{4, 5\} \xrightarrow{(\mathcal{M}, i_2)} \{1\} = T_2,$$
$$\{4, 5\} \xrightarrow{(\mathcal{M}, i_3)} \{1\} = T_3.$$

Thus $T_1 \subseteq \{4, 5, 6\}$ and $|T_2| = |T_3| = 1$, so that condition (2) is satisfied for each $i \in I$ for set $S = \{4, 5\}$. The reader may check that sets $\{2, 3\}$ and $\{5, 6\}$ also satisfy Definition 7.5.5, and thus $\Lambda = \{\{1, 2, 3\}, \{4, 5, 6\}\}$ is a nontrivial decomposition for $\mathcal{M}$. Hence from Theorem 7.5.3, any $C$-class $\Sigma$ for $\mathcal{M}$ has the form $\Sigma = \Sigma_1 \cup \Sigma_2$, where $\Sigma_1$ is a $P_1$-$C$-class for $\mathcal{M}$ and $\Sigma_2$ is a $P_2$-$C$-class for $\mathcal{M}$, where $P_1 = \{1, 2, 3\}$ and $P_2 = \{4, 5, 6\}$. In this example, the form of the final class and Corollary 7.4.2.2 immediately verify that any $C$-class $\Sigma$ for $\mathcal{M}$ must take on the desired form $\Sigma = \Sigma_1 \cup \Sigma_2$.

**Definition 7.5.6** Let $\Sigma$ and $\Pi$ be classes of sets of states of a machine $\mathcal{M}$, and let $P \subseteq Q$. We denote by $\Gamma(\Sigma, \Pi, \mathcal{M}, P)$ the class of sets of states of $\mathcal{M}$ resulting from the intersection of all classes $\Gamma$ of sets of states of $\mathcal{M}$ satisfying the following conditions.

1. $\Sigma \subseteq \Gamma$.

2. For each state $q \in P$, $\{q\} \in \Gamma$.

3. If $S \in \Gamma$ and $S \xrightarrow{(\mathcal{M}, i)} T$ for some $i \in I$ and $|T| > 1$; then $T \in \Gamma$.

4. If $S \in \Gamma$ and $\{S\} \not\in \Sigma$, then $V \in \Gamma$, where $V$ is the intersection of all elements of $\Pi$ which include $S$.

Although the class $\Gamma(\Sigma, \Pi, \mathcal{M}, P)$ has a rather complex definition, the next two theorems show how it enables one to delete certain compatible sets from consideration when searching for a single minimum $C$-class for $\mathcal{M}$.

**Theorem 7.5.4** Let $\Lambda$ be a decomposition for a machine $\mathcal{M}$, $P \in \Lambda$, and let $\Sigma$ and $\Pi$ be classes of subsets of $P$. If $\Omega$ is a $P$-$C$-class for $\mathcal{M}$ for which $\Sigma \subseteq \Omega \subseteq (\Sigma \cup \Pi)$, then $\Gamma(\Sigma, \Pi, \mathcal{M}, P)$ is covered by $\Omega$.

PROOF. Let $G \in \Gamma(\Sigma, \Pi, \mathcal{M}, P)$; then there exists a sequence $S_1, \ldots, S_n$ such that (1) either $S_1 \in \Sigma$ or $S_1 = \{q\}$ for some $q \in P$; (2) for $1 \leq j \leq n - 1$ either $S_j \xrightarrow{(\mathcal{M}, i)} S_{j+1}$ for some $i \in I$ or $S_j \not\in \Sigma$ and $S_{j+1} = \bigcap \{R \mid R \in \Pi \text{ and } R \supseteq S_j\}$; and (3) $S_n = G$. For, if this were not true, the class of all sets $G$ for which there is such a sequence would be a proper subclass of $\Gamma(\Sigma, \Pi, \mathcal{M}, P)$ which satisfies conditions (1) through (4) of Definition 7.5.6, and this contradicts the intersection part of the definition for $\Gamma(\Sigma, \Pi, \mathcal{M}, P)$. We apply induction to the index $n$

of the sequence $S_1, S_2, \ldots, S_n$. If $n = 1$, either $G \in \Sigma$ which, with the hypothesis that $\Sigma \subseteq \Omega$, implies that $\{G\} \, \mathcal{C} \, \Omega$; or else $G = \{q\}$ for some $q \in P$; and since $\Omega$ is a $P$-$C$-class for $\mathcal{M}$, $\Omega$ covers all states in $P$, and thus $\{G\} \, \mathcal{C} \, \Omega$. Now suppose $\{S_j\} \, \mathcal{C} \, \Omega$. If by (2), $S_j \xrightarrow{(\mathcal{M},i)} S_{j+1}$ for some $i \in I$, since $\Omega$ is closed $\{S_{j+1}\} \, \mathcal{C} \, \Omega$; and if by (2), $S_j \notin \Sigma$ and

$$S_{j+1} = \bigcap \{R \mid R \in \Pi \text{ and } R \supseteq S_j\},$$

since $\Omega \subseteq (\Sigma \cup \Pi)$, we have that $S_j \subseteq R$ for some $R \in (\Pi \cap \Omega)$; and since $S_{j+1} \subseteq R$, it follows that $\{S_{j+1}\} \, \mathcal{C} \, \Omega$. By induction on $n$, we have that $\{G\} \, \mathcal{C} \, \Omega$ for an arbitrary $G \in \Gamma(\Sigma, \Pi, \mathcal{M}, P)$, and thus $\Gamma(\Sigma, \Pi, \mathcal{M}, P) \, \mathcal{C} \, \Omega$, which completes the proof.

Note that the first part of the proof of this theorem provides a rather straightforward manner for computing $\Gamma(\Sigma, \Pi, \mathcal{M}, P)$.

**Theorem 7.5.5**  Let $P \in \Lambda$, where $\Lambda$ is a decomposition for $\mathcal{M}$, and let $\Sigma$ and $\Pi$ be classes of subsets of $P$. Let $R \in \Pi$ and $R' \in \Pi$ be such that $R \subseteq R'$, $R'$ is compatible, and $\Gamma(R', \mathcal{M})$ is covered by $\Gamma(\Sigma, \Pi, \mathcal{M}, P) \cup \{R'\}$. If $\Omega$ is a $P$-$C$-class for $\mathcal{M}$ such that $\Sigma \subseteq \Omega \subseteq (\Sigma \cup \Pi)$ and $R \in \Omega$, then $\Omega' = (\Omega - \{R\}) \cup \{R'\}$ is also a $P$-$C$-class for $\mathcal{M}$.

PROOF.  By Theorem 7.5.4, $\Gamma(\Sigma, \Pi, \mathcal{M}, P) \, \mathcal{C} \, \Omega$. Therefore $\Gamma(\Sigma, \Pi, \mathcal{M}, P) \cup \{R'\} \, \mathcal{C} \, \Omega'$, since $R \subseteq R'$. Now by $\Gamma(R', \mathcal{M}) \, \mathcal{C} \, \Gamma(\Sigma, \Pi, \mathcal{M}, P) \cup \{R'\}$, we have that $\Gamma(R', \mathcal{M}) \, \mathcal{C} \, \Omega'$. If $S \in \Omega'$ and $S \neq R'$, then $S \in \Omega$; hence $\Gamma(S, \mathcal{M}) \, \mathcal{C} \, \Omega$ by Corollary 7.5.2.1. Since $\Omega \, \mathcal{C} \, \Omega'$, it follows that $\Gamma(S, \mathcal{M}) \, \mathcal{C} \, \Omega'$. Thus $\Gamma(S, \mathcal{M}) \, \mathcal{C} \, \Omega'$ for each $S \, \mathcal{C} \, \Omega'$ and obviously $\Omega'$ covers all states of $P$, which implies that $\Omega'$ is weakly closed. Also $\phi \notin \Omega'$ since $\phi \notin \Omega$ so by Definition 7.5.4, $\Omega'$ is a $P$-$C$-class for $\mathcal{M}$.

**Corollary 7.5.5.1**  Let $P \in \Lambda$, where $\Lambda$ is a decomposition for $\mathcal{M}$, and let $\Omega$ be a $P$-$C$-class for $\mathcal{M}$. Let $R$ and $R'$ be compatible subsets of $P$ such that $R \subseteq R'$, $R \in \Omega$ and $\Gamma(R', \mathcal{M}) \, \mathcal{C} \, \Gamma(R, \mathcal{M}) \cup \{R'\}$. Then $\Omega' = (\Omega - \{R\}) \cup \{R'\}$ is a $P$-$C$-class for $\mathcal{M}$.

This corollary follows directly from Theorem 7.5.5 when $\Sigma = \{R\}$ and $\Pi$ is the class of all compatible subsets of $P$.

Note that this theorem and corollary shows that certain compatible sets need never be considered as elements of $P$-$C$-classes when one is attempting to find only one minimum $P$-$C$-class for $\mathcal{M}$. That is, the set $R$ of the theorem and corollary can always be replaced with an $R'$ where $R' \supseteq R$; this replacement is possible when the generated classes of $R$ and $R'$ are essentially equal. This elimination of certain compatible subsets of $P$ considerably reduces the number of possible classes in the search procedure for $P$-$C$-classes.

Another property of $C$-class and $P$-$C$-classes is given in Theorems 7.5.6 and 7.5.7.

Let $X_q$, where $q \in Q$, denote the set of all states $p \in Q$ such that $p \sim q$. For $S \subseteq Q$, we let $X(S) = \bigcap_{q \in S} X_q$. Thus $S$ is compatible if and only if $S \subseteq X(S)$. Also if $S \subseteq X(S) \subseteq X_q$, then $S \cup \{q\}$ is compatible.

**Definition 7.5.7** A collection $A$ (possibly empty) of ordered pairs $(S, q)$, where $S \subseteq Q$ and $q \in Q$, is called a *permissible collection for $\mathcal{M}$* when for all $(S, q) \in A$ and for all $i \in I$, when $S \xrightarrow{(\mathcal{M}, i)} T_i$ and $\tau(q, i) = r_i$, we have (1) $X(S) \subseteq X_q$ and (2) either $r_i \in T_i$ or there is a pair $(T_i', r_i) \in A$ with $T_i' \subseteq T_i$.

**Definition 7.5.8** A set $R \subseteq Q$ is called *closed with respect to $A$* when for each $(S, q) \in A$, $S \subseteq R$ implies that $q \in R$. The *closure of a set $R \subseteq Q$ with respect to $A$* is the intersection of all sets $S \subseteq Q$ which are closed with respect to $A$ and which include $R$.

Note that if $A = \phi$, $S$ is closed with respect to $A$ for every $S \subseteq Q$.

**Theorem 7.5.6** Let $\mathcal{M} = (Q, I, W, \tau, \omega)$ be a transition complete machine, let $P \in \Lambda$ where $\Lambda$ is a decomposition for $\mathcal{M}$, and let $\Sigma = \{S_1, \ldots, S_n\}$ be a $P$-$C$-class for $\mathcal{M}$. Let $A$ be a permissible collection for $\mathcal{M}$ and let $S_k'$ be the closure of $S_k$ with respect to $A$ for $1 \leq k \leq n$. Then $\Sigma' = \{S_j' \mid 1 \leq j \leq n\}$ is a $P$-$C$-class for $\mathcal{M}$. Also, for all $i \in I$ and $j$ $(1 \leq j \leq n)$ if $S_j \xrightarrow{(\mathcal{M}, i)} T$, $S_j' \xrightarrow{(\mathcal{M}, i)} T'$, and $T \subseteq S_k$, then $T' \subseteq S_k'$.

PROOF. Since $\Sigma$ is covered by $\Sigma'$, $\Sigma'$ also covers all states in $P$; and since $\phi \notin \Sigma$, $\phi \notin \Sigma'$. By definition of $S_k'$ there is a sequence $S_k^{(0)}, S_k^{(1)}, \ldots, S_k^{(a)}$, where $S_k^{(0)} = S_k$ and $S_k^{(a)} = S_k'$, and for $0 \leq m \leq a - 1$, we have $S_k^{(m+1)} = S_k^{(m)} \cup \{q_m\}$ where $S_k^{(m)} \supseteq T_m$ for some $(T_m, q_m) \in A$. If $S_k^{(m)}$ is compatible, then $S_k^{(m)} \subseteq X(S_k^{(m)})$. The permissibility of $A$ (condition 1) implies that $X(T_m) \subseteq X_{q_m}$. Thus $S_k^{(m)} \subseteq X_{q_m}$, so $S_k^{(m)} \cup \{q_m\} = S_k^{(m+1)}$ is compatible. Now since $S_k = S_k^{(0)}$ is compatible by hypothesis, it follows by induction that $S_k'$ is compatible. Now since $S_k'$ is compatible, $S_k \subseteq S_k'$, and $S_k \subseteq P$, then $S_k' \cap P \neq \phi$ so that $S_k' \subseteq P$ from condition (1) of the definition for a decomposition for $\mathcal{M}$. Thus $\Sigma'$ is a class of nonempty compatible subsets of $P$ which covers the states in $P$. Weak closure of $\Sigma'$ and the second assertion of the theorem remain to be shown.

It is sufficient to show that the second assertion of the theorem holds, and from this and the weak closure of $\Sigma$ will follow the weak closure of $\Sigma'$. Let $i \in I$. Suppose $S_k^{(m)} \xrightarrow{(\mathcal{M}, i)} R_m$, $T_m \xrightarrow{(\mathcal{M}, i)} T_m'$, and $\tau(q_m, i) = q_m'$ for $0 \leq m \leq a - 1$, since $\mathcal{M}$ is transition complete.

Since $\Sigma$ is a $P$-$C$-class, either $R_0 \subseteq P$ and $R_0 \subseteq S_u$ for some $S_u \in \Sigma$ or $R_0 \not\subseteq P$ and $|R_0| = 1$. In the latter case, since $S_k^{(a)}$ is compatible and

$R_a \nsubseteq P$, then $|R_a| = 1$ also, since $P \in \Lambda$. In the former case, $R_{m+1} = R_m \cup \{q_m'\}$ since $\tau(q_m, i) = q_m'$ and $T_m' \subseteq R_m$ since $T_m \subseteq S_k^{(m)}$, for $0 \le m \le a - 1$. By permissibility of $A$ [condition (2)] for $0 \le m \le a - 1$, either $q_m' \in T_m' \subseteq R_m$, so $R_{m+1} = R_m$, or there is a $T_m'' \subseteq T_m' \subseteq R_m$ with $(T_m'', q_m') \in A$. It follows from the definition of $S_u'$ that $R_a \subseteq S_u'$. This proves the second assertion of the theorem, and implies that $\Sigma'$ is weakly closed, and hence a $P$-$C$-class for $\mathcal{M}$.

This theorem allows one to disregard all compatibles which are not closed with respect to $A$ when one is attempting to find one minimum $P$-$C$-class for $\mathcal{M}$, since by the theorem we know that there exists a minimum $P$-$C$-class for $\mathcal{M}$ containing only elements which are closed with respect to $A$. If one is interested in finding all minimum machines for $\mathcal{M}$, the following other condition on a collection $A$ is required to get a result similar to Theorem 7.5.6.

**Definition 7.5.9**   A collection $A$ is called a *strongly permissible collection* for $\mathcal{M}$ when (1) $A$ is permissible for $\mathcal{M}$ and (2) for all $i \in I$ and $(S, q) \in A$ if $(q, i) \in D_\omega$, then $(p, i) \in D_\omega$ for some $p \in S$.

With this extra condition [(2) of Definition 7.5.9], the following corollaries are readily obtained.

**Corollary 7.5.6.1**   Let $\mathcal{M}$ be a transition complete machine and let $A$ be a strongly permissible collection for $\mathcal{M}$. If $\Sigma = \{S_1, \ldots, S_n\}$ is a $C$-class for $\mathcal{M}$ and $\Sigma' = \{S_1', \ldots, S_n'\}$, where $S_j'$ is the closure of $S_j$ with respect to $A$, then $\Sigma'$ is a $C$-class for $\mathcal{M}$ and any machine represented by $\Sigma$ is also represented by $\Sigma'$.

**Corollary 7.5.6.2**   Let $\mathcal{M}$ be nondegenerate and let $\mathcal{M}^*$ be the $T$-completion of $\mathcal{M}$ where $Q^* = Q \cup \{x\}$, and let $A$ be a strongly permissible collection for $\mathcal{M}^*$. Then any transition complete minimum machine for $\mathcal{M}$ is represented by a $C$-class for $\mathcal{M}^*$ consisting only of sets closed with respect to $A$.

A set of states of a machine $\mathcal{M}$ is called *closed* if it is closed with respect to some permissible collection for $\mathcal{M}$.

**Theorem 7.5.7**   For a transition complete machine $\mathcal{M}$, there exists a permissible collection $A$ (possibly empty) for $\mathcal{M}$ such that every closed compatible set of states of $\mathcal{M}$ is closed with respect to $A$.

PROOF.   Define $A_j'$ and $A_j$ inductively as follows: $(S, q) \in A_j'$ if and only if $q \notin S$, $S$ is compatible, $|S| = j$, $X(S) \subseteq X_q$, and $(S', q) \notin A_k$ for any $S' \subseteq S$ and $k < j$. $A_j$ is the unique maximum subset of $A_j'$ such that $A_1 \cup \cdots \cup A_j$ satisfies condition (2) of the permissible collection definition. The uniqueness of this maximum subset follows from the fact that a union of collections, each of which satisfies condition (2), also satisfies condition (2). Let $A = \bigcup\limits_{j=1}^{|Q|} A_j$. By construction, $A$ is permissible. If $A'$ is any permissible collection for $\mathcal{M}$ and $(S', q) \in A'$, where $S'$ is compatible and $q \in S'$, $(S, q) \in A$ for some $S \subseteq S'$. This follows immediately from the construction of $A$, and thus any set closed with respect to $A'$ is also closed with respect to $A$.

**Corollary 7.5.7.1** For any transition complete machine, there is a minimum $C$-class consisting only of closed sets.

Inputs

| States | $i_1$ | $i_2$ |
|--------|-------|-------|
| $q_1$ | $q_3/0$ | $-/-$ |
| $q_2$ | $q_4/0$ | $q_3/0$ |
| $q_3$ | $-/-$ | $q_5/1$ |
| $q_4$ | $q_5/-$ | $q_5/0$ |
| $q_5$ | $q_5/0$ | $q_5/-$ |

Figure 7.5.5 Machine example for Theorems 7.5.6 and 7.5.7.

We call a compatible set $R$ of states of $\mathcal{M}$ *redundant* if there is a compatible $R' \supseteq R$ $(R' \neq R)$ such that $\Gamma(R', \mathcal{M})$ is covered by $\Gamma(R, \mathcal{M}) \cup \{R'\}$. From Corollary 7.5.5.1, it follows that for $P \in \Lambda$, where $\Lambda$ is a decomposition for a transition complete machine $\mathcal{M}$ and $\Omega$ a minimum $P$-$C$-class for $\mathcal{M}$, there is a minimum $P$-$C$-class $\Omega'$ covering $\Omega$ and consisting only of nonredundant sets. From Theorems 7.5.6 and 7.5.7, it follows that for any minimum $P$-$C$-class $\Omega'$ for $\mathcal{M}$, there is a minimum $P$-$C$-class $\Omega''$ for $\mathcal{M}$ which covers $\Omega'$ and consists only of closed sets. If $\Omega''$ has redundant elements, this process can be iterated, so that after a finite number of iterations, a minimum $P$-$C$-class for $\mathcal{M}$ can be obtained containing only closed nonredundant sets of states of $\mathcal{M}$.

As an example for Theorems 7.5.6 and 7.5.7, we consider machine $\mathcal{M}$ depicted in Figure 7.5.5 by a flow table.

The $T$-completion machine $\mathcal{M}^*$ for $\mathcal{M}$ is shown in Figure 7.5.6.

For $\mathcal{M}^*$ we have

$$X_{q_1} = \{q_1, q_3, q_4, q_5, x\},$$
$$X_{q_2} = \{q_2, q_4, q_5, x\},$$
$$X_{q_3} = \{q_1, q_3, q_5, x\},$$
$$X_{q_4} = \{q_1, q_2, q_4, q_5, x\},$$
$$X_{q_5} = \{q_1, q_2, q_3, q_4, q_5, x\}.$$

Inputs

| States | $i_1$ | $i_2$ |
|:---:|:---:|:---:|
| $q_1$ | $q_3/0$ | $x/-$ |
| $q_2$ | $q_4/0$ | $q_3/0$ |
| $q_3$ | $x/-$ | $q_5/1$ |
| $q_4$ | $q_5/-$ | $q_5/0$ |
| $q_5$ | $q_5/0$ | $q_5/-$ |
| $x$ | $x/-$ | $x/-$ |

Figure 7.5.6    $T$-Completion $\mathcal{M}^*$ for $\mathcal{M}$ of Figure 7.5.5.

The permissible collection $A$ for $\mathcal{M}^*$ as constructed in the proof of Theorem 7.5.7 is

$$A = \{(\{q_1\}, q_5), (\{q_2\}, q_5), (\{q_3\}, q_5), (\{q_4\}, q_5),$$
$$(\{x\}, q_5), (\{q_1\}, x), (\{q_2\}, x), (\{q_3\}, x), (\{q_4\}, x),$$
$$(\{q_5\}, x), (\{q_2\}, q_4)\}.$$

Thus the closed compatible sets for $\mathcal{M}^*$ are $\{q_1, q_5, x\}$, $\{q_3, q_5, x\}$, $\{q_4, q_5, x\}$, $\{q_2, q_4, q_5, x\}$, $\{q_1, q_3, q_5, x\}$, $\{q_1, q_4, q_5, x\}$, and $\{q_5, x\}$. A minimum $C$-class for $\mathcal{M}^*$ consisting only of closed sets is $\Sigma^* = \{\{q_1, q_3, q_5, x\}, \{q_2, q_4, q_5, x\}\}$, and thus $\Sigma = \{\{q_1, q_3, q_5\}, \{q_2, q_4, q_5\}\}$ is a minimum $C$-class for $\mathcal{M}$.

A minimum state machine $\mathcal{M}'$ for $\mathcal{M}$ represented by $\Sigma$, with $S_1 = \{q_1, q_3, q_5\}$ and $S_2 = \{q_2, q_4, q_5\}$, is shown in Figure 7.5.7.

Various algorithms based on the theorems described in this section have been devised and these properties have been found to reduce greatly the search for minimum $C$-classes in difficult state minimization problems. We shall not discuss the intricacies of these algorithms or any statistics on their experimental results (see Reference [3] for this purpose). Since some calculation is required for the generation of classes $\Gamma(\Sigma, \Pi, \mathcal{M}, P)$ and permissible collections if the properties are to be applied, however, these calculations should probably be made only when a large search over possible $C$-classes is otherwise required. Furthermore, since these properties do not lead to a completely direct (that is, without search) algorithm

Inputs

| States | $i_1$ | $i_2$ |
|:---:|:---:|:---:|
| $s_1$ | $s_1/0$ | $s_1/1$ |
| $s_2$ | $s_2/0$ | $s_1/0$ |

Figure 7.5.7    Minimum State Machine $\mathcal{M}'$ for $\mathcal{M}$ represented by $\Sigma$.

for obtaining a minimum *C*-class, it may still be possible to obtain better techniques for obtaining minimum state machines.

State minimization for complete machines is particularly simple and well known, and is discussed next.

## 7.6 STATE MINIMIZATION FOR COMPLETE SEQUENTIAL MACHINES

The special case of state minimization for a complete sequential machine $\mathcal{M}$ is of interest, since in this case the final class is the only minimum *C*-class for $\mathcal{M}$ and the final class represents only one machine. These results are proved as follows.

**Theorem 7.6.1** If $\mathcal{M}$ is complete, the compatibility relation between states of $\mathcal{M}$ is an equivalence relation.

PROOF. Since the compatibility relation has already been seen to be reflexive and symmetric, it remains to show that if $\mathcal{M}$ is complete, then compatibility is also transitive. Suppose $q \in Q$, $q' \in Q$, and $q'' \in Q$, and that $q \sim q'$ and $q' \sim q''$, but $q \nsim q''$. From Definition 7.2.2, if $q \nsim q''$, there exists some sequence $i_1, i_2, \ldots, i_p$ which is applicable both to $\mathcal{M}$ in $q$ and $\mathcal{M}$ in $q''$ such that the output produced by $\mathcal{M}$ in $q$ is not equal to the output produced by $\mathcal{M}$ in $q''$ under $i_1, i_2, \ldots, i_p$. Let $w$ and $w''$ represent these respective outputs; then $w \neq w''$. Now $i_1, i_2, \ldots, i_p$ is applicable to $\mathcal{M}$ in $q'$ since $\mathcal{M}$ is complete. Let $w'$ be the output produced by $\mathcal{M}$ in $q'$ under $i_1, \ldots, i_p$.

By the assumption that $q \sim q'$ and $q \sim q''$, we have that $w' = w$ and $w' = w''$, but since $w \neq w''$, this is impossible. Thus $q \sim q''$, proving transitivity, and the theorem is proved.

Since compatibility is an equivalence relation, this relation partitions the set of states of a complete machine $\mathcal{M}$ into an equivalence class of sets. This equivalence class is the final class for $\mathcal{M}$.

From the definition of a *C*-class for $\mathcal{M}$, any *C*-class must cover all the states of $\mathcal{M}$ and only contain sets that are subsets of sets of the final class. It is thus readily seen that for a complete machine $\mathcal{M}$, the final class for $\mathcal{M}$ is the only minimum *C*-class for $\mathcal{M}$. This leads to the following theorem.

**Theorem 7.6.2** There exists only one minimum state machine $\mathcal{M}'$ for any complete machine $\mathcal{M}$, up to possible renaming of states of $\mathcal{M}'$.

PROOF. From our previous remarks, the final class $\Phi$ for $\mathcal{M}$ is the only minimum *C*-class for $\mathcal{M}$. Now by the definition of $\Phi$ represents $\mathcal{M}'$, it follows that for each $S_j \in \Phi$ there is an $s_j \in Q'$ of $\mathcal{M}'$. Since $\Phi$ is a partition, $\Sigma_{j,i}$ for $S_j$ and $i \in I$ contains exactly one $S_k \in \Phi$; thus, $\tau'(S_j, i)$ is uniquely determined for each $s_j$ and $i \in I$. In addition, since $(q, i) \in D_\omega$ for each $q \in S_j$, it follows that $(s_j, i) \in D_{\omega'}$ for each $s_j \in Q'$ and $i \in I$, so that $\omega'(s_j, i)$ is uniquely determined for each $j$ and $i$. Thus $\Phi$ represents a unique machine (up to possible renumbering of states) and the theorem is proved.

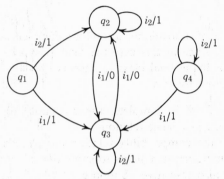

Figure 7.6.1    A complete machine example.

To illustrate state minimization for complete machines, consider $\mathcal{M}$ shown in Figure 7.6.1.

The final class for $\mathcal{M}$ is calculated as follows:

$$(1, 2, 3, 4)$$

$i_1$
$1, 4 \sim 2, 3$

$$(1, 4) \qquad (2, 3)$$

$i_2$
$1 \sim 4$

$$(1) \quad (4) \qquad (2, 3)$$

This final class is the minimum $C$-class for $\mathcal{M}$. The tabular form to get $\mathcal{M}'$ is

|       | $S_1$ (1) | $S_2$ (4) | $S_3$ (2, 3) |
|-------|-----------|-----------|--------------|
| $i_1$ | 3/1       | 3/1       | 3, 2/0       |
| $i_2$ | 2/1       | 4/1       | 2, 3/1       |

The unique minimum machine $\mathcal{M}'$ for $\mathcal{M}$ is shown in Figure 7.6.2.

A second example of complete machine state minimization is shown in Figure 7.6.3a and b.

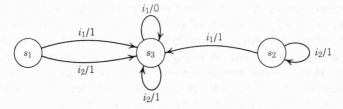

Figure 7.6.2   Minimum machine $\mathcal{M}'$ for $\mathcal{M}$ of Figure 7.5.1.

We make one concluding remark about the connection between state minimization for complete and incomplete machines. Since complete machine state minimization is much simpler than incomplete machine state minimization, one might attempt to obtain a minimum state machine for an incomplete machine $\mathcal{M}$ as follows. Complete $\mathcal{M}$ in all possible ways, and then obtain minimum state machines for each of these machines. Pick one of these minimum state machines having as few states as any other. Call it $\mathcal{M}'$ and let this be a minimum state machine for $\mathcal{M}$. Unfortunately, *in general, $\mathcal{M}'$ will not be a minimum state machine for $\mathcal{M}$.* This result, first discovered by Ginsburg [7], is closely related to the earlier mentioned fact that it is not always possible to obtain a minimum $C$-class that is a partition of the states of $\mathcal{M}$; and minimum $C$-classes for complete machines are always partitions. The three state machine $\mathcal{M}$ of Figure

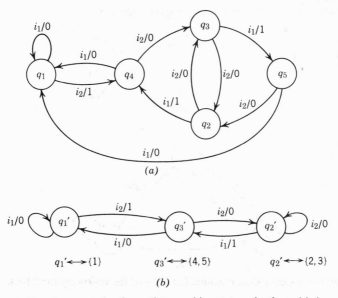

Figure 7.6.3   Another example of complete machine state reduction. (*a*) A complete machine $\mathcal{M}$ with final class $\{\{1\}, \{2, 3\}, \{4, 5\}\}$. (*b*) The minimum state machine for (*a*).

7.3.1 demonstrates this fact. The only undefined entry for this machine is $\omega(q_1, i_1)$. If $\omega(q_1, i_1)$ is defined either as $w_1$ or as $w_2$, it is readily seen that the three state machine is itself minimum, but we have already seen that the two state machine $\mathcal{M}'$ of Figure 7.4.1 is a minimum state machine for $\mathcal{M}$. It thus seems nondisjointness of sets in a $C$-class for $\mathcal{M}$ plays an essential role in the problem of state minimization for incomplete machines. For incomplete machines we mentioned in Section 7.3 that it was not immediately evident how to test if two machines $\mathcal{M}$ and $\mathcal{M}'$ were related by $\mathcal{M}' \supseteq \mathcal{M}$. For complete machines it follows from the fact that the compatibility relation is an equivalence relation that if $\mathcal{M}' \supseteq \mathcal{M}$ and $\mathcal{M}'$ is strongly connected* then $\mathcal{M}' \equiv \mathcal{M}$. Then since the minimum state machine is unique for a complete machine, one may readily determine if two complete machines $\mathcal{M}$ and $\mathcal{M}'$ are equivalent by simply finding the minimum state machines for $\mathcal{M}$ and $\mathcal{M}'$. Then $\mathcal{M}$ and $\mathcal{M}'$ are equivalent if and only if the two minimum state machines are identical.

**Exercises**

1. Prove that the inclusion relation for machines is transitive.
2. Prove that if $\mathcal{M} \equiv \mathcal{M}'$ and $\mathcal{M}'' \overset{min}{\supseteq} \mathcal{M}$, then $\mathcal{M}'' \overset{min}{\supseteq} \mathcal{M}'$.
3. What input sequences are applicable to each of the following machines starting in state $q_1$?
   (*Hint*: Use regular expressions to specify the sequences.)

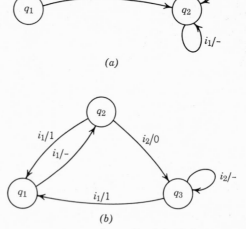

(a)

(b)

4. Find a minimum state machine for each of the following machines.

* A machine $\mathcal{M}'$ is called *strongly connected* if for any pair of states $q$ and $q'$ of $\mathcal{M}'$ there exists an input sequence which produces a state sequence starting with $q$ and ending with $q'$.

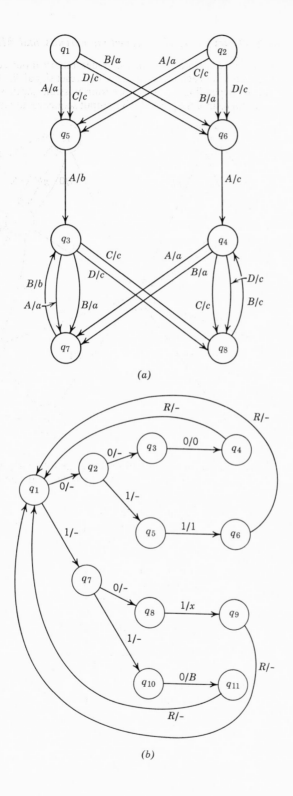

(a)

(b)

The machine in (*b*) is a decoder which decodes binary input sequences of length 3, being reset after each three inputs with a reset signal *R*. The outputs are 0, 1, *x*, or *B*, depending on which of four possible input sequences is obtained. Note that four of the possible eight input sequences are not specified.

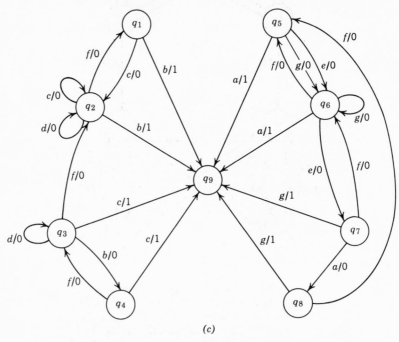

(*c*)

**5.** Find a minimum state machine that will produce the following input-output sequences when starting in some single starting state. Indicate which state is the starting state.

$$A_1 = \begin{cases} \text{input} & A \quad B \quad B \quad A \\ \text{output} & 1 \quad 0 \quad 0 \quad 1 \end{cases}$$
$$\underbrace{\phantom{000000000}}_{R}$$

$$A_2 = \begin{cases} \text{input} & A \quad A \quad B \quad A \\ \text{output} & 1 \quad 1 \quad 0 \quad 1 \end{cases}$$
$$\underbrace{\phantom{000000000}}_{R}$$

$$A_3 = \begin{cases} \text{input} & A \quad B \quad A \quad B \quad A \\ \text{output} & 1 \quad 0 \quad 1 \quad 0 \quad 1 \end{cases}$$
$$\underbrace{\phantom{0000000000000}}_{R}$$

$$A_4 = \begin{cases} \text{input} & A \quad A \quad A \quad A \\ \text{output} & 1 \quad 1 \quad 1 \quad 0 \end{cases}$$
$$\underbrace{\phantom{000000000}}_{R}$$

In this specification the $R$ indicates that this part of the sequence may be repeated as often as desired.

6. For the decoder of Exercise 2a, Chapter 6, transform the Moore model into a Mealy model, and then find a minimum state machine for the resulting Mealy model.

7. Modify the definitions and theorems of applicability, compatibility, $C$-classes, and state minimization and apply them to incompletely specified Moore model machines.

8. Prove that if $\mathcal{M} = (Q, I, W, \tau, \omega)$ and $\mathcal{M}' = (Q, I, W, \tau', \omega')$ are complete machines where $\mathcal{M}' \supseteq \mathcal{M}$ and $\mathcal{M}'$ is strongly connected, then $\mathcal{M}'$ is equivalent to $\mathcal{M}$.

### REFERENCE NOTATIONS

The first studies on machine equivalence and state minimization were done for complete machines by Moore [19] and Huffman [13]. Huffman's paper, as well as some other classical papers on sequential machines, can also be found in a recent book [20] edited by Moore. This book also includes an extensive bibliography by Moore on sequential machines, which unfortunately because of its concise nature is rather difficult to use. Later Mealy [17] discussed several techniques for finding the minimum $C$-class (also the final class) for complete machines. The final class algorithim given in Section 7.2 is somewhat similar to one of Mealy's techniques. Other algorithms for obtaining the final class are given by Paull and Unger in [22], and it was in this paper that the connection between $C$-classes and minimum state machines was first developed. Ginsburg first noticed that incomplete machine state minimization could not be accomplished using the methods developed for complete machines, and he developed several approaches to this problem [7–12]. The other references given here indicate the rather extensive study of this problem. Much of the presentation given in Sections 7.2 through 7.5 is based on the work of Beatty and Miller [2, 3]. In [3] a programmed algorithm for state minimization is described in detail, and some statistical results of this algorithm, which employs results of Section 7.5, are also described. In addition, certain lattice properties of normal $C$-classes are briefly mentioned in [3]. In [21] Narasimhan notes the connection between transition complete machines and incomplete machines. We have also treated this connection in Section 7.5. In [16] McCluskey shows that for a restricted class of incomplete machines only maximum compatibles need be considered for state minimization. References [1, 4, 14, 15, 17, 19] deal exclusively with complete machines.

### REFERENCES

1. Aufenkamp, D. D. and F. E. Hohn, "Analysis of Sequential Machines," *Trans. IRE*, Vol. EC-6, pp. 276–285, December 1957.

2. Beatty, J. and R. E. Miller, "Some Theorems for Incompletely Specified Sequential Machines with Applications to State Minimization," *AIEE Proceedings of the Third Annual Symposium on Switching Circuit Theory and Logical Design*, pp. 123–136, September 1962.

3. Beatty, J. and R. E. Miller, "An Approach to State Minimization for Incompletely Specified Sequential Machines," *IBM Research Report*, RC-1055, September 1963.

4. Cladwell, S. H., *Switching Circuits and Logical Design*, John Wiley and Sons, New York, 1958, Chapters 12, 13, and 14.

5. Elgot, C. C. and J. D. Rutledge, "Machine Properties Preserved Under State Minimization," *AIEE Proceedings of the Third Annual Symposium on Switching Circuit Theory and Logical Design*, pp. 61–70, September 1962.

6. Gillespie, R. G. and D. D. Aufenkamp, "On the Analysis of Sequential Machines," *IRE Transactions on Electronic Computers*, Vol. EC-7, pp. 119–122, June 1958.

7. Ginsburg, S., "A Synthesis Technique for Minimal State Sequential Machines," *IRE Transactions on Electronic Computers*, Vol. EC-8, No. 1, pp. 13–24, March 1959.

8. Ginsburg, S., "A Technique for the Reduction of a Given Machine to a Minimal State Machine," *IRE Transactions on Electronic Computers*, Vol. EC-8, No. 3, pp. 346–355, September 1959.

9. Ginsburg, S., "Connective Properties Preserved in Minimal State Machines," *Journal of the ACM*, Vol. 7, No. 4, pp. 311–325, October 1960.

10. Ginsburg, S., "On the Reduction of Superfluous States in a Sequential Machine," *Journal of the ACM*, Vol. 6, No. 2, pp. 259–282, April 1959.

11. Ginsburg, S., "Synthesis of Minimal-State Machines," *IRE Transactions on Electronic Computers*, Vol. EC-8, No. 4, pp. 441–449, December 1959.

12. Ginsburg, S., *An Introduction to Mathematical Machine Theory*, Addison-Wesley Publishing Co., Reading, Mass., 1962, Chapter 2.

13. Huffman, D. A., "The Synthesis of Sequential Switching Circuits," *Journal of the Franklin Institute*, Vol. 257, No. 3, pp. 161–190, March 1954; No. 4, pp. 275–303, April 1954.

14. Humphrey, W. S. Jr., *Switching Circuits with Computer Applications*, McGraw-Hill Book Co., New York, 1958, Chapter 10.

15. Huzino, Seiiti, "Theory of Finite Automata," *Memoirs of the Faculty of Science, Kyushu University, Mathematics*, Vol. XV, Series A, No. 2, January 1962.

16. McCluskey, E. J., Jr., "Minimum-State Sequential Circuits for a Restricted Class of Incompletely Specified Flow Tables," Princeton University, Department of Electrical Engineering, Digital Systems Laboratory, Technical Report No. 14, February 1962.

17. Mealy, G. H., "A Method for Synthesizing Sequential Circuits," BSTJ, Vol. 34, pp. 1045–1079, September 1955.

18. Miller, R. E., "State Reduction for Sequential Machines," *IBM Research Report*, RC-121, June 15, 1959.

19. Moore, E. F., "Gedanken-Experiments on Sequential Machines," *Automata Studies, Annals of Mathematics Studies* No. 34, pp. 129–153, Princeton University Press, New Jersey, 1956.

20. Moore, E. F. editor, *Sequential Machines: Selected Papers*, Addison-Wesley Publishing Co., Reading, Mass., 1964.

21. Narasimhan, R., "Minimizing Incompletely Specified Sequential Switching Functions," *IRE Transactions on Electronic Computers*, Vol. EC-10, pp. 531–532, September 1961.

22. Paull, M. C. and S. H. Unger, "Minimizing the Number of States in Incompletely Specified Sequential Switching Functions," *IRE Transactions on Electronic Computers*, Vol. EC-8, No. 3, pp. 356–367, September 1959.

23. Reed, I. S., "Mathematical Structure of Sequential Machines," Chapter 11 in *A Survey of Switching Circuit Theory*, McGraw-Hill Book Co., New York, 1962.

# 8

# State Assignment for Sequential Machines

## 8.1 INTRODUCTION

As an abstract model the sequential machine provides a straightforward representation for the basic concepts of states and transitions between states. In Chapter 7, we have seen that this model enables us to compare machines under the relations of inclusion and equivalence and also to obtain a minimum state machine for any given machine. In Chapter 6 it was demonstrated that sequential networks could be analyzed to obtain state diagrams that are complete sequential machine representations for the networks. Thus we can also compare sequential networks using the inclusion and equivalence relations on the sequential machine representations of the networks.

Further relationships between sequential networks are treated in this chapter. In particular, we are concerned with transforming a sequential machine into a set of output equations (Equations 6.2.1) and a set of next state equations (Equations 6.2.2) which represent a sequential network. Various properties of sequential machines will be derived that accomplish these transformations to output and next state equations.

For a sequential machine $\mathcal{M} = (Q, I, W, \tau, \omega)$, we shall assume that for each input $i \in I$ some configuration of 0 and 1 values of a set of input variables $x_1, x_2, \ldots, x_n$ are associated with the input and that a specific configuration of 0's and 1's represents each $i \in I$ such that no two inputs are represented by the same configuration. Similarly, we assume that each output $w \in W$ is given as a predetermined configuration of 0 and 1 values of a set of output variables $z_1, z_2, \ldots, z_m$.

These variables $x_1, x_2, \ldots, x_n$ and $z_1, z_2, \ldots, z_m$ can thus be considered as input lines and output lines, respectively, of a sequential network. The only remaining undetermined variables necessary to give a transformation from the sequential machine to the sets of equations are the internal variables $y_1, y_2, \ldots, y_k$. That is, for each state of $\mathcal{M}$, we must assign a configuration of $k$, 0's, and 1's to the state so that no two states are assigned the same configuration. This assigning of $k$-tuples of 0's and 1's for each of the states of $\mathcal{M}$ is called a *state assignment for* $\mathcal{M}$.

Since no two states may be assigned the same $k$-tuple, for $k$ internal variables we can have at most $2^k$ states in $\mathcal{M}$. Thus the number of states of $\mathcal{M}$ determines a minimum possible number $k_m$ of internal variables $y_1, y_2, \ldots, y_{k_m}$ for an assignment, where if $n$ equals the number of states in $\mathcal{M}$, $k_m = \lceil \log_2 n \rceil$.

For different state assignments, different output equations and next state equations result. Because the complexity of a sequential network is somewhat related to the complexity of the output and next state equations, we shall investigate techniques for state assignment that tend to simplify the resulting equations. First, however, we show how the equations, and appropriate "don't care" conditions, are obtained once a state assignment is given.

## 8.2   TRANSFORMATION FROM STATE ASSIGNMENT TO EQUATIONS

Given a state assignment for a sequential machine we now give rules for deriving the output and next state equations of the form of (6.2.1) and (6.2.2). We shall describe these functions in terms of cubical complexes.

Let the binary vector of $n$ bits $(x_{1r}, x_{2r}, \ldots, x_{nr})$, $x_{ir} = 0$ or 1 be called the *input* $i_r$ to the sequential machine, the binary vector $(z_{1s}, z_{2s}, \ldots, z_{ms})$ be called the *output* $w_s$ of the sequential machine, and the binary vector $(y_{1t}, y_{2t}, \ldots, y_{kt})$ be called the *state* $q_t$ of the sequential machine. Covers for each equation are then obtained as follows.

I. A cover $C(z_j)$ for the output equation $z_j$, $1 \leq j \leq m$ is formed by placing a 0-cube $(x_{1r}, x_{2r}, \ldots, x_{nr}, y_{1t}, y_{2t}, \ldots, y_{kt})$ in $C(z_j)$ for each $q_t$ and $i_r$ for which $(q_t, i_r) \in D_\omega$, $\omega(q_t, i_r) = w_s$, and $z_j = 1$ in $w_s$.

II. A cover $C(y_j')$ for the next state equation $y_j'$, $1 \leq j \leq k$ is formed by placing a 0-cube $(x_{1u}, x_{2u}, \ldots, x_{nu}, y_{1v}, y_{2v}, \ldots, y_{kv})$ in $C(y_j')$ for each $q_v$ and $i_u$ for which $(q_v, i_u) \in D_\tau$, $\tau(q_v, i_u) = q_w$, and $y_j = 1$ in $q_w$.

III. A cover for the "don't care" conditions for the output equations $C(N_z)$ is formed by placing an $n$-cube $(x, x, \ldots, x, y_{1w}, y_{2w}, \ldots, y_{kw})$ in $C(N_z)$ for each configuration $(y_{1w}, y_{2w}, \ldots, y_{kw})$ not used in the state assignment and a 0-cube $(x_{1u}, x_{2u}, \ldots, x_{nu}, y_{1v}, y_{2v}, \ldots, y_{kv})$ for each state $q_v$ and input $i_u$ in which $(q_v, i_u) \notin D_\omega$.

IV. A cover for the "don't care" conditions for the next state equations $C(N_{y'})$ is formed by placing an $n$-cube $(x, x, \ldots, x, y_{1w}, y_{2w}, \ldots, y_{kw})$ in $C(N_{y'})$ as in Rule III, and also a 0-cube $(x_{1u}, x_{2u}, \ldots, x_{nu}, y_{1v}, y_{2v}, \ldots, y_{kv})$ for each state $q_v$ and input $i_u$ for which $(q_v, i_u) \notin D_\tau$.

Note that Rule I creates a term in the output equation $z_j$ whenever the output, resulting from the input and state represented by the term, has a value 1 for $z_j$. The other rules may be interpreted similarly. We demonstrate these rules with the machine shown in Figure 8.2.1. In this figure we assume that the values of the state variables appear in the order $y_1 y_2$,

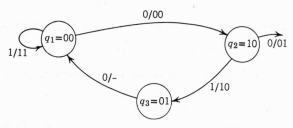

Figure 8.2.1  A machine with a given state assignment.

and the order of the output values is $z_1 z_2$. We have only one input variable which we call $x_1$, and we must form two output equations $z_1$ and $z_2$ and two next state equations $y_1'$ and $y_2'$. From Rule I we obtain covers for the outputs $z_1$ and $z_2$:

$$
\begin{array}{ccc}
x_1 & y_1 & y_2
\end{array}
$$

$$
C(z_1) = \begin{Bmatrix} 1 & 0 & 0 \\ 1 & 1 & 0 \end{Bmatrix}.
$$

$$
C(z_2) = \begin{Bmatrix} 1 & 0 & 0 \\ 0 & 1 & 0 \end{Bmatrix}.
$$

From Rule II we obtain the next state covers:

$$
\begin{array}{ccc}
x_1 & y_1 & y_2
\end{array}
$$

$$
C(y_1') = \{0 \quad 0 \quad 0\}
$$
$$
C(y_2') = \{1 \quad 1 \quad 0\}.
$$

From Rule III we obtain the "don't cares" for the outputs as

$$
\begin{array}{ccc}
x_1 & y_1 & y_2
\end{array}
$$

$$
C(N_z) = \begin{Bmatrix} x & 1 & 1 \\ 0 & 0 & 1 \\ 1 & 0 & 1 \end{Bmatrix}.
$$

From Rule IV we obtain the "don't cares" for the next states as

$$C(N_{y'}) = \begin{matrix} x_1 & y_1 & y_2 \\ \begin{pmatrix} x & 1 & 1 \\ 0 & 1 & 0 \\ 1 & 0 & 1 \end{pmatrix} \end{matrix}.$$

Thus, for example, the switching function for output $z_1$ would be

$$z_1 = x_1 \bar{y}_1 \bar{y}_2 \vee x_1 y_1 \bar{y}_2,$$

and the "don't cares" for the outputs could be represented by a function $q$ where

$$q = y_1 y_2 \vee \bar{y}_1 y_2.$$

As stated earlier, different state assignments will produce different sets of next state and output equations and also different "don't care" conditions. For a completely synchronous network any state assignment may be used, and the circuit operation will give the desired input-output behavior for the machine. For asynchronous networks, the state assignment must be restricted to one allowing transitions from any given state $q_j$ to any possible next state $q_k$ of $q_j$, under some input, so that the machine will actually arrive in state $q_k$ rather than some other state even if the

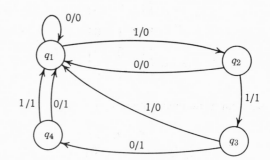

| State Assignment I | | |
| --- | --- | --- |
| | $y_1$ | $y_2$ |
| $q_1$ | 1 | 1 |
| $q_2$ | 0 | 0 |
| $q_3$ | 1 | 0 |
| $q_4$ | 0 | 1 |

| State Assignment II | | |
| --- | --- | --- |
| | $y_1$ | $y_2$ |
| $q_1$ | 0 | 0 |
| $q_2$ | 1 | 0 |
| $q_3$ | 1 | 1 |
| $q_4$ | 0 | 1 |

Figure 8.2.2   A machine and two different state assignments.

circuit operation speeds have some variation. Conditions known as "hazards" and "race conditions" must be avoided. We consider only synchronous machines in this chapter and consider asynchronous networks in Chapters 9 and 10.

To illustrate the effect of different state assignments on the output and next state equations, consider the sequential machine and the two assignments shown in Figure 8.2.2.

The simplified output and next state equations resulting from Assignment I are

$$z_1 = x_1\bar{y}_1 \vee \bar{y}_1 y_2 \vee \bar{x}_1 y_1 \bar{y}_2,$$

$$y_1' = \bar{y}_1 \vee x_1\bar{y}_2 \vee \bar{x}_1 y_2,$$

$$y_2' = \bar{x}_1 \vee \bar{y}_1 y_2 \vee y_1\bar{y}_2.$$

Similarly, for Assignment II we obtain

$$z_1 = \bar{y}_1 y_2 \vee \bar{x}_1 y_1 y_2 \vee x_1 y_1 \bar{y}_2,$$

$$y_1' = x_1\bar{y}_2,$$

$$y_2' = \bar{x}_1 y_1 y_2 \vee x_1 y_1 \bar{y}_2.$$

Multiple output AND-OR combinational networks are shown for Assignments I and II in Figure 8.2.3a and b, respectively, where common terms are used for more than one output whenever desirable. From these networks, it is readily seen that Assignment II leads to a much more economical network than Assignment I.

In the state assignment for synchronous machines, we attempt to obtain a design having economical combinational circuits. The general problem could thus be stated as follows. For a given sequential machine $\mathcal{M}$ and a set of decision elements with known costs, find a sequential machine $\mathcal{M}'$, where $\mathcal{M}' \supseteq \mathcal{M}$, and a state assignment for $\mathcal{M}'$ having $k$ or fewer state variables leading to a circuit having the least possible total cost, which consists of both the cost of the memory devices and that of the combinational circuits.

As one might expect from the methods of combinational network synthesis discussed in Chapters 3 and 4 of Volume 1, it is very difficult to find a solution to this general state assignment problem even when $\mathcal{M}$ contains only a few states.

Several factors, other than the complexity of obtaining minimum cost combinational networks, add to the difficulty of this problem. First, if one wishes to obtain an economical sequential network realization for some design specifications given in terms of a sequential machine $\mathcal{M}$, it may be both possible and desirable to perform state assignment on another machine $\mathcal{M}'$, where $\mathcal{M}'$ is from some class of machines related to $\mathcal{M}$.

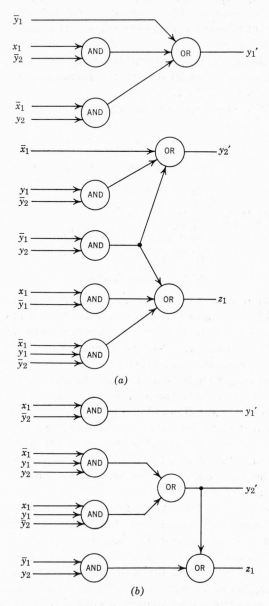

Figure 8.2.3   Combinational networks for Figure 8.2.2.   (*a*) Combinational network for Assignment I.   (*b*) Combinational network for Assignment II.

Usually, any machine $\mathcal{M}'$ including $\mathcal{M}$ will also satisfy the design specifications; thus applying a state assignment to $\mathcal{M}'$ may also yield a lower cost network than it is possible to attain from any direct state assignment of $\mathcal{M}$. In some cases, other considerations may impose further limits on the class of machines leading to satisfactory networks, but nevertheless it is usually possible to consider machines other than only $\mathcal{M}$ itself.

A second difficulty for finding an economical state assignment is that there are many possible assignments for $\mathcal{M}$. If one uses $k$ internal variables and $\mathcal{M}$ has $p$ states, there are $(2^k)!/(2^k - p)!$ possible assignments. Some of them are essentially equivalent, however, in the sense that they lead to identical combinational networks when simple permutations of the internal variables are allowed. Since there are $k!$ permutations of the $k$ internal variables and relabeling of the variables does not change the complexity of the combinational networks for the output and next state equations, there are $(2^k)!/(2^k - p)!\,k!$ essentially different assignments when these permutations are ignored. When a minimum number of internal variables are used in the assignment and both permutation and inversion of internal variables may be ignored, it has been shown that there are $(2^k - 1)!/(2^k - p)!\,k!$ distinct state assignments. Up to about four states, it is not very difficult to inspect all possible assignments, but as $p$ increases, it soon becomes impractical to explore all possibilities, even when using a computer.

A third factor adding to the difficulty is the many possible forms of combinational networks and storage elements which might be used to realize the sequential network. For example, for some types of storage elements, such as flip-flops rather than delay units, next state equations different from Equations 6.2.2 may be required to represent the network. Furthermore, the memory devices may be distributed throughout the network in a different form from the basic sequential network model. As can be imagined, both these structural changes in a network affect directly the way state assignments lead to least cost networks.

An effective method of solution for this general state assignment problem has not been developed. With some additional simplifying assumptions and through the development of sequential machine properties related to state assignment, however, various techniques for obtaining state assignments that produce reasonably economical sequential network designs have been found. We discuss these properties and techniques in the remainder of this chapter. Various algorithms based on some of these properties have been given in the literature. These algorithms will not be discussed in detail here, however, since the details of an algorithm are very dependent on the particular network structure and element costs assumed.

## 8.3 AN ELEMENTARY APPROACH FOR STATE ASSIGNMENT

To give further insight into state assignment, we assume first that rather than requiring lowest cost networks we find an assignment that produces next state and output equations of the form of Equations 6.2.2 and 6.2.1 which give "fairly economical" multiple output AND-OR networks. We can thus use the techniques of Chapters 3 and 4 to obtain minimum covers

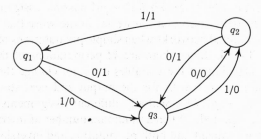

Figure 8.3.1   A three state machine with binary input and binary output.

and multiple output covers. For example, we prefer to obtain Assignment II for Figures 8.2.2 and 8.2.3 rather than Assignment I. We assume further that the machine for which we wish to make an assignment is determined (call it $\mathcal{M}$) and no searching over a class of machines $\mathcal{M}'$, where $\mathcal{M}' \supseteq \mathcal{M}$, will be attempted. We usually use a minimum state machine as determined by the techniques of Chapter 7, but the state assignment approach does not require that $\mathcal{M}$ must be minimum. Finally, we assume that the minimum possible number of storage elements $k_m$ for the state assignment will always be used.

With these assumptions we give a symbolic approach to the problem and thereby derive some rules of thumb for obtaining fairly economical networks. We use the example of Figure 8.3.1 to describe this approach. Any state assignment for the machine can be represented symbolically as shown in the following.

State Assignment

| State | $y_1$ | $y_2$ |
|:-----:|:-----:|:-----:|
| 1 | $y_{11}$ | $y_{21}$ |
| 2 | $y_{12}$ | $y_{22}$ |
| 3 | $y_{13}$ | $y_{23}$ |
| "Don't care" | $y_{14}$ | $y_{24}$ |

The sets of equations then can be expressed in this symbolic representation in which each $y_{ij}$ is either 0 or 1, and

$$y_i^{y_{ij}} = \begin{cases} \bar{y}_i & \text{if} \quad y_{ij} = 0, \\ y_i & \text{if} \quad y_{ij} = 1. \end{cases}$$

The output equation for $z_1$ is

$$z_1 = \bar{x}y_1^{y_{11}}y_2^{y_{21}} \vee y_1^{y_{12}}y_2^{y_{22}}.$$

The next state equations for $y_1'$ and $y_2'$ are

$$y_1' = y_{11}(xy_1^{y_{12}}y_2^{y_{22}}) \vee y_{12}(y_1^{y_{13}}y_2^{y_{23}}) \vee y_{13}(y_1^{y_{11}}y_2^{y_{21}} \vee \bar{x}y_1^{y_{12}}y_2^{y_{22}}),$$

$$y_2' = y_{21}(xy_1^{y_{12}}y_2^{y_{22}}) \vee y_{22}(y_1^{y_{13}}y_2^{y_{23}}) \vee y_{23}(y_1^{y_{11}}y_2^{y_{21}} \vee \bar{x}y_1^{y_{12}}y_2^{y_{22}}).$$

Since the example machine is complete, the only "don't care" condition here is $y_1^{y_{14}} y_2^{y_{24}}$, the unused state assignment vector.

Although this symbolism makes the equations appear rather complex, all possible assignments are represented, and thus the nature of the state assignment problem is displayed. In addition, the effect of any particular assignment on the equations can be readily evaluated by setting the $y_{ij}$'s equal to 0's and 1's. After completing the output and next state equations symbolically, we want to set the $y_{ij}$'s equal to 0's and 1's in order to simplify the equations and also have a state assignment where each state has a different binary vector. The following two rules of thumb help in this simplification.

I. Set the $y_{ij}$'s equal to 0 which have the most complex factors in the $y_m'$ equations.

II. Assign values to the $y_{ij}$'s such that the nonzero terms in the equations may be mutually simplified by combining terms.

In the example, we set $y_{13} = y_{23} = 0$ by Rule I since these two factors are obviously the most complex in equations $y_1'$ and $y_2'$. This leaves the equations

$$z_1 = \bar{x}y_1^{y_{11}}y_2^{y_{21}} \vee y_1^{y_{12}}y_2^{y_{22}},$$

$$\begin{cases} y_1' = y_{11}(xy_1^{y_{12}}y_2^{y_{22}}) \vee y_{12}(\bar{y}_1\bar{y}_2), \\ y_2' = y_{21}(xy_1^{y_{12}}y_2^{y_{22}}) \vee y_{22}(\bar{y}_1\bar{y}_2). \end{cases}$$

If we set $y_{11} = 0$, we must have $y_{21} = 1$ and $y_{12} = 1$ because no two state assignments may be equal. Setting $y_{22} = 0$ eliminates one further term, and the only possible remaining assignment for $y_{14}$ and $y_{24}$ is $y_{14} = y_{24} = 1$, giving the "don't care" condition $y_1y_2$. The equations for this assignment are

$$z_1 = \bar{x}\bar{y}_1y_2 \vee y_1\bar{y}_2,$$

$$\begin{cases} y_1' = \bar{y}_1\bar{y}_2, \\ y_2' = xy_1\bar{y}_2. \end{cases}$$

By using the "don't care" condition $y_1 y_2$, we may further simplify the equations to

$$z_1 = \bar{x}_1 y_2 \vee y_1,$$

$$\begin{cases} y_1{}' = \bar{y}_1 \bar{y}_2, \\ y_2{}' = x y_1. \end{cases}$$

Thus we get a fairly simple set of equations by using these two rules on this example. Some other state assignments would give more complex equations, as can be checked by the reader.

These rules of thumb are not precise and they become increasingly difficult to apply in more complex examples since it is not clear exactly to which $y_{ij}$'s the rules should be applied first.

A further application of this approach is the four state machine of Figure 8.2.2. The symbolic representation of a state assignment is

State Assignment

| State | $y_1$ | $y_2$ |
|:---:|:---:|:---:|
| 1 | $y_{11}$ | $y_{21}$ |
| 2 | $y_{12}$ | $y_{22}$ |
| 3 | $y_{13}$ | $y_{23}$ |
| 4 | $y_{14}$ | $y_{24}$ |

The symbolic equations for the machine are thus

$$z_1 = x_1 y_1^{y_{14}} y_2^{y_{24}} \vee \bar{x}_1 y_1^{y_{14}} y_2^{y_{24}} \vee \bar{x}_1 y_1^{y_{13}} y_2^{y_{23}} \vee x_1 y_1^{y_{12}} y_2^{y_{22}},$$

$$\begin{aligned} y_1{}' = y_{11}(x_1 y_1^{y_{14}} y_2^{y_{24}} &\vee \bar{x}_1 y_1^{y_{14}} y_2^{y_{24}} \vee x_1 y_1^{y_{13}} y_2^{y_{23}} \vee \bar{x}_1 y_1^{y_{11}} y_2^{y_{21}} \\ &\vee \bar{x}_1 y_1^{y_{12}} y_2^{y_{22}}) \vee y_{12}(x_1 y_1^{y_{11}} y_2^{y_{21}}) \vee y_{13}(x_1 y_1^{y_{12}} y_2^{y_{22}}) \\ &\vee y_{14}(\bar{x}_1 y_1^{y_{13}} y_2^{y_{23}}), \end{aligned}$$

$$\begin{aligned} y_2{}' = y_{21}(x_1 y_1^{y_{14}} y_2^{y_{24}} &\vee \bar{x}_1 y_1^{y_{14}} y_2^{y_{24}} \vee x_1 y_1^{y_{13}} y_2^{y_{23}} \vee \bar{x}_1 y_1^{y_{11}} y_2^{y_{21}} \\ &\vee \bar{x}_1 y_1^{y_{12}} y_2^{y_{22}}) \vee y_{22}(x_1 y_1^{y_{11}} y_2^{y_{21}}) \vee y_{23}(x_1 y_1^{y_{12}} y_2^{y_{22}}) \\ &\vee y_{24}(\bar{x}_1 y_1^{y_{13}} y_2^{y_{23}}). \end{aligned}$$

Because this machine is complete and the number of states is an exact power of 2, there are no "don't care" conditions.

To simplify these symbolic equations, we apply Rules I and II. From Rule I, it is clear that both $y_{11}$ and $y_{21}$ should be set equal to 0 since the corresponding factors in $y_1{}'$ and $y_2{}'$ are obviously the most complex factors in the equations. This step reduces the equations to

$$z_1 = x_1 y_1^{y_{14}} y_2^{y_{24}} \vee \bar{x}_1 y_1^{y_{14}} y_2^{y_{24}} \vee \bar{x}_1 y_1^{y_{13}} y_2^{y_{23}} \vee x_1 y_1^{y_{12}} y_2^{y_{22}},$$

$$y_1{}' = y_{12}(x_1 \bar{y}_1 \bar{y}_2) \vee y_{13}(x_1 y_1^{y_{12}} y_2^{y_{22}}) \vee y_{14}(\bar{x}_1 y_1^{y_{13}} y_2^{y_{23}}),$$

$$y_2{}' = y_{22}(x_1 \bar{y}_1 \bar{y}_2) \vee y_{23}(x_1 y_1^{y_{12}} y_2^{y_{22}}) \vee y_{24}(\bar{x}_1 y_1^{y_{13}} y_2^{y_{23}}).$$

At this point, since each factor in the $y_1'$ and $y_2'$ equations is as complex as each other factor, we employ Rule II for further simplification. Rule II does not indicate clearly the next values to assign, but the factors $\bar{x}_1 y_1^{y_{13}} y_2^{y_{23}}$ and $x_1 y_1^{y_{12}} y_2^{y_{22}}$ appear in $z_1$ and are also potential factors in $y_1'$ and $y_2'$. We shall choose to make them factors of $y_2'$, which means that $y_{23} = y_{24} = 1$. Assigning $y_{13} = 1$ and $y_{14} = 0$ allows $y_1'$ to be further simplified since the $x_1 \bar{y}_1 \bar{y}_2$ and $x_1 y_1^{y_{12}} y_2^{y_{22}}$ factors can then be combined, since the only assignment left for $y_{12}$ and $y_{22}$ is $y_{12} = 1$ and $y_{22} = 0$. Thus the equations become

$$z_1 = x_1 \bar{y}_1 y_2 \vee \bar{x}_1 \bar{y}_1 y_2 \vee \bar{x}_1 y_1 y_2 \vee x_1 y_1 \bar{y}_2,$$

$$y_1' = x_1 \bar{y}_1 \bar{y}_2 \vee x_1 y_1 \bar{y}_2,$$

$$y_2' = x_1 y_1 \bar{y}_2 \vee \bar{x}_1 y_1 y_2.$$

These equations simplify to

$$z_1 = \bar{y}_1 y_2 \vee \bar{x}_1 y_1 y_2 \vee x_1 y_1 \bar{y}_2,$$

$$y_1' = x_1 \bar{y}_2,$$

$$y_2' = \bar{x}_1 y_1 y_2 \vee x_1 y_1 \bar{y}_2.$$

This is the same assignment as Assignment II, Figure 8.2.2, and thus the combinational network of Figure 8.2.3*b* is obtained. It should be noted, however, that other assignments could have been obtained from Rule II since no clearcut assignment is indicated for this example, except that one should assign $y_{11} = y_{21} = 0$.

Finally, we demonstrate the application of these simple assignment rules to an incomplete machine by reconsidering the machine of Figure 8.2.1. The symbolic representation is

| | State Assignment | |
| State | $y_1$ | $y_2$ |
| --- | --- | --- |
| 1 | $y_{11}$ | $y_{21}$ |
| 2 | $y_{12}$ | $y_{22}$ |
| 3 | $y_{13}$ | $y_{23}$ |
| "Don't care" | $y_{14}$ | $y_{24}$ |

The symbolic equations are

$$z_1 = x_1 y_1^{y_{11}} y_2^{y_{21}} \vee x_1 y_1^{y_{12}} y_2^{y_{22}},$$

$$z_2 = x_1 y_1^{y_{11}} y_2^{y_{21}} \vee \bar{x}_1 y_1^{y_{12}} y_2^{y_{22}},$$

$$y_1' = y_{11}(x_1 y_1^{y_{11}} y_2^{y_{21}} \vee \bar{x}_1 y_1^{y_{13}} y_2^{y_{23}}) \vee y_{12}(\bar{x}_1 y_1^{y_{11}} y_2^{y_{21}}) \vee y_{13}(x_1 y_1^{y_{12}} y_2^{y_{22}}),$$

$$y_2' = y_{21}(x_1 y_1^{y_{11}} y_2^{y_{21}} \vee \bar{x}_1 y_1^{y_{13}} y_2^{y_{23}}) \vee y_{22}(\bar{x}_1 y_1^{y_{11}} y_2^{y_{21}}) \vee y_{13}(x_1 y_1^{y_{12}} y_2^{y_{22}}).$$

The "don't care" conditions for the outputs and next states are

$$N_z = y_1^{y_{14}} y_2^{y_{24}} \vee y_1^{y_{13}} y_2^{y_{23}}$$

and

$$N_{y'} = y_1^{y_{14}} y_2^{y_{24}} \vee x_1 y_1^{y_{13}} y_2^{y_{23}} \vee \bar{x}_1 y_1^{y_{12}} y_2^{y_{22}}$$

Thus the equations can be immediately simplified before any $y_{ij}$ are assigned as follows:

$$z_1 = x_1,$$
$$z_2 = x_1 y_1^{y_{11}} y_2^{y_{21}} \vee \bar{x}_1 y_1^{y_{12}} y_2^{y_{22}}$$
$$y_1' = y_{11}(x_1 y_1^{y_{11}} y_2^{y_{21}} \vee y_1^{y_{13}} y_2^{y_{23}}) \vee y_{12}(\bar{x}_1 y_1^{y_{11}} y_2^{y_{21}}) \vee y_{13}(y_1^{y_{12}} y_2^{y_{22}}),$$
$$y_2' = y_{21}(x_1 y_1^{y_{11}} y_2^{y_{21}} \vee y_1^{y_{13}} y_2^{y_{23}}) \vee y_{22}(\bar{x}_1 y_1^{y_{11}} y_2^{y_{21}}) \vee y_{23}(y_1^{y_{12}} y_2^{y_{22}}).$$

From Rule I we now assign $y_{11} = y_{21} = 0$ to simplify the $y_1'$ and $y_2'$ equations, giving

$$z_1 = x_1,$$
$$z_2 = x_1 \bar{y}_1 \bar{y}_2 \vee \bar{x}_1 y_1^{y_{12}} y_2^{y_{22}},$$
$$y_1' = y_{12}(\bar{x}_1 \bar{y}_1 \bar{y}_2) \vee y_{13}(y_1^{y_{12}} y_2^{y_{22}}),$$
$$y_2' = y_{22}(\bar{x}_1 \bar{y}_1 \bar{y}_2) \vee y_{23}(y_1^{y_{12}} y_2^{y_{22}}).$$

By assigning arbitrarily the encoding $y_{12} = 0$, $y_{22} = 1$, and $y_{13} = 1$, $y_{23} = 0$, we eliminate one factor in each of the $y_j'$ equations and force $y_{14} = y_{24} = 1$. The equations and "don't care" conditions then become

$$\begin{cases} z_1 = x_1 \\ z_2 = x_1 \bar{y}_1 \bar{y}_2 \vee \bar{x}_1 \bar{y}_1 y_2, \end{cases}$$

$$\begin{cases} y_1' = \bar{y}_1 y_2 \\ y_2' = \bar{x}_1 \bar{y}_1 \bar{y}_2, \end{cases}$$

$$\begin{cases} N_z = y_1 y_2 \vee y_1 \bar{y}_2 = y_1 \\ N_{y'} = y_1 y_2 \vee x_1 y_1 \bar{y}_2 \vee \bar{x}_1 \bar{y}_1 y_2. \end{cases}$$

These equations can then be simplified to

$$\begin{cases} z_1 = x_1, \\ z_2 = x_1 \bar{y}_2 \vee \bar{x}_1 y_2, \end{cases}$$

$$\begin{cases} y_1' = y_2, \\ y_2' = \bar{x}_1 \bar{y}_1. \end{cases}$$

The resulting combinational network is shown in Figure 8.3.2.

The two rules of thumb, I and II, indicate roughly some relationships between the transition and output structure of a machine and an economical state assignment. For example, Rule I indicates that a state having a large number of transitions entering the state should have many 0's in the $y_{ij}$'s for that state. Rule II indicates that a pair of states having many

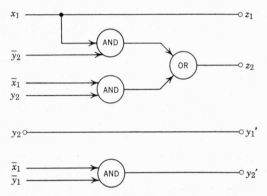

Figure 8.3.2.  Combinational network from incomplete machine state assignment example.

transitions between each other should have assignments differing in only one $y_j$ variable (that is, adjacent) so that terms can be combined. Other properties of sequential machines tending to simplify the equations are developed in more detail in the following two sections.

## 8.4  PARTITIONS ON STATES FOR REDUCED DEPENDENCY OF NEXT STATE EQUATIONS

Here, we consider some algebraic properties of sequential machines that help to simplify the next state equations:

$$y_1' = y_1'(x_1, \ldots, x_n, y_1, \ldots, y_k),$$

.

.

.

$$y_k' = y_k'(x_1, \ldots, x_n, y_1, \ldots, y_k),$$

used to realize a sequential machine. In general, each $y_j'$ equation is dependent on all the input variables $x_1, \ldots, x_n$ and all the state variables $y_1, \ldots, y_k$. The approach for obtaining simplified next state equations, which we describe here, is to find assignments of the $y_1, \ldots, y_k$ variables such that each next state equation depends on as few of the $y_1, \ldots, y_k$

variables as possible. This approach, due to Hartmanis and Stearns, is shown to be closely related to the existence of certain partitions on the states of a sequential machine. It is usually true that a switching function of $r$ variables is more economically realized by a combinational network than a switching function of $s$ variables when $r < s$. Thus finding state assignments that create reduced dependence in the $y_j'$ equations often yields a more economical combinational network than other types of assignments.

With this motivation, we develop a method for finding this reduced dependence in the $y_j'$ equations. Several simplifying assumptions are made. First, we assume that we apply the methods directly to some $\mathcal{M}$, where $\mathcal{M}$ is a complete machine. Second, since the output equations are not considered here, we ignore the complexity of the output equations when obtaining an assignment; and third, we assume a two-level AND-OR network configuration in comparing the complexity of the combinational networks. This last assumption simplifies the comparison of various state assignments; however, reduced dependence of the equations tends to give more economical combinational networks for other network configurations as well.

The sequential machine and two state assignments in Figure 8.4.1 illustrate how reduced dependence simplifies the resulting equations.

For Assignment I, the next state equations are

$$y_1' = \bar{x}_1\bar{y}_1y_2\bar{y}_3 \vee x_1\bar{y}_1y_2y_3 \vee \bar{x}_1\bar{y}_1\bar{y}_2y_3,$$

$$y_2' = \bar{x}_1y_1\bar{y}_2y_3 \vee x_1\bar{y}_1\bar{y}_2y_3 \vee x_1\bar{y}_1\bar{y}_2y_3 \vee \bar{x}_1\bar{y}_1\bar{y}_2y_3 \vee x_1y_1\bar{y}_2y_3 \vee x_1y_1\bar{y}_2y_3,$$

$$y_3' = \bar{x}_1\bar{y}_1y_2y_3 \vee x_1\bar{y}_1y_2y_3 \vee \bar{x}_1\bar{y}_1\bar{y}_2y_3 \vee x_1y_1\bar{y}_2y_3 \vee x_1y_1\bar{y}_2y_3 \vee \bar{x}_1\bar{y}_1\bar{y}_2y_3,$$

and the "don't care" conditions are $N_{y'} = y_1y_2$. The equations simplify to

$$y_1' = \bar{x}_1y_2\bar{y}_3 \vee x_1y_2y_3 \vee \bar{x}_1\bar{y}_1\bar{y}_2y_3,$$

$$y_2' = y_1y_3 \vee x_1\bar{y}_2 \vee \bar{y}_1\bar{y}_2\bar{y}_3,$$

$$y_3' = \bar{x}_1\bar{y}_1y_3 \vee \bar{x}_1\bar{y}_1\bar{y}_2 \vee x_1y_1 \vee x_1y_2\bar{y}_3,$$

and each equation is dependent on each of the variables $x_1$, $y_1$, $y_2$, and $y_3$.

For Assignment II, the next state equations are

$$y_1' = \bar{x}_1\bar{y}_1\bar{y}_2y_3 \vee \bar{x}_1\bar{y}_1\bar{y}_2y_3 \vee x_1y_1\bar{y}_2y_3 \vee \bar{x}_1y_1y_2\bar{y}_3 \vee x_1y_1\bar{y}_2y_3 \vee x_1y_1y_2\bar{y}_3,$$

$$y_2' = \bar{x}_1\bar{y}_1\bar{y}_2y_3 \vee \bar{x}_1y_1\bar{y}_2y_3,$$

$$y_3' = x_1y_1\bar{y}_2y_3 \vee \bar{x}_1\bar{y}_1\bar{y}_2y_3 \vee \bar{x}_1y_1\bar{y}_2y_3 \vee x_1\bar{y}_1\bar{y}_2y_3,$$

and the "don't care" conditions are $N_{y'} = y_2y_3$. These equations simplify to

$$y_1' = \bar{x}_1\bar{y}_1 \vee x_1y_1,$$

$$y_2' = \bar{x}_1y_3,$$

$$y_3' = \bar{y}_2\bar{y}_3.$$

Obviously, the equations for Assignment II are much simpler than those for Assignment I. Note that the equations for Assignment II also display reduced dependence, since $y_1'$ depends only on $x_1$ and $y_1$, but not on $y_2$ or $y_3$; similarly, equation $y_2'$ depends only on $x_1$ and $y_3$, but not on $y_1$ or $y_2$; finally, $y_3'$ depends only on $y_2$ and $y_3$, but not on $x_1$ or $y_1$. If we consider

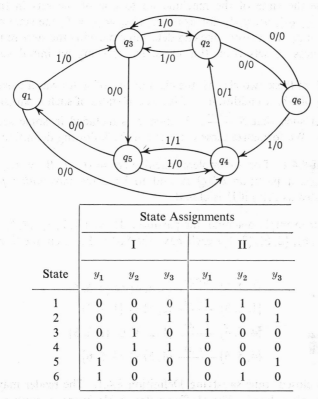

| | State Assignments | | | | | |
|---|---|---|---|---|---|---|
| | | I | | | II | |
| State | $y_1$ | $y_2$ | $y_3$ | $y_1$ | $y_2$ | $y_3$ |
| 1 | 0 | 0 | 0 | 1 | 1 | 0 |
| 2 | 0 | 0 | 1 | 1 | 0 | 1 |
| 3 | 0 | 1 | 0 | 1 | 0 | 0 |
| 4 | 0 | 1 | 1 | 0 | 0 | 0 |
| 5 | 1 | 0 | 0 | 0 | 0 | 1 |
| 6 | 1 | 0 | 1 | 0 | 1 | 0 |

Figure 8.4.1 Example of state assignment with reduced dependence.

the set $\{y_1', y_2', y_3'\}$ and ignore input dependences, we see that $y_1'$ is "self-dependent;" that is, it depends only on the present value of $y_1$. Similarly, $\{y_2', y_3'\}$ is self-dependent. This self-dependence is reflected in the states of the machine in the following way. If the value of $y_1$ is known, we know that we are either in one of the states of the set $\{q_1, q_2, q_3\}$ when $y_1 = 1$ or in one of the states $\{q_4, q_5, q_6\}$ when $y_1 = 0$. Thus the class $\{\{q_1, q_2, q_3\}, \{q_4, q_5, q_6\}\}$ is determined by $y_1$; however, from the equation for $y_1'$ we know that $y_1'$ can be computed knowing only the input value and $y_1$ value. Thus for any input sequence applied to $\mathcal{M}$ and knowing an initial value of $y_1$, we can compute all the succeeding values of $y_1$ for the given input sequence; thus we can partially determine the state sequence of the machine because at each of its points we must have either a state in the set $\{q_1, q_2, q_3\}$ if the preceding $y_1'$ was equal to 1, or a state in the set $\{q_4, q_5, q_6\}$ if the preceding $y_1'$ value was 0.

Similarly, knowing only the value of the pair of variables $(y_2, y_3)$ will determine the state of the machine up to one of the sets in the class $\{\{q_1, q_6\}, \{q_2, q_5\}, \{q_3, q_4\}\}$; for example, if $y_2 = y_3 = 0$, the state of $\mathcal{M}$ is either $q_3$ or $q_4$. As before, one can determine partially the state sequences, as sequences of sets from this class, by knowing an initial value for $(y_2, y_3)$.

In each of these two classes, the class of sets of states was a partition of the set $Q$ of $\mathcal{M}$. In addition, if $S$ is a set of states of such a partition and $T$ is a set such that $S \xrightarrow{(\mathcal{M},i)} T$, then $T$ is included in some set of the partition. We formalize these concepts in the following definition.

**Definition 8.4.1** For a complete machine $\mathcal{M} = (Q, I, W, \tau, \omega)$, a class $\Pi$ which is a partition of $Q$ is said to have the *substitution property* (abbreviated as S.P.) if $\Pi$ is closed.

For our example machine, the partitions $\Pi_1 = \{\{1, 2, 3\}, \{4, 5, 6\}\}$ and $\Pi_2 = \{\{1, 6\}, \{2, 5\}, \{3, 4\}\}$ each have the S.P.* For example, for $\Pi_1$ we have

$$\{1, 2, 3\} \xrightarrow{(\mathcal{M},0)} \{4, 5, 6\} \subseteq \{4, 5, 6\},$$
$$\{1, 2, 3\} \xrightarrow{(\mathcal{M},1)} \{2, 3\} \subseteq \{1, 2, 3\},$$
$$\{4, 5, 6\} \xrightarrow{(\mathcal{M},0)} \{1, 2, 3\} \subseteq \{1, 2, 3\},$$
$$\{4, 5, 6\} \xrightarrow{(\mathcal{M},1)} \{4, 5\} \subseteq \{4, 5, 6\}.$$

So $\Pi_1$ is closed, thus satisfying Definition 8.4.1. The reader may check that $\Pi_2$ is also closed. The Huffman flow table (where outputs need not be specified) is a very convenient model for checking closure, and we shall use it in the remainder of this section.

The general relation between state assignments with reduced dependence and partitions having the S.P. is given in the following theorem.

**Theorem 8.4.1** Let $\mathcal{M}$ be a complete sequential machine with $|Q| = n$, having a state assignment using internal variables $y_1, y_2, \ldots, y_k$. If the first $r$ next state equations, $1 \leq r \leq k$, depend on only the input variables and the first $r$ internal variables $y_1, y_2, \ldots, y_r$, then a partition $\Pi$ exists with the S.P. for $\mathcal{M}$ where states $q$ and $q'$ are in the same set of $\Pi$ if and

---

* As in Chapter 7, we denote $q_j$ simply by the index $j$ to simplify the notation.

only if the combinations of $y_1, y_2, \ldots, y_r$ values in the assignments for $q$ and $q'$ are equal.

PROOF. By definition of $\Pi$, it is a partition of $Q$, and thus we have only to show that $\Pi$ is closed to prove that $\Pi$ has the S.P. Suppose $q$ and $q'$ belong to the same set of $\Pi$; then the configuration of values $y_1, y_2, \ldots, y_r$ is equal for $q$ and $q'$. Let it be denoted by $\hat{y}_1, \hat{y}_2, \ldots, \hat{y}_r$.

By hypothesis, the $y_j'$ equations for $1 \leq j \leq r$ are dependent only on the variables $x_1, \ldots, x_n, y_1, \ldots, y_r$. Any input $i \in I$ is represented by a configuration of values for $x_1, x_2, \ldots, x_n$, which we denote by $x_{1i}, x_{2i}, \ldots, x_{ni}$. Thus the values of $y_j'$, $1 \leq j \leq r$, are uniquely determined by $x_{1i}, x_{2i}, \ldots, x_{ni}, \hat{y}_1, \ldots, \hat{y}_r$. That is, for any input $i$ the values of $y_1', \ldots, y_r'$ are equal both for $q$ and $q'$. Thus, if $\tau(q, i) = p$ and $\tau(q', i) = p'$, both $p$ and $p'$ have equal $y_1, \ldots, y_r$ encodings. Thus $\Pi$ is closed if and only if $p$ and $p'$ are included in a single set of $\Pi$, thus proving the theorem.

As an example of this theorem, Assignment II for the machine of Figure 8.4.1 has reduced dependency where $y_1, y_2, y_3$ are the internal variables and $y_1'$ depends only on the input and $y_1$. Thus by partitioning $Q$ for this machine into sets of states that have equal values for $y_1$, we obtain $\Pi = \{\{1, 2, 3\}, \{4, 5, 6\}\}$. This partition is identical to $\Pi_1$ which was shown earlier to have the S.P.

We now wish to show how a partition with S.P. for a sequential machine, for which a state assignment is desired, can lead to an assignment with reduced dependence. Suppose $\Pi$ is a partition with S.P. for $\mathcal{M}$. The minimum number of internal variables required to denote the set of $\Pi$ in which the next state of $\mathcal{M}$ will be contained, given an input and the set of $\Pi$ containing the present state, is $\lceil \log_2 |\Pi| \rceil$, since there are $|\Pi|$ sets of states in $\Pi$.* Other internal variables may then be used to distinguish between states in each set of $\Pi$. Thus, if $n(\Pi)$ denotes the number of states contained in the largest set of $\Pi$, we require at least $\lceil \log_2 n(\Pi) \rceil$ such variables. If we use a minimum number $k$ of variables and $r = \lceil \log_2 |\Pi| \rceil$, then $k - r = \lceil \log_2 n(\Pi) \rceil$. That is, the total number of variables required to use $\Pi$ for an assignment is $k = r + \lceil \log_2 n(\Pi) \rceil = \lceil \log_2 |\Pi| \rceil + \lceil \log_2 n(\Pi) \rceil$. If $n = |Q|$, we have seen previously that the minimum number of variables for any state assignment is $k_m = \lceil \log_2 n \rceil$. Thus, if $\Pi$ is to be used, the minimum number of internal variables can be employed if

$$\lceil \log_2 n \rceil = \lceil \log_2 |\Pi| \rceil + \lceil \log_2 n(\Pi) \rceil.$$

To illustrate these results, consider the machine shown in Figure 8.4.2. For this machine, $\Pi_1 = \{\{1\}, \{2\}, \{3, 4\}\}$ and $\Pi_2 = \{\{1, 2\}, \{3, 4\}\}$ can be seen to have S.P. and $k_m = 2$.

---

* The sets of states of a partition $\Pi$ are also commonly called the *blocks* of $\Pi$.

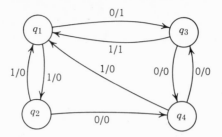

Figure 8.4.2   Example for state assignments using partitions with S.P.

For $\Pi_1$ we have

$$\lceil \log_2 |\Pi_1| \rceil = \lceil \log_2 3 \rceil = 2,$$

and

$$\lceil \log_2 n(\Pi)_1 \rceil = \lceil \log_2 2 \rceil = 1.$$

Hence $2 + 1 = 3$ internal variables are required if $\Pi_1$ is used. However, for $\Pi_2$

$$\lceil \log_2 |\Pi_2| \rceil + \lceil \log_2 n(\Pi_2) \rceil = 1 + 1 = 2,$$

so that only the minimum number of internal variables are required to use partition $\Pi_2$.

By using the notation of the previous section, a symbolic assignment for this example is

State Assignment

| State | $y_1$ | $y_2$ |
|-------|-------|-------|
| 1 | $y_{11}$ | $y_{21}$ |
| 2 | $y_{12}$ | $y_{22}$ |
| 3 | $y_{13}$ | $y_{23}$ |
| 4 | $y_{14}$ | $y_{24}$ |

If $\Pi_2$ is used to obtain an assignment and variable $y_1$ is used to denote the sets of $\Pi_2$, we require that $y_{11} = y_{12} \neq y_{13} = y_{14}$. Since no two states may be assigned the same configuration, it follows that $y_{21} \neq y_{22}$ and $y_{23} \neq y_{24}$. Even with these restrictions on the $y_{ij}$'s, the complete assignment is not determined. By using the rules of thumb, further simplifications can be obtained. The next state symbolic equations are

$$y_1' = y_{11}(x_1 y_1^{y_{12}} y_2^{y_{22}} \vee x_1 y_1^{y_{14}} y_2^{y_{24}} \vee x_1 y_1^{y_{13}} y_2^{y_{23}}) \vee y_{12}(x_1 y_1^{y_{11}} y_2^{y_{21}})$$
$$\vee y_{13}(\bar{x}_1 y_1^{y_{11}} y_2^{y_{21}} \vee \bar{x}_1 y_1^{y_{14}} y_2^{y_{24}}) \vee y_{14}(\bar{x}_1 y_1^{y_{12}} y_2^{y_{22}} \vee \bar{x}_1 y_1^{y_{13}} y_2^{y_{23}}),$$

$$y_2' = y_{21}(x_1 y_1^{y_{12}} y_2^{y_{22}} \vee x_1 y_1^{y_{14}} y_2^{y_{24}} \vee x_1 y_1^{y_{13}} y_2^{y_{23}}) \vee y_{22}(x_1 y_1^{y_{11}} y_2^{y_{21}})$$
$$\vee y_{23}(\bar{x}_1 y_1^{y_{11}} y_2^{y_{21}} \vee \bar{x}_1 y_1^{y_{14}} y_2^{y_{24}}) \vee y_{24}(\bar{x}_1 y_1^{y_{12}} y_2^{y_{22}} \vee \bar{x}_1 y_1^{y_{13}} y_2^{y_{23}}).$$

Since $y_{11} = y_{12}$ and $y_{13} = y_{14}$, equation $y_1'$ simplifies to

$$y_1' = y_{11}x_1 \vee y_{13}\bar{x}_1.$$

Similarly, using also that $y_{21} \neq y_{22}$, $y_{23} \neq y_{24}$, and $y_{12} \neq y_{13}$, the $y_2'$ equation becomes

$$y_2' = y_{21}(x_1 y_2^{y_{22}} \vee x_1 y_1^{y_{13}}) \vee y_{22}(x_1 y_1^{y_{11}} y_2^{y_{21}})$$
$$\vee\ y_{23}(\bar{x}_1 y_1^{y_{11}} y_2^{y_{21}} \vee \bar{x}_1 y_1^{y_{14}} y_2^{y_{24}}) \vee y_{24}(\bar{x}_1 y_1^{y_{12}} y_2^{y_{22}} \vee \bar{x}_1 y_1^{y_{13}} y_2^{y_{23}}).$$

The $y_2'$ equation is the only one to be simplified since $y_1'$ is either equal to $x_1$ or $\bar{x}_1$, depending on the value picked for $y_{11}$. For $y_2'$, either $y_{21} = y_{23}$ and $y_{22} = y_{24}$ or $y_{21} = y_{24}$ and $y_{22} = y_{23}$. If this second choice is made, both the factors for $y_{23}$ and $y_{24}$ can be simplified. Thus, letting $y_{21} = y_{24}$ and $y_{22} = y_{23}$, we obtain

$$y_2' = y_{21}(x_1 y_2^{y_{22}} \vee x_1 y_1^{y_{13}}) \vee y_{22}(x_1 y_1^{y_{11}} y_2^{y_{21}})$$
$$\vee\ y_{23}(\bar{x}_1 y_2^{y_{24}}) \vee y_{24}(\bar{x}_1 y_2^{y_{22}}).$$

By Rule I, we let $y_{21} = 0$; then by our previous restrictions $y_{24} = 0$, $y_{22} = 1$, and $y_{23} = 1$. Thus

$$y_1' = y_{11}x_1 \vee y_{13}\bar{x}_1,$$
$$y_2' = x_1 y_1^{y_{11}} \bar{y}_2 \vee \bar{x}_1 \bar{y}_2.$$

Since the complexity is not changed by the value chosen for $y_{11}$, we arbitrarily set $y_{11} = 1$, giving the simplified next state equations

$$y_1' = x_1,$$
$$y_2' = y_1 \bar{y}_2 \vee \bar{x}_1 \bar{y}_2.$$

In this example, it is important to note that using a partition with S.P. did not specify completely the exact state assignment for the machine. Thus other rules could be used to specify further which one of the many possible assignments satisfying the partition is actually used, so that the resulting equations are further simplified.

Partitions with S.P. for any machine can be generated by a simple iterative procedure using the properties of closure and partition. First, note that the partitions $\Pi(0) = \{\{q_1\}, \{q_2\}, \ldots, \{q_n\}\}$ and $\Pi(1) = \{\{q_1, q_2, \ldots, q_n\}\}$ trivially have the S.P. for any machine $\mathcal{M}$ in which $Q = \{q_1, q_2, \ldots, q_n\}$. To find other nontrivial partitions, start by assuming that some pair of states $(q_j, q_k)$ is in a single set of a partition. We say that we *identify* $q_j$ and $q_k$. Then by closure for any $i \in I$ and

$$\tau(q_j, i) = q_{ji},$$
$$\tau(q_k, i) = q_{ki},$$

it follows that $(q_{ji}, q_{ki})$ must be identified. If some $q'$ has been identified with $q$ and a $q''$ has also identified with $q$, $(q', q'')$ are also identified since we desire to obtain a partition of $Q$. We repeat this process until no new pairs are identified; it is readily seen that the $\Pi$ so constructed has S.P. for $\mathcal{M}$. To obtain other partitions, we repeat the process for each possible starting pair of states $(q_j, q_k)$, that is, for $n(n - 1)/2$ pairs of states.

We use Figure 8.4.2 to illustrate this process. Here $\Pi(0) = \{\{1\}, \{2\}, \{3\}, \{4\}\}$ and $\Pi(1) = \{\{1, 2, 3, 4\}\}$. Identifying states 1 and 2 gives

$$\{\{1, 2\}, \{3\}, \{4\}\},$$

but

$$\{1, 2\} \xrightarrow{(\mathcal{M},0)} \{3, 4\},$$

$$\{1, 2\} \xrightarrow{(\mathcal{M},1)} \{1, 2\},$$

so that we require $\{3, 4\}$ to be identified, giving

$$\{\{1, 2\}, \{3, 4\}\}.$$

Then

$$\{3, 4\} \xrightarrow{(\mathcal{M},0)} \{3, 4\},$$

and

$$\{3, 4\} \xrightarrow{(\mathcal{M},1)} \{1\}.$$

Thus no further identifications are required and $\Pi_2 = \{\{1, 2\}, \{3, 4\}\}$ has the S.P.

Now if states 1 and 3 are identified, we obtain the partition $\{\{1, 3\}, \{2\}, \{4\}\}$. The next sets of states are most readily checked by a flow table format

|         |   | $\{1, 3\}$ | $\{2\}$ | $\{4\}$ |
|---------|---|------------|---------|---------|
| Inputs  | 0 | 3, 4       | 4       | 3       |
|         | 1 | 2, 1       | 1       | 1       |

Thus, $\{1, 2\}$ and $\{3, 4\}$ must be identified, and to maintain a partition we need both state 4 to be identified with set $\{1, 3\}$ and also state 2 to be identified with $\{1, 3\}$. Thus, we obtain $\Pi(1)$. The reader may check that $\Pi(1)$ is also obtained if $\{1, 4\}$ is the starting pair. Starting with pair $\{2, 3\}$, we find the partition $\Pi_4 = \{\{1\}, \{2, 3\}, \{4\}\}$ with S.P. Starting with $\{2, 4\}$, we get

|         |   | $\{2, 4\}$ | $\{1\}$ | $\{3\}$ |
|---------|---|------------|---------|---------|
| Inputs  | 0 | 4, 3       | 3       | 4       |
|         | 1 | 1, 1       | 2       | 1       |

so that $\{3, 4\}$ must be identified, giving $\Pi_3 = \{\{1\}, \{2, 3, 4\}\}$ as a partition with S.P. Finally, identifying $\{3, 4\}$ gives $\Pi_1 = \{\{1\}, \{2\}, \{3, 4\}\}$ as a partition with S.P. Note that by this procedure we have derived $\Pi_1$ and $\Pi_2$ for $\mathcal{M}$ discussed earlier and have also found two new partitions $\Pi_3$ and $\Pi_4$.

With the introduction of several algebraic operations between partitions, it is possible to generate all the partitions with S.P. for $\mathcal{M}$.

**Definition 8.4.2** Partition $\Pi_1$ is said to be *smaller than* $\Pi_2$ (denoted by $\Pi_1 \leq \Pi_2$) if $\Pi_1$ is covered by $\Pi_2$.

This ordering can be seen to be a partial ordering of the partitions of $Q$. For example, $\Pi_1 \leq \Pi_2$ for the partitions generated for Figure 8.4.2, but $\Pi_2 \nleq \Pi_3$, and $\Pi_3 \nleq \Pi_2$.

Note that $\Pi(0)$ is the unique smallest partition and $\Pi(1)$ the unique largest partition under this partial ordering.

**Definition 8.4.3** Let $\Pi$ and $\Pi'$ be partitions of $Q$. We denote $\Pi \cdot \Pi' = \Pi''$ as a partition of $Q$ where a set is an element of $\Pi''$ only if it is a nonempty intersection of sets in $\Pi$ and $\Pi'$.

For example, $\Pi_2 = \{\{1, 2\}, \{3, 4\}\}$, and $\Pi_3 = \{\{1\}, \{2, 3, 4\}\}$ for the machine of Figure 8.4.2, and so

$$\Pi_2 \cdot \Pi_3 = \{\{1\}, \{2\}, \{3, 4\}\},$$

since

$$\{1\} \cap \{1, 2\} = \{1\},$$

$$\{1\} \cap \{3, 4\} = \phi,$$

$$\{2, 3, 4\} \cap \{1, 2\} = \{2\},$$

$$\{2, 3, 4\} \cap \{3, 4\} = \{3, 4\}.$$

It can be shown that $\Pi_1 \cdot \Pi_2$ is the greatest lower bound of $\Pi_1$ and $\Pi_2$ under the $\leq$ partial ordering of Definition 8.4.2. Similarly, we can obtain a least upper bound of $\Pi_1$ and $\Pi_2$, namely, $\Pi_1 + \Pi_2$ as defined in the following.

**Definition 8.4.4.** If $\Pi$ and $\Pi'$ are partitions of $Q$, we denote by $\Pi + \Pi' = \Pi''$ the minimum partition of $Q$ such that if $P$ is an element of either $\Pi$ or $\Pi'$ and $P \cap S \neq \phi$ for some $S \in \Pi''$, then $P \subseteq S$.

For example, using the $\Pi_2$ and $\Pi_3$ of the example, we obtain

$$\Pi_2 + \Pi_3 = \{\{1, 2\}, \{3, 4\}\} + \{\{1\}, \{2, 3, 4\}\} = \{\{1, 2, 3, 4\}\}.$$

Another example of these operations is

If                     $\Pi = \{\{1, 2\}, \{3, 4\}, \{5, 6\}, \{7, 8, 9\}\}$,

and                   $\Pi' = \{\{1, 6\}, \{2, 3\}, \{4, 5\}, \{7, 8\}, \{9\}\}$,

then         $\Pi \cdot \Pi' = \{\{1\}, \{2\}, \{3\}, \{4\}, \{5\}, \{6\}, \{7, 8\}, \{9\}\}$

and         $\Pi + \Pi' = \{\{1, 2, 3, 4, 5, 6\}, \{7, 8, 9\}\}$.

In relation to partitions with the S.P. for some machine $\mathcal{M}$ the following theorem can be proved.

**Theorem 8.4.2**  If $\Pi$ and $\Pi'$ are two partitions with S.P. for $\mathcal{M}$, the partitions $\Pi \cdot \Pi'$ and $\Pi + \Pi'$ also have the S.P. for $\mathcal{M}$.

We can see that $\Pi \cdot \Pi'$ has the S.P. as follows.  By definition $\Pi \cdot \Pi'$ is a partition.  Thus it remains only to show that $\Pi \cdot \Pi'$ is closed.  Suppose $S^* \in \Pi \cdot \Pi'$; then $S^* = S \cap S'$ for some $S \in \Pi$ and $S' \in \Pi'$.  Now since $\Pi$ and $\Pi'$ have S.P. for any $i \in I$ of $\mathcal{M}$

$$S \xrightarrow{(\mathcal{M},i)} T$$

such that $T \subseteq S_1$ for some $S_1 \in \Pi$ and

$$S' \xrightarrow{(\mathcal{M},i)} T'$$

such that $T' \subseteq S_1'$ for some $S_1' \in \Pi'$.  Also

$$S \cap S' \xrightarrow{(\mathcal{M},i)} T \cap T',$$

so that

$$S^* \xrightarrow{(\mathcal{M},i)} T \cap T'.$$

From these inclusion properties we have that

$$T \cap T' \subseteq S_1 \cap S_1',$$

and, of course, we need to check for closure only when neither of these sets is empty.

From Definition of $\Pi \cdot \Pi'$, $(S_1 \cap S_1') \in \Pi \cdot \Pi'$ if $S_1 \cap S_1' \neq \phi$, and thus $\Pi \cdot \Pi'$ is closed.  The reader may find it interesting to verify that $\Pi + \Pi'$ also has the S.P.

From this theorem it follows that the collection of all partitions with S.P. for $\mathcal{M}$ forms a lattice under the ordering of Definition 8.4.2.*  This theorem also allows us to generate new partitions with the S.P. from ones generated by the procedure of identifying pairs of states.  In fact, if $\Pi(q_j, q_k)$ denotes the smallest partition with S.P. for $\mathcal{M}$ that identifies $q_j$

* A lattice is a partially ordered set in which every two elements have a l.u.b. and a g.l.b.

and $q_k$, it can be shown that any partition $\Pi$ with S.P. for $\mathcal{M}$ can be generated by a sum over some subset of pairs $(j, k)$.

$$\Pi = \sum_{j,k} \Pi(q_j, q_k).$$

Thus all partitions with S.P. for $\mathcal{M}$ can be obtained by first finding all $\Pi(q_j, q_k)$ by the procedure of identifying pairs discussed earlier, and then summing over all possible subsets of these $\Pi(q_j, q_k)$ to obtain all the other partitions with S.P.

In the previous discussion, we considered how one partition with S.P. can be used to give reduced dependence to the first $r$ of the $k$ next state equations. We now show how two partitions with S.P. can be used to obtain assignments for which the first $r$ equations are self-dependent and also that last $k - r$ equations are self-dependent. In Assignment II for the machine of Figure 8.4.1 $y_1'$ depends only on $x_1$ and $y_1$, and $y_2'$ and $y_3'$ depend only on $x_1$ and $y_2, y_3$. This assignment is related to the two partitions $\Pi_1 = \{\{1, 2, 3\}, \{4, 5, 6\}\}$ and $\Pi_2 = \{\{1, 6\}, \{2, 5\}, \{3, 4\}\}$ of $\mathcal{M}$. Note that for these two partitions

$$\Pi_1 \cdot \Pi_2 = \{\{1\}, \{2\}, \{3\}, \{4\}, \{5\}, \{6\}\} = \Pi(0).$$

Thus, if we know the set in $\Pi_1$ and the set in $\Pi_2$ in which a certain state of $\mathcal{M}$ is contained, the exact state is determined. To use $\Pi_1$ we need one variable and for $\Pi_2$ we need two variables. Thus, using the first variable $y_1$ to distinguish sets of $\Pi_1$ and the last two variables $y_2, y_3$ to distinguish sets of $\Pi_2$, with a given input and a value of $y_1$, we can compute $y_1'$. Similarly, with a given input and configuration of values for $y_2, y_3$, we can determine values for $y_2'$ and $y_3'$. It can be seen that Assignment II of Figure 8.4.1 is of this form. The general result for such pairs of partitions is given in the following theorem.

**Theorem 8.4.3**  Let $\mathcal{M}$ have $n$ states, then $\mathcal{M}$ has a state assignment using $k_m = \lceil \log_2 n \rceil$ internal variables, for which $y_1', y_2', \ldots, y_r'$ are dependent only on the input and $y_1, y_2, \ldots, y_r$ variables, and for which $y_{r+1}', y_{r+2}',$ $\ldots y_{k_m}'$ are dependent only on the input and $y_{r+1}, y_{r+2}, \ldots, y_{k_m}$ variables if and only if there are two partitions $\Pi$ and $\Pi'$ with the S.P. for $\mathcal{M}$ where $\Pi$ and $\Pi'$ satisfy the conditions

1. $\Pi \cdot \Pi' = \Pi(0)$.
2. $\lceil \log_2 |\Pi| \rceil + \lceil \log_2 |\Pi'| \rceil = k_m$.

This theorem gives a type of decomposition to a machine into two self-dependent sets of next state equations. If condition (1) of the theorem is satisfied, but $\lceil \log_2 |\Pi| \rceil + \lceil \log_2 |\Pi'| \rceil = k > k_m$, one can make an assignment using $k$ variables which decomposes the next state equations into two self-dependent sets. Also, more than two partitions may be used to get further decomposition. For example, consider the machine described by the flow table of Figure 8.4.3.

Inputs

| States | $x_1$ $x_2$<br>0   0 | $x_1$ $x_2$<br>0   1 | $x_1$ $x_2$<br>1   0 | $x_1$ $x_2$<br>1   1 |
|:---:|:---:|:---:|:---:|:---:|
| $q_1$ | $q_2/0$ | $q_3/0$ | $q_4/0$ | $q_1/1$ |
| $q_2$ | $q_1/1$ | $q_3/0$ | $q_4/0$ | $q_1/1$ |
| $q_3$ | $q_2/0$ | $q_1/1$ | $q_4/0$ | $q_1/1$ |
| $q_4$ | $q_2/0$ | $q_3/0$ | $q_1/1$ | $q_1/0$ |

Figure 8.4.3   Example of multiple partitions.

The nontrivial partitions with S.P. for this machine are

$$\Pi_1 = \{\{1, 2\}, \{3\}, \{4\}\}, \qquad \Pi_2 = \{\{1, 3\}, \{2\}, \{4\}\},$$
$$\Pi_3 = \{\{1, 4\}, \{2\}, \{3\}\}, \qquad \Pi_4 = \{\{1, 2, 3\}, \{4\}\},$$
$$\Pi_5 = \{\{1, 3, 4\}, \{2\}\}, \quad \text{and} \quad \Pi_6 = \{\{1, 2, 4\}, \{3\}\}.$$

No two of these partitions satisfy Theorem 8.4.3; however, $\Pi_4 \cdot \Pi_5 \cdot \Pi_6 = \Pi(0)$. Thus using $y_1$, $y_2$, and $y_3$ for distinguishing sets in $\Pi_4$, $\Pi_5$, and $\Pi_6$, respectively, and using 0's to distinguish the three element sets, we obtain the following assignment:

State Assignment

| State | $y_1$ | $y_2$ | $y_3$ |
|:---:|:---:|:---:|:---:|
| 1 | 0 | 0 | 0 |
| 2 | 0 | 1 | 0 |
| 3 | 0 | 0 | 1 |
| 4 | 1 | 0 | 0 |

The resulting next state equations then become

$$y_1' = x_1\bar{x}_2\bar{y}_1,$$
$$y_2' = \bar{x}_1\bar{x}_2\bar{y}_2,$$
$$y_3' = \bar{x}_1 x_2 \bar{y}_3.$$

For this machine it is advantageous to use three internal variables. The reader should check that the two variable assignments require more complex logic, thus demonstrating the usefulness of partitions with S.P.

to help give economical combinational network realizations even when the minimum number of internal variables is not used.

Partitions with S.P. are quite helpful in obtaining economical state assignments, as demonstrated by the three examples of this section. For many machines, however, no nontrivial partitions with S.P. exist. This is the case, for example, for the machines of Figures 8.2.2 and 8.3.1. For this reason, partitions with S.P. are quite limited in their application to the state assignment problem. In fact, a very small proportion of machines have nontrivial partitions with S.P., especially for machines with many states and inputs.

Until now we have restricted our study of reduced dependence to that of self-dependence between sets of variables. That is, if $x_1, \ldots, x_n$ are the input variables and $y_1, \ldots, y_k$ are the set of internal variables, we have seen how to reduce the dependence of some subset of the next state equations

$$y_i' = y_i'(x_1, \ldots, x_n, y_1, \ldots, y_k)$$

to the form

$$y_i' = y_i'(x_1, \ldots, x_n, y_1, \ldots, y_r)$$

in the case that

$$i = 1, 2, \ldots, r \qquad \text{and} \quad r < k.$$

A more general type of reduced dependence is possible, however, if the subset of indices for internal variables $y_1, \ldots, y_r$ on the right-hand side of these equations is not restricted to be the same as the range of $i$ for the $y_i'$ equations displaying reduced dependence. For example, we would like to be able to identify a reduced dependence or "cross dependence" such as

$$y_i' = y_i'(x_1, \ldots, x_n, y_1, \ldots, y_r),$$

in which $i = r + 1, \ldots, k$. We shall now discuss some of the generalized concepts of partitions on states which are appropriate for displaying reduced dependence of this generalized type, but we shall omit all detailed proofs of these results.

**Definition 8.4.5** A *partition pair* $(\Pi, \Pi')$ on the states of a complete machine $\mathcal{M}$ is an ordered pair of partitions on $Q$ such that if $S \in \Pi$, $i \in I$, and $S \xrightarrow{(\mathcal{M}, i)} T_i$, then $T_i$ is included in some element of $\Pi'$.

In special case that $\Pi = \Pi'$, we see that $\Pi$ has the S.P., and thus partition pairs are a generalization of the concept of partitions with the S.P.

To demonstrate how partition pairs play a role in finding reduced "cross dependence," we consider the example machine of Stearns and Hartmanis shown in Figure 8.4.4.

Inputs

| States | $x_1$ $x_2$ 0   0 | $x_1$ $x_2$ 0   1 | $x_1$ $x_2$ 1   0 | $x_1$ $x_2$ 1   1 |
|--------|-------|-------|-------|-------|
| $q_1$ | $q_1$ | $q_2$ | $q_3$ | $q_4$ |
| $q_2$ | $q_3$ | $q_4$ | $q_1$ | $q_2$ |
| $q_3$ | $q_2$ | $q_1$ | $q_4$ | $q_3$ |
| $q_4$ | $q_4$ | $q_3$ | $q_2$ | $q_1$ |

Figure 8.4.4   Example machine for a state assignment using a partition pair.

The outputs are not included in this example since we are interested only in the next state equations. The only nontrivial partition with S.P. for this machine is $\Pi_1 = \{\{1, 4\}, \{2, 3\}\}$. The following assignment uses $\Pi_1$ to reduce the dependence in the $y_1'$ equation,

State Assignment

| State | $y_1$ | $y_2$ |
|-------|-------|-------|
| 1 | 0 | 0 |
| 2 | 1 | 0 |
| 3 | 1 | 1 |
| 4 | 0 | 1 |

and gives next state equations

$$y_1' = \bar{x}_1\bar{x}_2 y_1 \vee \bar{x}_1 x_2 \bar{y}_1 \vee x_1 \bar{x}_2 \bar{y}_1 \vee x_1 x_2 y_1,$$
$$y_2' = \bar{x}_1 y_1 \bar{y}_2 \vee \bar{x}_1 \bar{y}_1 y_2 \vee x_1 \bar{y}_1 \bar{y}_2 \vee x_1 y_1 y_2.$$

Can you find an assignment using $\Pi_1$ which yields a simpler set of $y_1'$, $y_2'$ equations?

Now consider the pair of partitions $\Pi = \{\{1, 2\}, \{3, 4\}\}$ and $\Pi' = \{\{1, 3\}, \{2, 4\}\}$. It is readily seen from Figure 8.4.4, that both $(\Pi, \Pi')$ and $(\Pi', \Pi)$ are partition pairs for this machine, even though neither $\Pi$ nor $\Pi'$ have S.P. We use these partitions by assigning $y_1$ values as equal for states in the same set of $\Pi$, and $y_2$ values as equal for states in the same set of $\Pi'$. Such an assignment is

State Assignment

| State | $y_1$ | $y_2$ |
|-------|-------|-------|
| 1 | 0 | 0 |
| 2 | 0 | 1 |
| 3 | 1 | 0 |
| 4 | 1 | 1 |

and the resulting next state equations are

$$y_1' = \bar{x}_1 y_2 \vee x_1 \bar{y}_2,$$

$$y_2' = \bar{x}_2 y_1 \vee x_2 \bar{y}_1.$$

These next state equations are considerably more economical than those for the previous assignment. Note how the reduced dependency arrived at by using these partition pairs gives a "cross dependence" of $y_1'$ being dependent on the input plus $y_2$ and $y_2'$ being dependent on the input plus $y_1$.

In this example, to each state of any given set of states of $\Pi$ we assigned equal values to $y_1$. Similarly, we used $y_2$ to designate sets of states of $\Pi'$. In general, if we have a particular state assignment of $\mathcal{M}$ using variables $y_1$, $y_2, \ldots, y_k$, and $C$ is a subset of these variables indices, $C \subseteq \{1, 2, \ldots, k\}$, let $\Pi_C$ designate the partition of states of $\mathcal{M}$ such that two states $q$ and $q'$ belong to the same set of $\Pi_C$ if and only if the value of $y_j$ assigned to $q$ equals the value of $y_j$ assigned to $q'$ for each $j \in C$. The following theorem for partition pairs, analogous to Theorem 8.4.1 for partitions with S.P., can now be stated.

**Theorem 8.4.4** Let $\mathcal{M}$ be a complete sequential machine having a state assignment using the internal variables $y_1, y_2, \ldots, y_k$, and let $C \subseteq \{1, 2, \ldots, k\}$ and $D \subseteq \{1, 2, \ldots, k\}$. Then the next state equations $y_j'$ for $j \in D$ depend only on the input variables and the internal variables $y_r$ for $r \in C$ if and only if $(\Pi_C, \Pi_D)$ is a partition pair.

We can now use Definition 8.4.2 to extend the partial ordering on partitions to partition pairs.

**Definition 8.4.6** If $(\Pi, \Pi')$ and $(\theta, \theta')$ are partition pairs, then $(\Pi, \Pi') \leq (\theta, \theta')$ if and only if $\Pi \leq \theta$ and $\Pi' \leq \theta'$.

Algebraic properties can also be extended to partition pairs. In particular, if $(\Pi, \Pi')$ and $(\theta, \theta')$ are partition pairs then $(\Pi \cdot \theta, \Pi' \cdot \theta')$ is also a partition pair and is the g.l.b. of $[(\Pi, \Pi'), (\theta, \theta')]$. Similarly $(\Pi + \theta, \Pi' + \theta')$ is a partition pair and is the l.u.b. of $[(\Pi, \Pi'), (\theta, \theta')]$. Thus the set of partition pairs for a machine $\mathcal{M}$ forms a lattice. Also, if $(\Pi, \Pi')$ is a partition pair, $\theta \leq \Pi$ and $\Pi' \leq \theta'$, then $(\theta, \theta')$ is a partition pair.

In order to look for partition pairs of a sequential machine $\mathcal{M}$, so that state assignments with reduced dependence can be derived, it would be desirable to be able to generate a family of partition pairs of $\mathcal{M}$ which characterize (or from which can be generated) all possible partition pairs of $\mathcal{M}$. Toward this goal we introduce the following definitions.

**Definition 8.4.7** If $\Pi$ is a partition of states of $\mathcal{M}$, let $M(\Pi) = \sum_i \Pi_i$, where the sum ranges over all $i$ such that $(\Pi_i, \Pi)$ is a partition pair. Similarly, let $m(\Pi) = \prod_i (\Pi_i)$ where the product ranges over all $i$ such that $(\Pi, \Pi_i)$ is a partition pair.

By the algebraic properties of partition pairs it follows that $(M(\Pi), \Pi)$ and $(\Pi, m(\Pi))$ are partition pairs, and if $\Pi \leq \theta$, then $m(\Pi) \leq m(\theta)$ and $M(\Pi) \leq M(\theta)$. The partition $M(\Pi)$ is the unique coarsest partition $\Pi'$ such that $(\Pi', \Pi)$ is a partition pair (that is, $M(\Pi)$ covers any $\Pi'$ such that $(\Pi', \Pi)$ is a partition pair.) Similarly, $m(\Pi)$ is the finest partition such that $(\Pi, m(\Pi))$ is a partition pair.

**Definition 8.4.8** A partition pair $(\Pi, \Pi')$ is called an *Mm-pair* if and only if $\Pi = M(\Pi')$ and $\Pi' = m(\Pi)$.

Let $\theta$ and $\theta'$ be partitions such that $\theta \leq \Pi$, $\theta' \geq \Pi'$, and $(\Pi, \Pi')$ is an *Mm*-pair. It then follows that $(\theta, \theta')$ is a partition pair. Also if $(\theta, \theta')$ is any partition pair of a machine $\mathcal{M}$, then there must exist at least one *Mm*-pair $(\Pi, \Pi')$ such that $\theta \leq \Pi$ and $\theta' \geq \Pi'$. In this way, the *Mm*-pairs characterize the set of all partition pairs for a machine $\mathcal{M}$.

The computation of all *Mm*-pairs for a complete sequential machine $\mathcal{M}$ proceeds as follows. We let $\Pi_{q_jq_k}$ denote that partition of $\mathcal{M}$ for which $\{q_j, q_k\}$ is the only set of states having more than one element and compute $m(\Pi_{q_jq_k})$ for all possible pairs $(q_j, q_k)$. For this computation $q_r \equiv q_s$ if there exists an $i$ such that $\{q_j, q_k\} \xrightarrow{(\mathcal{M}, i)} \{q_r, q_s\}$. Then $m(\Pi_{q_jq_k})$ is the partition formed by the transitive closure of this equivalence relation. By taking all possible sums of the $m(\Pi_{q_jq_k})$ partitions, we obtain all possible $\Pi'$ such that $(\Pi, \Pi')$ is an *Mm*-pair. For any such $\Pi'$, the respective $\Pi$ is

$$\Pi = \sum \Pi_{q_jq_k},$$

where the sum ranges over all $\Pi_{q_jq_k}$ such that $m(\Pi_{q_jq_k}) \leq \Pi'$.

| States | Inputs | | | |
|---|---|---|---|---|
| | $x_1$ $x_2$ <br> 0　0 | $x_1$ $x_2$ <br> 0　1 | $x_1$ $x_2$ <br> 1　0 | $x_1$ $x_2$ <br> 1　1 |
| $q_1$ | $q_1$ | $q_1$ | $q_4$ | $q_1$ |
| $q_2$ | $q_3$ | $q_3$ | $q_4$ | $q_1$ |
| $q_3$ | $q_4$ | $q_1$ | $q_1$ | $q_1$ |
| $q_4$ | $q_2$ | $q_1$ | $q_4$ | $q_2$ |
| $q_5$ | $q_5$ | $q_3$ | $q_1$ | $q_2$ |

Figure 8.4.5 Example for *Mm*-pairs.

We now illustrate the calculation of *Mm*-pairs and their application to state assignment by the example of Figure 8.4.5.

The calculation of the *Mm*-pairs proceeds by first calculating the $m(\Pi_{q_j q_k})$ for all pairs $(j, k)$. This gives

$$m(\Pi_{q_1 q_2}) = \{\{1, 3\}, \{2\}, \{4\}, \{5\}\} = \Pi_1',$$

$$m(\Pi_{q_1 q_3}) = \{\{1, 4\}, \{2\}, \{3\}, \{5\}\} = \Pi_2',$$

$$m(\Pi_{q_1 q_4}) = \{\{1, 2,\}, \{3\}, \{4\}, \{5\}\} = \Pi_3',$$

$$m(\Pi_{q_1 q_5}) = \{\{1, 2, 3, 4, 5\}\} = \Pi(1),$$

$$m(\Pi_{q_2 q_3}) = \{\{1, 3, 4\}, \{2\}, \{5\}\} = \Pi_4',$$

$$m(\Pi_{q_2 q_4}) = \{\{1, 2, 3\}, \{4\}, \{5\}\} = \Pi_5',$$

$$m(\Pi_{q_2 q_5}) = \{\{1, 2, 4\}, \{3, 5\}\} = \Pi_6',$$

$$m(\Pi_{q_3 q_4}) = \{\{1, 2, 4\}, \{3\}, \{5\}\} = \Pi_7',$$

$$m(\Pi_{q_3 q_5}) = \{\{1, 2, 3\}, \{4, 5\}\} = \Pi_8',$$

$$m(\Pi_{q_4 q_5}) = \{\{1, 3, 4\}, \{2, 5\}\} = \Pi_9'.$$

Other than $\Pi(0)$, we find the other $\Pi'$ partitions for which $(\Pi, \Pi')$ is an *Mm*-pair by summing over all possible subsets of $\Pi_1'$ through $\Pi_9'$. The only new partition obtained in this way is

$$\Pi_1' + \Pi_7' = \{\{1, 2, 3, 4\}, \{5\}\} = \Pi_{10}'.$$

Letting $(\Pi_i, \Pi_i')$ be the desired *Mm*-pairs we now compute the $\Pi_i$ partitions using the formula $\Pi_i = \sum_{jk} \Pi_{q_j q_k}$ for $j$ and $k$ such that $m(\Pi_{q_j q_k}) \leq \Pi_i'$. We obtain

$$\Pi_1 = \Pi_{q_1 q_2} = \{\{1, 2\}, \{3\}, \{4\}, \{5\}\},$$

$$\Pi_2 = \Pi_{q_1 q_3} = \{\{1, 3\}, \{2\}, \{4\}, \{5\}\},$$

$$\Pi_3 = \Pi_{q_1 q_4} = \{\{1, 4\}, \{2\}, \{3\}, \{5\}\},$$

$$\Pi_4 = \Pi_{q_1 q_2} + \Pi_{q_1 q_3} + \Pi_{q_2 q_3} = \{\{1, 2, 3\}, \{4\}, \{5\}\},$$

$$\Pi_5 = \{\{1, 2, 4\}, \{3\}, \{5\}\},$$

$$\Pi_6 = \{\{1, 3, 4\}, \{2, 5\}\},$$

$$\Pi_7 = \{\{1, 3, 4\}, \{2\}, \{5\}\},$$

$$\Pi_8 = \{\{1, 2, 4\}, \{3, 5\}\},$$

$$\Pi_9 = \{\{1, 2, 3\}, \{4, 5\}\},$$

$$\Pi_{10} = \{\{1, 2, 3, 4\}, \{5\}\}.$$

Also, of course, $M(\Pi(0)) = \Pi(0)$ and $M(\Pi(1)) = \Pi(1)$, so that $(\Pi(0), \Pi(0))$ and $(\Pi(1), \Pi(1))$ are $Mm$-pairs.

From the $Mm$-pairs $(\Pi_i, \Pi_i')$ any pair $(\Pi, \Pi')$ can be checked to be a partition pair simply by seeing if $\Pi \leq \Pi_i$ and $\Pi' \geq \Pi_i'$ for some $i$. In particular, $(\Pi, \Pi)$ is a partition pair if and only if $\Pi$ has the S.P., and thus all partitions with the S.P. can be obtained from the $Mm$-pairs. In our example we see that the only nontrivial partition with S.P. is $\Pi_{10}$.

State Assignment

| State | $y_1$ | $y_2$ | $y_3$ |
|-------|-------|-------|-------|
| 1 | 0 | 0 | 0 |
| 2 | 1 | 0 | 0 |
| 3 | 0 | 1 | 0 |
| 4 | 0 | 0 | 1 |
| 5 | 1 | 1 | 1 |

Figure 8.4.6    State assignment for machine of Figure 8.4.5.

In general, we say that a state assignment, having variables $y_1, y_2, \ldots,$ $y_k$, *uses* a partition $\Pi$ if for some subset $C$ of the variable indices we have that $\Pi_C = \Pi$. Since each state of a machine must be assigned a different configuration of $k$ values for a state assignment if the $\Pi_1, \Pi_2, \ldots, \Pi_p$ is the set of partitions used by the assignment, it follows that $\Pi_1 \cdot \Pi_2 \cdots \cdot \Pi_p = \Pi(0)$. Thus in seeking an assignment with reduced dependence, we attempt to find partitions with S.P. or partition pairs so that the product of partitions is $\Pi(0)$ and then we assign subsets of binary variables to these partitions. If the reduced dependence thus attained is to be of any benefit, the number $k$ of internal variables usually also has to remain small; for example, we may desire to consider only assignments using $k_m$, the minimum possible number of internal variables. With a bound on $k$ it is, in general, a rather difficult combinatorial problem to find partitions suitable for a state assignment. We show simply that, in the example, a judicious choice of partition pairs does, in fact, lead to a desirable state assignment.

Consider the following partition pairs for the example

$$(\Pi_6, \Pi_6') = (\{\{1, 3, 4\}, \{2, 5\}\}, \{\{1, 2, 4\}, \{3, 5\}\}),$$

$$(\Pi_8, \Pi_8') = (\{\{1, 2, 4\}, \{3, 5\}\}, \{\{1, 2, 3\}, \{4, 5\}\}),$$

$$(\Pi_9, \Pi_9') = (\{\{1, 2, 3\}, \{4, 5\}\}, \{\{1, 3, 4\}, \{2, 5\}\}).$$

Here $\Pi_6' = \Pi_8$, $\Pi_8' = \Pi_9$, and $\Pi_9' = \Pi_6$, so there are only three different partitions involved, and since each has only two blocks, we can use a single variable to determine the block of each partition. Furthermore, $\Pi_6 \cdot \Pi_8 \cdot \Pi_9 = \Pi(0)$, so we should be able to distinguish completely between states by these three variables; finally, since there are five states in the machine, we need at least three variables in any state assignment. Figure 8.4.6 shows an assignment using these three partitions in which $y_1$ is associated with $\Pi_6$, $y_2$ is associated with $\Pi_8$, and $y_3$ is associated with $\Pi_9$. The resulting next state equations are

$$y_1' = \bar{x}_1\bar{x}_2y_3 \vee x_1x_2y_3,$$

$$y_2' = \bar{x}_1y_1,$$

$$y_3' = \bar{x}_1\bar{x}_2y_2 \vee x_1\bar{x}_2\bar{y}_2.$$

The cross dependence obtained by using these partition pairs is evident in the equations.

The concepts of partition pairs can be readily extended to a discussion of partitions on the sets of inputs and outputs as well as on the set of states. Thus problems of the assignments of variable values to inputs or outputs can also be treated from the results on partitions. Some work has also been done on finding which partitions can be used to yield a good state assignment and on extending the concepts of partition pairs to incompletely specified machines. Since considerable work in these areas is still necessary, we shall not discuss them further.

## 8.5   ADJACENCY SETS AND SUBCUBE PROPERTIES FOR STATE ASSIGNMENT

In this section, we describe briefly an approach to the simplification of the next state equations which is different from Section 8.4. It is more closely related to the two rules of thumb given in Section 8.3. As before, we assume two-level AND-OR type circuits for computing the cost of the circuits. Roughly speaking, the transition structure of the machine is used to find sets of states of a machine $\mathcal{M}$ (either complete or incomplete) such that if the states of any such set are assigned as mutually adjacent vertices on a $k$-cube (that is, as a single or several relatively large subcubes on the $k$-cube for $y_1, y_2, \ldots, y_k$), there is a corresponding simplification of some of the next state equations. This simplification is the type indicated by Rule II of Section 8.3.

As an example, reconsider the machine of Figure 8.2.2. The symbolic equations for $y_1'$ and $y_2'$ given in Section 8.3 can be written as

$$y_j' = y_{j1}(x_1 y_1^{y_{14}} y_2^{y_{24}} \lor x_1 y_1^{y_{13}} y_2^{y_{23}} \lor \bar{x}_1 y_1^{y_{11}} y_2^{y_{21}} \lor \bar{x}_1 y_1^{y_{14}} y_2^{y_{24}}$$

$$\lor \bar{x}_1 y_1^{y_{12}} y_2^{y_{22}}) \lor y_{j2}(x_1 y_1^{y_{11}} y_2^{y_{21}}) \lor y_{j3}(x_1 y_1^{y_{12}} y_2^{y_{22}})$$

$$\lor y_{j4}(\bar{x}_1 y_1^{y_{13}} y_2^{y_{23}}),$$

where $j = 1$ or 2.

Thus, if $q_1$ and $q_2$ are given adjacent assignments in the state assignment, the

$$\bar{x}_1 y_1^{y_{12}} y_2^{y_{22}} \quad \text{and} \quad \bar{x}_1 y_1^{y_{11}} y_2^{y_{21}}$$

terms of the $y_{j1}$ factor can be combined. Also if $y_{j2}$ and $y_{j3}$ are both equal to 1 for some $j$ (thus implying that $q_2$ is adjacent to $q_3$), the

$$x_1 y_1^{y_{11}} y_2^{y_{21}} \quad \text{and} \quad x_1 y_1^{y_{12}} y_2^{y_{22}}$$

terms can be combined in the $j$th equation. The assignment given in Section 8.3 did, in fact, create these two adjacencies to give an economical assignment. Here, however, we shall develop a method of generating desirable mutual adjacencies between sets of states directly from the sequential machine, instead of writing the symbolic next state equations. In this development, however, the state adjacencies will be justified by reference to the symbolic equations.

As seen in writing the symbolic next state equations for each transition into a state $q_i$, a term is formed in the equations representing the input on the transition times the "previous state" of the transition. This symbolic term occurs in each equation $y_j'$ with a coefficient $y_{ji}$, where $y_{ji} = 0$ if state $q_i$ has an assignment of 0 for $y_j$, and $y_{ji} = 1$ if $q_i$ has an assignment of 1 for $y_j$. Since the $y_{ji}$ coefficients are not initially determined, it is not evident exactly which terms will appear in the final equations. Since the terms arise from inputs and "previous states," we define an *inverse state table* for depicting the previous states for any present state and input.

This inverse state table has one column for each input and one row for each "present state." An entry in row $i$, column $j$, lists the "previous states" of the machine by which it is possible to reach state $q_i$ under the input given by column $j$. For example, the inverse state table for the machine for Figure 8.2.2 is shown in Figure 8.5.1.

The entry 1, 2, 4, for example, in the row for present state 1 and input 0, means that having had an input of 0 we could have arrived at state 1 from state 1 or state 2 or state 4. An entry of $\phi$, which appears in three places in this table, means that it is impossible to arrive in the present state indicated by the row of the table under that input. Thus, for example, in Figure 8.2.2 there is no transition into state 2 having an input of 0. It should be obvious that the inverse state table contains the same information about transitions of a machine as does the flow table or state diagram, and that the inverse state table can be generated readily from either of these two descriptions of $\mathcal{M}$.

The states appearing together in a row $i$ entry of the inverse state table also appear together as terms in the $y_{ji}$ factor of the $y_j'$ equation. Thus the terms having input $x_1$ and encodings of states 3 and 4 appear in the factor of the $y_j'$ equation which has coefficient $y_{j1}$. If these terms for

| Input | | Present |
|---|---|---|
| 0 | 1 | State |
| 1, 2, 4 | 3, 4 | 1 |
| $\phi$ | 1 | 2 |
| $\phi$ | 2 | 3 |
| 3 | $\phi$ | 4 |

Figure 8.5.1   Inverse state table for Figure 8.2.2.

states 3 and 4 are to be combined in the equations, the encoding for states 3 and 4 must differ only in one coordinate; that is, be adjacent vertices on the $k$-cube. Similarly, adjacencies between states 1, 2, and 4 are desired since they are common entries to row 1 under input 0. In this case, however, if 1 and 4 are both made adjacent to state 2, then 1 cannot be adjacent to state 4, since this is impossible on a $k$-cube. Thus it is not always possible to satisfy all the adjacencies indicated as desirable from the inverse state table. In state Assignment II of Section 8.2 for this example, the following pairs of states are adjacent pairs (1, 2), (2, 3), (3, 4), and (1, 4). Hence as many as possible of the adjacencies indicated by the inverse state table are satisfied in this assignment. Since combining terms is possible when states appearing in the same entry of the inverse state table are given adjacent assignments, we call sets of states appearing in a single entry of the inverse state table *Type I adjacency sets.*

Another type of adjacency is also displayed by this assignment, the pair (2, 3). Once states 1 and 2 are made adjacent, if the states for the pair of rows for which 1 and 2 appear in a column (such as states 2 and 3 under input 1) are also assigned to adjacent vertices, then the

$$x_1 y_1^{y_{11}} y_2^{y_{21}} \quad \text{and} \quad x_1 y_1^{y_{12}} y_2^{y_{22}}$$

terms will combine into a single term whenever the assignment is such that $y_{j2} = y_{j3} = 1$. This type of adjacency is called a *Type II adjacency set*. In general, both of these types of adjacencies on pairs of states can be generalized to placing $r = 2^s$ states on vertices of a single subcube to obtain simplification. If $r$ is not an exact power of 2, however, then partial satisfaction of adjacencies between them can be obtained by placing the states on several closely connected subcubes.

The adjacency sets can also be considered as special mappings formed by the transitions of the machine. For example, Type I adjacency sets are characterized as follows. A subset of states $S$ is a Type I adjacency set for a machine $\mathscr{M}$ if and only if there exists some input $i \in I$ such that $S \xrightarrow{(\mathscr{M},i)} q$, where $q$ is a single state of $\mathscr{M}$. Also Type II adjacency sets are obtained as follows: Given $S$ as a Type I adjacency set, and $S \xrightarrow{(\mathscr{M},i')} T$ for some $i' \in I$, then $T$ is a Type II adjacency set. This description of adjacency sets shows some relation between adjacency sets and partitions discussed in the previous section.

By extending these mappings, other higher order adjacency and subcube requirements can be found, both by looking for mappings using more than a single input $i$ and also by using a Type II adjacency set to find another set of states that follows the Type II adjacency set under some input or set of inputs.

Usually, many more adjacencies arise from the inverse state table and higher order adjacency requirements than can be realized by fitting the states into subcubes of the $k$-cube.

For example, in the example $k_m = 2$, we saw that it was desirable to make the following pairs of states have adjacent encodings: $(1, 2), (2, 4), (1, 4), (2, 3),$ and $(3, 4)$. Obviously, all these pairs cannot be made adjacent, since the three states 1, 3, and 4 are all to be adjacent to state 2, but it is only possible to have two states adjacent to any other state as is noted by the structure of the 2-cube.

In general, it is very difficult to determine for which states it is most desirable to have the adjacency requirements satisfied and also to find the largest set of these adjacencies which can be simultaneously realized on the $k$-cube. Neither of these two problems has been solved. There are usually too many possibilities to inspect them all. Various approximations are used in the algorithms presented in the literature.

Since the choice of the most desirable adjacencies is not readily determined, we shall discuss the use of adjacency sets in another example rather than give complex techniques for evaluating the desirability of the various adjacencies. First, however, we wish to see how using Rule I, that is, the setting of certain $y_{ij}$ coefficients to 0 and 1, can also be partially determined from the inverse state table.

In equation $y_j{'}$, the factor with coefficient $y_{ji}$ has exactly the same number of terms as there are appearances of states in entries of row $i$ in the inverse state table. Let $s_i$ denote the sum of the number of state entries in row $i$ of the inverse state table. For our example of Figure 8.5.1,

$$s_1 = 5$$

$$s_2 = s_3 = s_4 = 1.$$

Thus as can be seen from the $y_j{'}$ equation, there are five terms in the $y_{j1}$ factor and one term each in the $y_{j2}$, $y_{j3}$, and $y_{j4}$ factors. Using Rule I alone, with no concern to the adjacency sets, we would attempt to assign the $0, 0, \ldots, 0$ encoding to the state having the largest $s_i$ sum, then assign the $k$ encodings having only one 1 to the next higher $s_i$ sums, etc. For our example, we thus have assignment $0\,0$ dictated for state 1 and a tie for all other assignments, since only two of the three remaining states may be given encodings having only a single 1. In general, there are exactly $\binom{k}{m}$ encodings with exactly $m$ out of $k$ ones.

The assignment of $0, 0, \ldots, 0$ to a state $q_i$ with large $s_i$ has the additional effect of setting all $y_{ji}$ coefficients equal to 0. Thus none of the terms in any $y_{ji}$ factor appear in any $y_j{'}$ equation. Thus the Type I adjacency sets implied by row $i$ no longer pertain to the simplification of any $y_j{'}$ equation, so that these adjacencies are no longer required for a desirable assignment. More generally, if state $q_i$ is assigned a vertex with exactly $m$ out of $k$ ones, then the Type I adjacency sets for state $q_i$ apply to simplifying only those $m$ out of the $k$ next state equations that have ones in the assignment. The $s_i$ row sums can therefore be used to indicate which states should have assignments with many (or few) zeros, where realizing the respective adjacency sets for the machine is also considered when choosing the assignment.

We illustrate how the adjacency sets and row sums are used to obtain an assignment by the example of an inverse flow table shown in Figure 8.5.2.

Since $s_1$ is by far the largest row sum, we let the assignment for state 1 be $0\,0\,0$. We also let the "don't care" be assigned $1\,1\,1$. From the Type I adjacency sets, we desire the following pairs of states to be adjacent: $(2, 6)$, $(1, 5)$, and $(2, 3)$. The Type II adjacency sets generated by these three Type I adjacency sets for this particular example are $(6, 7)$ and $(3, 6)$. It is also possible to assign states 1, 5, 2, 6 to a single 2-cube; then any $y$ variables that are equal to 1 for states 3 and 4 will have a subsequent combining of factors in the respective $y'$ equations.

| Previous State | | | |
|:---:|:---:|:---:|:---:|
| Input | | Present State | |
| 0 | 1 | | |
| 1, 7, 4, 5 | 4, 7 | 1 | $s_1 = 6$ |
| $\phi$ | $\phi$ | 2 | $s_2 = 0$ |
| $\phi$ | 2, 6 | 3 | $s_3 = 2$ |
| $\phi$ | 1, 5 | 4 | $s_4 = 2$ |
| $\phi$ | $\phi$ | 5 | $s_5 = 0$ |
| 6 | 3 | 6 | $s_6 = 2$ |
| 2, 3 | $\phi$ | 7 | $s_7 = 2$ |

Figure 8.5.2   Inverse flow table for another example.

Not all of these adjacencies are possible. For example, we cannot satisfy all three of the adjacencies (2, 6), (2, 3), and (3, 6). An assignment satisfying many of these adjacencies, however, is the following:

| State | State Assignment | | |
|:---:|:---:|:---:|:---:|
| | $y_1$ | $y_2$ | $y_3$ |
| 1 | 0 | 0 | 0 |
| 2 | 0 | 0 | 1 |
| 3 | 1 | 0 | 1 |
| 4 | 1 | 0 | 0 |
| 5 | 0 | 1 | 0 |
| 6 | 0 | 1 | 1 |
| 7 | 1 | 1 | 0 |
| "Don't care" | 1 | 1 | 1 |

The next state equations resulting from this assignment gives the following fairly simple equations:

$$y_1' = x\bar{y}_1 \vee \bar{x}\bar{y}_2 y_3,$$

$$y_2' = y_1 y_3 \vee \bar{x} y_3,$$

$$y_3' = x y_3 \vee y_2 y_3.$$

The reader may check that some other state assignments, which do not use the indicated adjacencies between states, give more complex $y_1'$, $y_2'$, and $y_3'$ equations.

**Exercises**

1. Find all partitions with the substitution property for each of the machines represented by the following flow charts. Also obtain economical state assignments having reduced dependency for each machine and give the resulting next state and output equations.

(a)

|  | Input | |
|---|---|---|
| State | $\bar{x}$ 0 | $x$ 1 |
| $q_1$ | $q_2/0$ | $q_2/1$ |
| $q_2$ | $q_3/0$ | $q_1/1$ |
| $q_3$ | $q_2/1$ | $q_4/0$ |
| $q_4$ | $q_3/0$ | $q_3/1$ |

(b)

|  | Input | | | |
|---|---|---|---|---|
| State | $\bar{x}_1 \ \bar{x}_2$ 0 0 | $\bar{x}_1 \ x_2$ 0 1 | $x_1 \ \bar{x}_2$ 1 0 | $x_1 \ x_2$ 1 1 |
| $q_1$ | $q_1/0$ | $q_2/0$ | $q_4/1$ | $q_2/1$ |
| $q_2$ | $q_3/1$ | $q_2/0$ | $q_5/1$ | $q_3/1$ |
| $q_3$ | $q_1/1$ | $q_1/0$ | $q_6/1$ | $q_3/1$ |
| $q_4$ | $q_1/0$ | $q_1/0$ | $q_5/1$ | $q_4/1$ |
| $q_5$ | $q_2/0$ | $q_2/0$ | $q_5/0$ | $q_6/1$ |
| $q_6$ | $q_1/0$ | $q_3/0$ | $q_4/0$ | $q_6/1$ |

(c)

|  | Input | |
|---|---|---|
| State | $\bar{x}$ 0 | $x$ 1 |
| $q_1$ | $q_3/0$ | $q_5/1$ |
| $q_2$ | $q_4/0$ | $q_5/0$ |
| $q_3$ | $q_2/0$ | $q_5/0$ |
| $q_4$ | $q_2/1$ | $q_5/0$ |
| $q_5$ | $q_1/1$ | $q_3/0$ |

2. Redesign the following synchronous sequential network to obtain the simplest possible synchronous network, having "equivalent input and output characteristics," that you can find. Use AND-OR logic as done in the existing design.

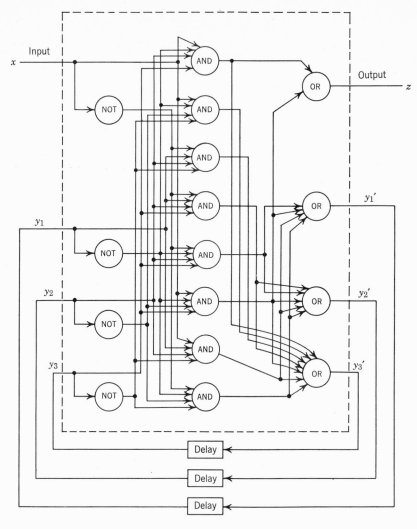

**3.** Combining the techniques of Sections 8.2 through 8.5 find economical sequential networks for the machines given by the following flow tables.

(*a*)

| State | Input $\bar{x}$ 0 | $x$ 1 |
|:---:|:---:|:---:|
| $q_1$ | $q_2/0$ | $q_7/0$ |
| $q_2$ | $q_6/1$ | $q_5/0$ |
| $q_3$ | $q_6/0$ | $q_2/0$ |
| $q_4$ | $q_1/0$ | $q_4/0$ |
| $q_5$ | $q_8/0$ | $q_3/0$ |
| $q_6$ | $q_8/0$ | $q_2/0$ |
| $q_7$ | $q_3/0$ | $q_4/0$ |
| $q_8$ | $q_5/0$ | $q_3/1$ |

(b)

|  | Input | |
| State | $\bar{x}$<br>0 | $x$<br>1 |
| --- | --- | --- |
| $q_1$ | $q_2/0$ | $q_3/0$ |
| $q_2$ | $q_1/1$ | $q_3/0$ |
| $q_3$ | $q_1/0$ | $q_2/0$ |

(c)

|  | Input | | | |
| State | $\bar{x}_1\ \bar{x}_2$<br>0   0 | $\bar{x}_1\ x_2$<br>0   1 | $x_1\ \bar{x}_2$<br>1   0 | $x_1\ x_2$<br>1   1 |
| --- | --- | --- | --- | --- |
| $q_1$ | $q_2/00$ | $q_3/01$ | $q_1/11$ | $q_1/11$ |
| $q_2$ | $q_2/00$ | $q_4/01$ | $q_3/01$ | $q_2/11$ |
| $q_3$ | $q_4/00$ | $q_3/01$ | $q_3/01$ | $q_1/11$ |
| $q_4$ | $q_4/00$ | $q_4/01$ | $q_1/11$ | $q_2/11$ |

(d)

|  | Input | |
| State | $\bar{x}$<br>0 | $x$<br>1 |
| --- | --- | --- |
| $q_1$ | $q_5/00$ | $q_4/10$ |
| $q_2$ | $q_5/01$ | $q_1/00$ |
| $q_3$ | $-/-$ | $q_3/01$ |
| $q_4$ | $q_7/11$ | $q_2/-$ |
| $q_5$ | $q_7/10$ | $q_1/00$ |
| $q_6$ | $q_2/00$ | $q_3/11$ |
| $q_7$ | $q_4/01$ | $q_2/-$ |

**4.** Find all $Mm$-pairs for each of the machines of Exercise 1.

**5.** Find the $Mm$-pairs for the following machines.

(a)

|  | Input | |
| State | $\bar{x}$<br>0 | $x$<br>1 |
| --- | --- | --- |
| $q_1$ | $q_1$ | $q_3$ |
| $q_2$ | $q_1$ | $q_2$ |
| $q_3$ | $q_4$ | $q_3$ |
| $q_4$ | $q_4$ | $q_2$ |

(b)

|  | Input | | | |
| State | $\bar{x}_1\ \bar{x}_2$<br>0   0 | $\bar{x}_1\ x_2$<br>0   1 | $x_1\ \bar{x}_2$<br>1   0 | $x_1\ x_2$<br>1   1 |
| --- | --- | --- | --- | --- |
| $q_1$ | $q_1$ | $q_3$ | $q_1$ | $q_4$ |
| $q_2$ | $q_1$ | $q_2$ | $q_2$ | $q_4$ |
| $q_3$ | $q_3$ | $q_3$ | $q_1$ | $q_3$ |
| $q_4$ | $q_3$ | $q_2$ | $q_2$ | $q_3$ |

What partitions, if any, lead to assignments using only two state variables that also have reduced dependence?

6. (a) Using the techniques of Sections 8.3 and 8.5 find an economical state assignment for the following machine and give the next state and output equations.

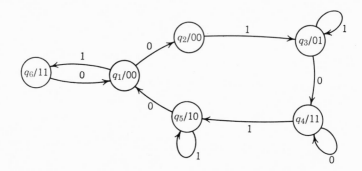

(b) Find the partitions with S.P. for this machine and describe the restrictions on $\tau(q_2, 0)$ and $\tau(q_6, 1)$ for these partitions to remain valid.

7. For the following sequential machine find:
   (a) A minimum state machine.
   (b) A state assignment for this machine which gives approximately minimum cost logical circuits. Give the next state and output equations.

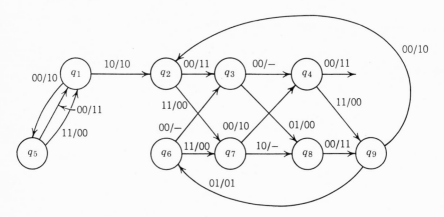

REFERENCE NOTATIONS

The development of partitions with S.P. discussed in Section 8.4 was first introduced by Hartmanis [10, 11]. Later, Stearns and Hartmanis [23] generalized this to partition pairs and illustrated the use of partition pairs for state assignment. These papers also included some comments showing how to apply the results to incompletely specified machines and partitions on the input and output sets of a machine. An algorithm to determine which partitions to use in an assignment was proposed by Curtis [5]. Later,

Karp [15] corrected some errors in this algorithm and introduced the concept of critical pairs to characterize the set of all partition pairs for an incompletely specified machine, since the *Mm*-pairs do not suffice in this case. Some other papers which deal with reduced dependence are [8, 12, 13, 24]. Approaches to state assignment similar to that discussed in Section 8.5 are presented in detail by Armstrong [1, 2] Davidow [6], Haring [9], and Schneider [22]. The number of possible state assignments is discussed by McCluskey and Unger in [19].

## REFERENCES

1. Armstrong, D. B., "A Programmed Algorithm for Assigning Internal Codes to Sequential Machines," *IRE Transactions on Electronic Computers*, Vol. EC-11, No. 4, pp. 466–472, August 1962.
2. Armstrong, D. B., "On the Efficient Assignment of Internal Codes to Sequential Machines," *IRE Transactions on Electronic Computers*, Vol. EC-11, No. 5, pp. 611–622, October 1962.
3. Caldwell, S. H., *Switching Circuits and Logical Design*, John Wiley and Sons, New York 1958, Chapter 13.
4. Crowley, T. H., "Recent Developments in the State Assignment Problem," *Proceedings of the Fourth Annual IEEE Symposium on Switching Circuit Theory and Logical Design*, 1963, Conference Paper CP-63-1464.
5. Curtis, H. A., "Multiple Reduction of Variable Dependency of Sequential Machines," *Journal of the Association for Computing Machinery*, Vol. 9, No. 3, pp. 324–344, July 1962.
6. Davidow, W. H., *A State Assignment Technique for Synchronous Sequential Networks*, Stanford Electronics Laboratory, Stanford University, Stanford, California, May 1961.
7. Dolotta, T. A. and E. J. McCluskey, Jr., "The Coding of Internal States of Sequential Circuits" *IEEE Transactions on Electronic Computers*, Vol. EC-13, No. 5, pp. 549–562, October 1964.
8. Gill, A., "Cascaded Finite-State Machines," *IRE Transactions on Electronic Computers*, Vol. EC-10, No. 3, pp. 366–370, September 1961.
9. Haring, D. R., "Some Aspects of the State Assignment Problem for Sequential Circuits," Massachusetts Institute of Technology, Electronic Systems Laboratory, Report ESL-R-147, September 1962.
10. Hartmanis, J., "Symbolic Analysis of a Decomposition of Information Processing Machines," *Information and Control*, Vol. 3, pp. 154–178, June 1960.
11. Hartmanis, J., "On the State Assignment Problem for Sequential Machines I," *IRE Transactions on Electronic Computers*, Vol. EC-10, No. 2, pp. 157–165, June 1961.
12. Hartmanis, J., "Further Results on the Structure of Sequential Machines," *Journal of the Association for Computing Machinery*, Vol. 10, No. 1, pp. 78–88, January 1963.
13. Hartmanis, J. and R. E. Stearns, "Pair Algebra and Its Application to Automata Theory," *Information and Control*, Vol. 7, pp. 485–507, 1964.
14. Hirschhorn, Edwin, "Simplification of a Class of Boolean Functions," *Journal of the Association for Computing Machinery*," Vol. 5, No. 1, pp. 67–75, January 1958.
15. Karp, R. M., "Some Techniques of State Assignment for Synchronous Sequential Machines," *IBM Research Report*, RC-938, May 1963 and also *IEEE Transactions on Electronic Computers*, Vol. EC-13, No. 5, pp. 507–518, October 1964.

16. Kautz, W. H., "State-Logic Relations in Autonomous Sequential Networks," *Proceedings of the Eastern Joint Computer Conference*, December 3–5, 1958.
17. Kohavi, Zvi, "Secondary State Assignment for Sequential Machines," *IEEE Transactions on Electronic Computers*, Vol. EC-13, No. 3, pp. 193–203, June 1964.
18. Liu, C. N., "A State Variable Assignment Method for Asynchronous Sequential Switching Circuits," *Journal of the Association for Computing Machinery*, Vol. 10, No. 2, pp. 209–216, April, 1963.
19. McCluskey, E. J. Jr., and S. H. Unger, "A Note on the Number of Internal Variable Assignments for Sequential Switching Circuits," *IRE Transactions on Electronic Computers*, Vol. EC-8, No. 4, pp. 439–440, December 1959.
20. McCluskey, E. J., Jr., "Assignment of Carry-Variables in Iterative Networks," *AIEE General Fall Meeting*, Paper No. 60-12111, October 1960.
21. Miller, R. E., "Switching Theory and Logical Design of Automatic Digital Computer Circuits," *IBM Research Report*, RC-473, pp. 155–162, June 1961.
22. Schneider, M. I., "State Assignment Algorithm for Clocked Sequential Machines," Massachusetts Institute of Technology, Lincoln Laboratory Technical Report No. 270, May 1962.
23. Stearns, R. E., and J. Hartmanis, "On the State Assignment Problem for Sequential Machines II," *IRE Transactions on Electronic Computers*, Vol. EC-10, No. 4, pp. 593–603. December 1961.
24. Yoeli, M., "The Cascade Decomposition of Sequential Machines." *IRE Transactions on Electronic Computers*, Vol. EC-10, No. 4, pp. 587–592, December 1961.

# 9

# *Asynchronous Switching Networks*

## 9.1 INTRODUCTION

No matter what types of physical elements we use to construct a sequential network, there will be an inherent time delay associated with the operation of each of the physical switching elements. If the elements are relays and relay contacts, one delay occurs between the time of excitation of a relay coil and the time that the contacts of this relay are actually operated. If the elements are decision and delay elements, such a delay occurs between the time that new inputs are applied to any element and the time that the output changes to the value specified by the switching function associated with the decision element. In addition, time delays occur for signals to be transmitted along the interconnecting wires from the output of an element to the inputs of other elements. For our previous studies of synchronous networks we assumed that the circuits and inputs were controlled by appropriate clocking signals so that no further consideration of timing was required. Thus, for example, in Chapter 8 we did not need to impose any constraints on the state assignment given to a machine to insure that erroneous operation would not occur in the network.

Even when the exact delays which occur in a network are unknown, however, it is often possible to obtain a desired behavior without providing clocking signals to synchronize the circuit. If synchronization is not provided to the network, say by clock signals or by knowing the exact delays in the network, we call the network *asynchronous*. The asynchronous network of Figure 6.3.3, briefly discussed in Chapter 6, illustrates the invariance of circuit behavior even when delay times were not precisely known.

In this chapter we consider asynchronous operation in more detail. For this purpose we must consider both the internal time delays within the network and the interaction of the network with its external environment. This interaction occurs through the sequence of inputs obtained from, and the sequence of outputs supplied to, the external environment. Throughout Chapters 9 and 10 we shall assume level-type signals on inputs and outputs, as well as internally, for the networks. We discuss the influences that various assumptions on the relative delay times of circuit operation, the application of inputs, and the reading of outputs have on network operation. For this discussion two varieties of internal stray delays are defined first. We then consider the problem of synthesizing an asynchronous network described by a sequential machine when particular relative timing assumptions between the network and the external environment can be made. In this synthesis we shall see that it is sometimes necessary to insert additional delay elements in the network to insure correct operation and to restrict our attention to asynchronous machines (Definition 6.4.3). We shall also find that a special type of "hazard-free" design of combinational networks will be important for asynchronous operation and that state assignment techniques differing considerably from those of Chapter 8 are required for insuring that the correct transitions from one state to another will actually take place.

In Section 9.7 we show how the external environment might be signaled by the network to indicate when the outputs of the network are ready and when the network may be supplied with new inputs. In addition, we discuss extending this approach to an external environment consisting of one or more other networks so that a system of individually designed networks can be obtained.

## 9.2  TYPES OF NETWORK STRAY DELAYS

We shall discuss the types of stray delays that can occur in a switching network in terms of networks of gate circuits displaying level-type signals that take on the binary values 0 and 1; much of the discussion, however, can be seen to apply to networks of other types of switching elements as well. Consider the decision element idealization of a gate circuit as shown in Figure 9.2.1.

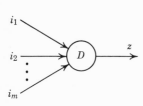

Figure 9.2.1 A decision element.

The value assumed by the output of the element $D$ can be expressed as a Boolean function of the inputs $x_1, x_2, \ldots, x_m$; that is, $z = f(x_1, x_2, \ldots, x_m)$. No delay is assumed either for the output of the decision element to react to the inputs of the element or in the lines interconnecting a network of these elements. In an actual network of gate circuits, however, such delays would occur. The delay which occurs between the time that inputs are supplied to an element $D$ and the time that the output assumes the value designated by the function $z = f(x_1, x_2, \ldots, x_m)$ is called an *element delay*. Similarly, the delay for transmission from the output of an element to an interconnected input is called the *line delay*. The element delays and line delays which can occur within a switching network are also called the *stray delays* of the network. We may model the stray delays of a network by inserting elements of delay in the lines interconnecting decision elements. This delay is depicted in Figure 9.2.2. Roughly speaking, the value of the output $o$ of a delay is to be equal to some previous value of its input $i$. The element delay is simulated by a delay attached to the output of a decision

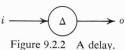

Figure 9.2.2   A delay.

element, and the line delay is simulated by a delay attached to the input of a decision element. The resulting structure of a gate circuit is shown in Figure 9.2.3.

Various types of terminal behavior of delays may be defined for simulating the stray delays.

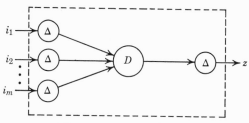

Figure 9.2.3   A gate circuit.

**Definition 9.2.1**   Let $\Delta$ be a nonnegative real number, and $i(t)$ and $o(t)$ denote the input and output signal values of a delay, respectively, at time $t$. If $o(t + \Delta) = i(t)$ for any time $t \geq 0$, the delay is called a *perfect stray delay*, and the constant $\Delta$ is called the *delay time* of the element.

**Definition 9.2.2**   A delay is called a $\Delta$-*inertial stray delay* if its terminal behavior satisfies the following conditions.

Let $t$ be a time such that $i(t - \epsilon) \neq i(t)$ for $\epsilon > 0$, $\Delta$ be a positive constant, and $i(\tau) = i(t)$ in the interval $t \leq \tau < t + \Delta$; then

1. $o(t + \Delta) = i(t)$.
2. If there exists a $t^*$, $t \leq t^* \leq t + \Delta$, such that $o(t^*) = i(t)$, and if $i(\tau) = i(t - \varepsilon)$ in the interval $t^* - \Delta \leq \tau < t$, then $o(\tau') = i(t)$ in the interval $t^* \leq \tau' \leq t + \Delta$.

**Definition 9.2.3**   Given a delay, if for each time $t$ there exists a $\Delta(t)$ such that the delay satisfies the conditions for a $\Delta(t)$ inertial stray delay, it is called an *inertial stray delay*.

The output of the perfect stray delay at any time $t$ is an exact replica of its input at time $t - \Delta$. Thus the element must remember the past inputs over a time interval $\Delta$. If no upper bound is placed on the number of different input signal values that can occur within a time interval $\Delta$, there is also no upper bound on the number of binary signals that the perfect stray delay must store. Although certain kinds of wires, like coaxial cables, used in a network may be able to store and transmit more than one signal value at any given time, it is certainly unrealistic to allow an unbounded amount of storage. For this reason, and since the inertial stray delays (Definitions 9.2.2 and 9.2.3) resemble more closely the stray delay behavior of most gate-type networks, we shall use inertial stray delays in studying network behavior resulting from stray delays.

In a $\Delta$-inertial stray delay the input $i(t)$ must be held constant for a time interval of $\Delta$ before the output can be assured to assume the value of the input. If $i(t)$ is not held constant for a time interval $\Delta$, however, Definition 9.2.2 does not necessarily define an output. From condition (2) of the definition we see that the output may indeed change to the value of the input at some time $t^* < t + \Delta$. In this case if the change in the input at time $t$ was the only change in the interval $t^* - \Delta$ to $t^*$, then condition (2) also insures that the output will remain constant from $t^*$ until the next input change. The only situation in which the output is undefined is when there is more than one input change in an interval $t \leq \tau \leq t + \Delta$.

In both the $\Delta$-inertial stray delay and inertial stray delay, only the most recent input change over a time interval $\Delta$ [or $\Delta(t)$] needs to be remembered to define the output. Thus, no matter how often the input changes, only one bit must be stored by the element.

The inertial delay element is more general than the $\Delta$-inertial delay element in that its delay $\Delta(t)$ is a function of $t$ rather than a constant $\Delta$ for all times. If for all $t$, $\Delta(t)$ is bounded from above by some number $T$, giving $0 \leq \Delta(t) \leq T$, the inertial stray delay is said to be *bounded*. In this case, if $i(t)$ is held constant for a time interval $T$ after each change of input, the output value will also be assured of changing to the most recent value of the input and will be defined at all times. In a network of gate circuits having no feedback in which the delays are bounded, it follows that certain restrictions on the rate of changes on the network inputs may be sufficient to insure that the input to each delay element never changes more than once in any time interval $T$. We consider these restrictions in the next section.

On the other hand, $\Delta(t)$ may not have such a universal upper bound $T$. Rather, it may be appropriate to assume only that $0 \leq \Delta(t) < \infty$. We call such a delay *unbounded*. In this case, holding $i(t)$ constant for any predetermined time is not sufficient to insure that the output be defined. We shall consider the effect of such a delay assumption on networks in Section 9.7 and also in Chapter 10.

## 9.3 ANALYSIS OF NETWORK BEHAVIOR WITH STRAY DELAYS

To study the propagation of signals within a switching network from its inputs to its outputs, we consider first networks of gate circuits containing no feedback. Such networks are, of course, combinational, but may be included as part of a sequential network as shown in the basic model for sequential networks (Figure 6.2.2).

Consider the network shown in Figure 9.3.1.

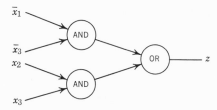

Figure 9.3.1. A switching network with no feedback.

If the elements of a network having no feedback are considered to be decision elements having no delays, and no delays occur in the lines, the behavior of the network can be described completely by expressing each output as a switching function of its inputs. With these assumptions the behavior of the network of Figure 9.3.1 is expressed by the function

$$z = \bar{x}_1 \bar{x}_3 \vee x_2 x_3.$$

If each element of the network is considered to be a switching circuit with inertial stray delays as shown in Figure 9.2.3, however, the switching function does not suffice as a description of the behavior. In a network of these elements, any line from the output of a decision element to the input of another element need contain only one delay element. Thus, without any loss of generality, we can simplify the analysis by considering the delay on the output and that on the input to be combined into a single delay on the input to the element. With these delays considered in the network of Figure 9.3.1 we obtain the configuration shown in Figure 9.3.2. We can illustrate with this example that the function

$$z = \bar{x}_1 \bar{x}_3 \vee x_2 x_3$$

does not completely describe the relationship between the inputs and output of the network. Suppose that each inertial stray delay is bounded, that the initial inputs are $x_1 = 0$, $x_2 = 1$, and $x_3 = 0$, and that all elements

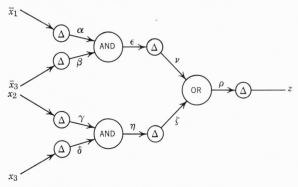

Figure 9.3.2.   Network with stray delays shown.

have reacted to these inputs.   In this case the output $z = 1$ since the $\bar{x}_1\bar{x}_3$ term equals 1.   Also the signal values of the circuit are

$$\alpha = 1,\ \beta = 1,\ \gamma = 1,\ \delta = 0,\ \epsilon = 1,\ \eta = 0,\ \nu = 1,$$
$$\zeta = 0,\quad\text{and}\quad \rho = 1.$$

Now if input $x_3$ changes from 0 to 1, the $x_2x_3$ term of the function becomes 1 and $z$ should remain 1.   Notice, however, that when $x_3$ changes from 0 to 1, both the $\beta$ and $\delta$ lines will change eventually.   These changes will force both $\epsilon$ and $\eta$ lines to change, followed by changes on the $\nu$ and $\zeta$ lines.   In these two chains of changes, if the $\nu$ line changes to 0 before the $\zeta$ line changes from 0 to 1, it is possible to have a temporary value of 0 on the $\rho$ and $z$ lines.   Such a temporary erroneous value on an output line could cause erroneous circuit operation, especially if the output were attached to other networks or used as part of a sequential network.   This erroneous behavior caused by the value on more than one line in the network being changed at any time is called a *hazard* in the combinational network.   We call it a *transient hazard* because the output is only temporarily in error.   Hazards can occur by giving both a temporary output of 0, as in this example, or by a temporary output of 1 when the desired output is 0.   Since the hazard produces only a temporary erroneous output, it may not appear very serious.   If the output is connected to another network, and the reaction time of this network is made slow enough, the hazard would not even be noticed.   With the extensive efforts to construct fast circuits, however, it seems undesirable to slow down the reaction times simply to circumvent a hazard.   It would be more desirable to eliminate the hazard, if possible. For this purpose consider modifying the network of Figure 9.3.2 by adding an AND-element for $\bar{x}_1 x_2$. The resulting network, with stray delays shown, is depicted in Figure 9.3.3. The Boolean function for this network is

$$z = \bar{x}_1 \bar{x}_3 \vee x_2 x_3 \vee \bar{x}_1 x_2,$$

which is identical to the function $\bar{x}_1 \bar{x}_3 \vee x_2 x_3$. In this network the reader may verify that no erroneous output can occur when changing the inputs from $x_1 = 0$, $x_2 = 1$, $x_3 = 0$ to $x_1 = 0$, $x_2 = 1$, $x_3 = 1$; also it can be seen that for this network no other erroneous output can be obtained by any input change of only a single variable. This type of network is called *hazard-free*; we describe briefly in the next section how to design hazard-free networks.

With the assumption of bounded delays for stray delays, temporary erroneous outputs on networks without feedback can be readily eliminated by the following precautions:

1. Insuring that the network is hazard-free.
2. Restricting changes of inputs to a single variable changing at a time.
3. Waiting a sufficient length of time between input changes for all elements to become stable.

Sufficient time for the third precaution is easily calculated as follows: if $k$ is the maximum number of decision elements that occur in any connection from any input to any output, the time is $[2(k - 1) + 2]T$, where $T$ is the upper bound on each stray delay. The time $[2(k - 1) + 2]T$ allows the maximum time for each stray delay in the longest chain of delays to react to an input change. Condition 1 imposes a constraint on the internal design of the network, whereas conditions (2) and (3) impose constraints on the external environment in order to obtain the desired behavior.

What happens if we change our assumption from bounded stray delays to unbounded delays? In this case the sufficient time for condition (3) used for bounded delays cannot be found, since there is no finite maximum stray delay time. Considering the hazard-free network of Figure 9.3.3, assume that we have an initial input $(0, 1, 0)^*$ and change the input to $(0, 1, 1)$. Since the output remains 1 for both these input combinations, we cannot test for an output change to tell whether the network has reacted to the input change. After waiting some time in hopes that the network completes reacting to the input change, suppose we change the input to $(1, 1, 1)$. With this sequence of two input changes an erroneous

* The input combination $(0, 1, 0)$ indicates the ordered values on $(x_1, x_2, x_3)$.

output can occur even though the output should remain equal to 1. For example, suppose after the first input change from $(0, 1, 0)$ to $(0, 1, 1)$, lines $\beta$, $\epsilon$ and $\nu$ reacted to the change so that $\nu = 0$, but that some delay in the circuits for lines $\delta$, $\eta$, and $\zeta$ has not reacted so that $\zeta = 0$. Of course, line $\xi = 1$ for both of these input configurations so that $\rho = z = 1$ as desired. Now assume that the second input change to $(1, 1, 1)$ occurs while $\zeta$ still is equal to 0. Now it is possible that line $\xi$ would change to 0

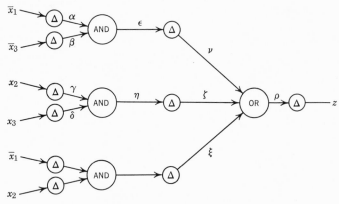

Figure 9.3.3.    Modification of Figure 9.3.2.

before line $\zeta$ changes to 1. In this case the OR-element could react giving an output $\rho = 0$ which may then create a temporary output of $z = 0$. To eliminate this erroneous behavior we would need some way of detecting that the signal $\zeta$ had actually changed to a 1 before the second input change is allowed. In other words, we desire to generate some *reply* to the external environment to indicate that the network is ready to accept a new input.

An impractical solution to this problem would be to bring each internal signal line in the network out to the external environment, and insist that the external environment test that all these lines are of correct value before any input change is allowed. This requires a complex decision by the external environment, however, and it would be much more desirable to supply only a single reply line to the external environment. A straightforward approach for generating a reply is not immediately evident, however. The reader may see this by attempting to generate a foolproof reply for the network we have been discussing. In Section 9.7 we consider generating reply signals and describe certain conditions under which it is possible to do so.

To summarize, in our analysis of network behavior without feedback we have illustrated how hazards can produce a temporary erroneous output. Of course, any errors must be temporary since the networks have no feedback. Furthermore, if there are no stray delays, the Boolean functions for each output describe the circuit behavior and no errors are possible. If the stray delays are bounded, the hazards may be circumvented by designing hazard-free networks, by changing only one input variable

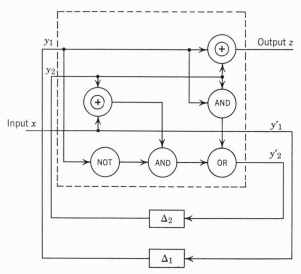

Figure 9.3.4. A network with feedback.

at a time, and by providing sufficient time between input changes. If the stray delays are unbounded, however, we cannot generally determine a sufficient time to wait between input changes, and it appears that extra "reply signals" are required to insure error-free operation.

We now consider the extra complications which arise when a network contains feedback. A simple example in the form of the basic model for a sequential network is shown in Figure 9.3.4. The equations for this network are

$$\begin{cases} z = \bar{y}_1 y_2 \lor y_1 \bar{y}_2 = y_1 \oplus y_2 \\ y_1' = x \\ y_2' = y_1 y_2 \lor \bar{y}_1(x \oplus y_2). \end{cases}$$

The part of the network shown within the dotted lines has no feedback. The two delay elements $\Delta_1$ and $\Delta_2$ are assumed to be actual elements designed to give some nonzero delay in the feedback loops. That is, they are not simply stray delays. We shall assume that the delay times of $\Delta_1$ and $\Delta_2$ act like bounded inertial stray delays except that they also have some lower bound on their delay. Thus if $\Delta(t)$ is the delay, $T_1 \leq \Delta(t) \leq T_2$, where $T_1$ and $T_2$ are positive real numbers.

To analyze the operation of this network let us assume that $x = y_1 = y_2 = 0$; then from the functions for the network we obtain that $z = 0$, $y_1' = 0$, and $y_2' = 0$. If we assume further that there are no stray delays in the network, the network signal values cannot change until the input changes. If the input $x$ is changed from 0 to 1, then both $y_1'$ and $y_2'$ instantaneously change to 1. Now if after a delay, $\Delta_1$ and $\Delta_2$ transmit these new values of $y_1'$ and $y_2'$ simultaneously to the $y_1$ and $y_2$ lines and a new input is also supplied to the network, we arrive at a synchronous operation for the network. In this case the next state and output equations describe adequately the network behavior.

In contrast, suppose there are some stray delays (either bounded or unbounded) within the network so that from the initial condition $y_1'$ changes to 1 but $y_2'$ remains 0. If these signals pass through $\Delta_1$ and $\Delta_2$ giving $y_1 = y_1' = 1$ and $y_2 = y_2' = 0$ while the input is still at the value $x = 1$, the combinational circuit may react to this new input on $y_1$. From the functions we would obtain $z = 1$, $y_1' = 1$, and $y_2' = 0$. If these values were actually produced, the output would be in error as well as the state (indicated by values on $y_1$ and $y_2$). The state $y_1 = 1, y_2 = 0$ is also a stable state for the input $x = 1$, so that no matter how long the input was held to 1, the circuit would not reach the desired state $y_1 = 1, y_2 = 1$ or give the desired output $z = 0$. Such a static error is called a *steady-state hazard*.

This behavior illustrates that the erroneous operation of the circuit, because of stray delays or variable delay times in the $\Delta_1$ and $\Delta_2$ delay elements, can cause a static or permanent error in the operation of a circuit having feedback, whereas for circuits without feedback only temporary erroneous outputs are possible. If, in a network, more than one signal can change at any time, we call this a *race condition*. Thus the condition of both $y_1'$ and $y_2'$ changing from 0 to 1, which arose from the input changing from 0 to 1, is an example of a race condition. When a race condition can lead to a steady-state hazard, as in the example, it is called a *critical race condition*; otherwise it is called a *noncritical race condition*.

If all the stray delays are bounded, then if the desired behavior is described by an asynchronous machine, it is possible to obtain desired network behavior by making the delay elements in each feedback loop sufficiently long for all combinational circuits to settle down before transmitting a change of state and by causing the inputs to change sufficiently infrequently so as to allow all feedback delay elements to operate before the input is changed. In Section 9.5 we discuss several approaches for this type of design. In the general case, when stray delays of a network with feedback are unbounded, no convenient method of description and design is known. A detailed analysis of any particular circuit is possible, but this provides no general theory. If the stray delays are limited to element delays alone, however (that is, no line delays in any part of the network), then behavior described by sequential machines can be obtained, as shown in Section 9.7. Also, the theory of speed independent networks, discussed in Chapter 10, applies to this assumption when it is also assumed that the network has no inputs from an external environment.

## 9.4   HAZARD-FREE COMBINATIONAL NETWORKS

To discuss methods for obtaining hazard-free operation of gate-type networks it is desirable to define hazards somewhat more precisely than was necessary in Section 9.3. In this section when we say network we mean a network of gate elements having no feedback. We shall also assume that stray delays occur on the input and output lines for each decision element (usually we shall not specifically show the delays) and that all stray delays are bounded.

For a network having one output and $n$ independent inputs we associate a switching function $f(x_1, x_2, \ldots, x_n)$ of $n$ variables. We say that $(e_1, e_2, \ldots, e_n)$ is an *input combination* to the network, where $e_i = 0$ or 1 for $1 \leq i \leq n$. Two input combinations $(e_1, e_2, \ldots, e_n)$ and $(e_1', e_2', \ldots, e_n')$ are said to be *adjacent* if $e_i \neq e_i'$ for one $i$; $1 \leq i \leq n$ and $e_j = e_j'$ otherwise. An input combination is applied to the network by having $x_i$ assume the value $e_i$ for each $i$. A network is *stable* under an input combination $(e_1, e_2, \ldots, e_n)$ when the output of each element in the network assumes the value indicated by its inputs for the function associated with the element and the output of each stray delay is equal to its input. When a network is stable under a given input combination, it will remain stable until another input combination is applied to the network, and the output of the network will take on the value $f(e_1, e_2, \ldots, e_n)$; that is, of the function $f(x_1, x_2, \ldots, x_n)$ evaluated at $(e_1, e_2, \ldots, e_n)$.

**Definition 9.4.1** Suppose a network whose switching function is $f(x_1, x_2, \ldots, x_n)$ is stable under the input combination $(e_1, e_2, \ldots, e_n)$, that $(e_1', e_2', \ldots, e_n')$ is an adjacent input combination, and $f(e_1, e_2, \ldots, e_n) = f(e_1', e_2', \ldots, e_n')$. If $(e_1', e_2', \ldots, e_n')$ is applied to the network, the change of input from $(e_1, e_2, \ldots, e_n)$ to $(e_1', e_2', \ldots, e_n')$ is called a *static hazard* for the network if it is possible for the output to assume a value not equal to $f(e_1', e_2', \ldots, e_n')$ before the network becomes stable.

We saw that the network of Figures 9.3.1 and 9.3.2 has a static hazard for the input transition from $(0, 1, 0)$ to $(0, 1, 1)$.

Another type of hazard is also possible, as seen by the following definition.

**Definition 9.4.2**  Suppose a network, with associated switching function $f(x_1, x_2, \ldots, x_n)$, is stable under an input combination $(e_1, e_2, \ldots, e_n)$, and an adjacent input combination $(e_1', e_2', \ldots, e_n')$ is applied to the network, where $f(e_1', e_2', \ldots, e_n') \neq f(e_1, e_2, \ldots, e_n)$. The transition from $(e_1, e_2, \ldots, e_n)$ to $(e_1', e_2', \ldots, e_n')$ is called a *dynamic hazard* for the network if it is possible for the output to assume the transient sequence of values $f(e_1', e_2', \ldots, e_n')$ followed by $f(e_1, e_2, \ldots, e_n)$ before it becomes stable under $(e_1', e_2', \ldots, e_n')$.

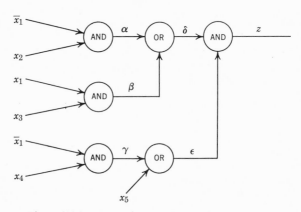

Figure 9.4.1.   Dynamic hazard example.

Both static and dynamic hazards for a network are changes of single input variables which can cause an erroneous temporary output between two stable conditions of the network and are thus transient hazards.  For a static hazard the sequence of outputs could be $0, \ldots, 1, \ldots, 0$, where the stable output is 0; or $1, \ldots, 0, \ldots, 1$, where the stable output is 1. The sequence of outputs might include more than a single temporary value.  For a dynamic hazard the sequence of outputs must include at least four elements; $0, \ldots, 1, 0, \ldots, 1$, or $1, \ldots, 0, 1, \ldots, 0$.

The network of Figure 9.4.1 has a dynamic hazard for the input combination transition from $(0, 1, 1, 1, 0)$ to $(1, 1, 1, 1, 0)$. We demonstrate this as follows.  Suppose that the initial input combination to this network is $(0, 1, 1, 1, 0)$, the network is stable, and input $x_1$ is then changed to 1.  By envisioning stray delays in the circuit we see that the value on line $\alpha$ will change later from 1 to 0. Similarly, line $\beta$ changes from 0 to 1 and lines $\gamma$ and $\epsilon$ change from 1 to 0. If the $\alpha$ line changes before the $\beta$ line, the $\delta$ line can have a sequence of values $1, 0, 1$ (that is, a static hazard). If the $\epsilon$ line changes to 0 only after the $\delta$ line has gone through the sequence $1, 0, 1$, the output $z$ may take on the sequence of values $1, 0, 1, 0$, thus displaying a dynamic hazard.

**Definition 9.4.3** A network is *hazard-free* if it has no static or dynamic hazards.

The network of Figure 9.3.3 has been claimed to be hazard-free and can be checked by inspecting the possible sequences of outputs under any transition between adjacent input combinations. Thus, if hazard-free operation were desired in a network to realize the function

$$z = \bar{x}_1 \bar{x}_3 \vee x_2 x_3,$$

we would use the network of Figure 9.3.3 rather than the minimal network of Figure 9.3.1. Here the redundant AND-element for $\bar{x}_1 x_2$ eliminates the static hazard.

We now discuss a technique for designing a hazard-free two-level AND-OR network for any Boolean function. Thus, when it is to our advantage, we can assume hazard-free operation of the combinational networks included in asynchronous sequential network designs.

**Definition 9.4.4** A *lift set* of a network is any minimum subset of input lines, which when set equal to 1 causes the output to equal 1.

The lift sets for Figure 9.3.1 are $\{\bar{x}_1, \bar{x}_3\}$ and $\{x_2, x_3\}$. For the hazard-free network of Figure 9.3.3, we have the additional lift set $\{\bar{x}_1, x_2\}$, where in both examples we use $x_i$ and $\bar{x}_i$ to indicate specific input lines. The lift sets for the network of Figure 9.4.1 are $\{\bar{x}_1, x_2, x_5\}$, $\{\bar{x}_1, x_2, x_4\}$, and $\{x_1, x_3, x_5\}$.

**Definition 9.4.5** An input combination $(e_1, e_2, \ldots, e_n)$ is said to be *covered* by a lift set $S$ if the following conditions hold.

1. If $x_i \in S$, then $e_i = 1$.
2. If $\bar{x}_j \in S$, then $e_j = 0$.

If a lift set does not contain $k$ of the variables of $f(x_1, x_2, \ldots, x_n)$ either complemented or not, the lift set covers $2^k$ input combinations. For a two-level AND-OR network each lift set corresponds to the inputs that enter a single AND-element.

**Theorem 9.4.1** A two-level AND-OR network is hazard-free if and only if each pair of adjacent input combinations, for which $f(x_1, x_2, \ldots, x_n) = 1$, is covered by at least one lift set of the network.

PROOF. Let $E = (e_1, e_2, \ldots, e_n)$ and $E' = (e_1', e_2', \ldots, e'_n)$ be a pair of adjacent input combinations for which

$$f(e_1, e_2, \ldots, e_n) = f(e_1', e_2', \ldots, e_n') = 1.$$

If both $E$ and $E'$ are not covered by a lift set of the network, then no single AND-element is equal to 1 for both $E$ and $E'$. During the transition from $E$ to $E'$ if the stray delays are such that the AND-elements which

| $x_1\,x_2$ \ $x_3$ | 0 | 1 |
|---|---|---|
| 0 0 | 1 | 0 |
| 0 1 | 1 | 1 |
| 1 1 | 0 | 1 |
| 1 0 | 0 | 0 |

Figure 9.4.2. Karnaugh map for $f = \bar{x}_1\bar{x}_3 \vee x_2x_3$.

equal 1 for $E$ change to 0 before any AND-element which equals 1 for $E'$ actually changes to 1, then the OR-element can produce a temporary erroneous output of 0. In this case, the network has a static hazard for the transition from $E$ to $E'$, thus proving half the theorem. Conversely, if each pair $(E, E')$ are covered by a lift set, then a single AND-element holds an output of 1 during the transition from $E$ to $E'$, showing that no static hazard giving a temporary output of 0 can exist for the network. In addition, for any transition between adjacent input combinations for which $f(x_1, x_2, \ldots, x_n) = 0$ for both combinations, no AND-element can ever provide a temporary output of 1. Thus the network has no static hazards. Finally, consider a transition between two adjacent input combinations which changes the output of the network. If the output change is from 1 to 0, the output cannot change to 0 until the OR-element has sensed that all its inputs are equal to 0. Since no AND-element is tending to change to 1 in this transition, no dynamic hazard can occur. Similar reasoning proves that no dynamic hazard can occur for an output change from 0 to 1. This completes the proof.

The necessary and sufficient condition of this theorem gives us an easily tested criterion for the design of hazard-free two-level AND-OR networks. For functions $f(x_1, x_2, \ldots, x_n)$ with few variables the requirement is readily tested by inspecting the Karnaugh map.

The Karnaugh map for

$$f(x_1, x_2, x_3) = \bar{x}_1\bar{x}_3 \vee x_2x_3$$

is shown in Figure 9.4.2. From this map and Theorem 9.4.1 we see that $\{\bar{x}_1, x_2\}$, $\{\bar{x}_1, \bar{x}_3\}$, and $\{x_2, x_3\}$ must be a lift sets of any hazard-free two-level

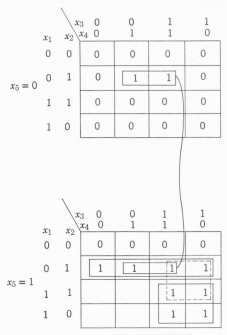

Figure 9.4.3   Karnaugh map for network of Figure 9.4.1.

AND-OR network to realize this function. This, of course, was the case for the network of Figure 9.3.3.

As another example, consider designing a hazard-free network to replace the network of Figure 9.4.1. The Karnaugh map is shown in Figure 9.4.3. In this example the three subcubes shown within solid lines would produce a minimum network. However, for hazard-free operation the additional AND-element indicated by the dotted subcube is required so that transitions $(0, 1, 1, 1, 1)$ to $(1, 1, 1, 1, 1)$ and $(0, 1, 1, 0, 1)$ to $(1, 1, 1, 0, 1)$ are each covered by a single lift set of the network. The hazard-free network is shown in Figure 9.4.4.

For functions of more variables than convenient to treat by map methods, it is readily seen that the techniques of cubical complexes, or charts, for obtaining minimum two-level networks can be generalized to include the condition of Theorem 9.4.1 whenever hazard-free designs are required. Prime implicants are generated as before, but the cover selected must also include cubes that cover transitions between adjacent input

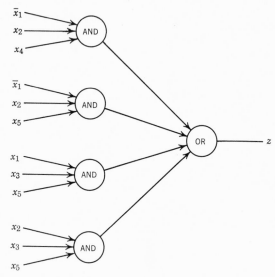

Figure 9.4.4    Hazard-free replacement for Figure 9.4.1.

combinations. For the example of Figure 9.4.4 a minimum cover is

$$\left\{ \begin{matrix} 0 & 1 & x & 1 & x \\ 0 & 1 & x & x & 1 \\ 1 & x & 1 & x & 1 \end{matrix} \right\},$$

but a hazard-free cover must include cube $\{x\ 1\ 1\ x\ 1\}$.

The results of hazard-free operation can be extended in several ways. By a dual development, conditions for designing hazard-free two-level OR-AND networks can be obtained. Conditions can be found for analyzing any network for static or dynamic hazards. The terminology and results on hazards are easily generalized to multiple-output networks. Finally, the concept of a hazard may be generalized to more than single input changes. In this case, however, it is not generally possible to design hazard-free networks for every switching function.

The basic conditions of Theorem 9.4.1 are sufficient to show that hazard-free operation can be obtained for any switching function specification when limiting changes of input to single changes, and this is all required in the following.

## 9.5 THE DESIGN OF ASYNCHRONOUS NETWORKS ASSUMING BOUNDED STRAY DELAYS

We now consider the design of asynchronous sequential networks under the assumption that all stray delays within the network are bounded and that all signals are the level type. The desired network behavior (or specification) is assumed to be given by a sequential machine. If desired,

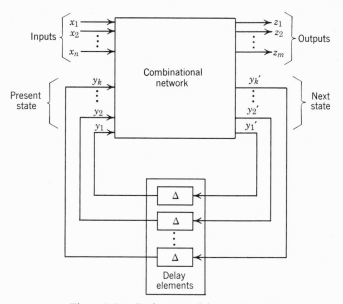

Figure 9.5.1   Basic sequential network model.

the states of the machine may have been minimized as discussed in Chapter 7; we shall not consider state minimization further in this chapter. The designs we consider will be of the general form of the basic model for sequential networks in Figure 6.2.2 and redrawn in Figure 9.5.1. The $k$ delay elements shown in the figure are assumed to satisfy the following definition.

**Definition 9.5.1**   A $\Delta$-*inertial delay element* is a delay element whose input $i(t)$ and output $o(t)$ satisfy the following condition.

Let $t$ be a time such that $i(t - \varepsilon) \neq i(t)$ for $\varepsilon > 0$, $\Delta$ be positive constant, and $i(\tau) = i(t)$ in the interval $t \leq \tau < t + \Delta$; then $o(t + \Delta) = i(t)$ and $o(\tau) = i(t - \varepsilon)$ for $t \leq \tau < t + \Delta$.

Note that the definition of a $\Delta$-inertial delay element is similar to that for a $\Delta$-inertial stray delay, Definition 9.2.2, except that the exact delay time of the $\Delta$-inertial delay element is specified as a constant time $\Delta$. The stray delay is meant to simulate an uncontrollable delay of a decision element or line, whereas the $\Delta$-inertial delay element is assumed to be a specially designed element placed in the network for the specific purpose of providing a controllable delay. Indeed, as is true in the reaction time of a decision element, the actual delay time of a $\Delta$-inertial delay element may be somewhat variable, but this can be modeled by visualizing stray delays in the input and output lines of the delay elements.

Since we are assuming that all stray delays within the network are bounded, we shall assume that each output of the combinational part of the sequential network is designed as a hazard-free network. Now if we can restrict the input changes into the combinational network to be transitions between adjacent input combinations and if an input change is allowed to follow a previous input change only after the network becomes stable, then the combinational network will operate in a hazard-free manner—with no temporary erroneous outputs. If no further conditions are imposed on the sequential machine and network delays, however, we cannot insure this desired hazard-free operation. The most apparent requirement for attaining adjacent input transitions is that only one of the inputs $x_1, x_2, \ldots, x_n$ be changed at any time. When one of the input variables changes, we must also insure that the present state variables do not change until the combinational network becomes stable. This is accomplished by assuming that the delay $\Delta$ of the delay elements is larger than the maximum stray delay that can occur in any input to output chain of lines and elements in the combinational network. If adjacent transitions of the state variables to the combinational network are also required during the change of state, this imposes a constraint on the state assignment for the sequential machine. (In some cases, single state variable changes are not required, and race conditions can be allowed as long as they are noncritical races.) Furthermore, after the state variables change, the combinational network should again become stable before another input variable change is allowed; this imposes a restriction on the rate at which input changes may be supplied to the network.

Because there are stray delays both in the combinational networks to provide the next state variables $y_1', y_2', \ldots, y_k'$ and in the feedback lines to the present state variables, we cannot insure that the next state actually occurs as a $k$-tuple of values on the $y_1, y_2, \ldots, y_k$ lines at any prespecified time, or even that all next state values arrive on these lines simultaneously. Therefore it is not generally apparent, how to synchronize the next input and next state to obtain the behavior as specified by a sequential machine.

By assuming that the sequential machine is an asynchronous machine, however, this problem is alleviated. For, in an asynchronous machine, if an input combination of $x_1, x_2, \ldots, x_n$ is applied and held on the input lines, the machine will change state only once; that is, the next state will be a stable state under the input, and if no critical race conditions occur in changing from the present state to the next state, the sequential network will become stable and will remain stable until a new input is applied. To accomplish the transition from present state to next state, however, we

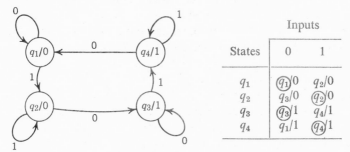

Figure 9.5.2.   Flow table for asynchronous machine.

may require a sequence of internal variable changes, and the time between input changes should be sufficient to allow for the longest possible sequence of changes to occur.

To insure proper operation, we shall make all these assumptions for the designs considered in this section. Summarizing our assumptions, we require that

1. The machine specified is an asynchronous machine.
2. The combinational networks are designed as hazard-free.
3. The input transitions are restricted to adjacent input combinations.
4. The feedback delay element time $\Delta$ is sufficiently large to allow the combinational network to become stable before the state changes, and the rate of changing the inputs is sufficiently slow to allow the network to reach its stable state before the inputs are changed.
5. No critical race conditions occur during a state change.

Condition (4) requires the designer to control three interrelated network and external environment delays.   Conditions (1), (2), and (5) are restrictions on the network design.  As should be apparent, methods for attaining condition (5) are a significant part of asynchronous network design. Finally, condition (3) and the input rate of condition (4) are restrictions on the external environment.  Although the five assumptions may not be necessary, they are sufficient and prove to be convenient restrictions for designing asynchronous networks for behaviors described by asynchronous sequential machines.

The Huffman flow tables* are a convenient means for representing sequential machines when designing asynchronous networks. Figure 9.5.2 shows a state diagram and flow table for a "scale of two counter." This machine is asynchronous because each state is stable. In the flow table, state entries are encircled to indicate this stability of state. Thus, for example, $q_1$ is encircled in the $q_1$ row and the 0-input column, since if we are in state $q_1$ and have an input of 0 we remain in state $q_1$.

In a flow table suppose we encircle a next state entry $q_i$ whenever $q_i$ appears in the $q_i$ row. The machine is asynchronous if and only if in each column of the flow table there is a circled $q_i$ for each $q_i$ that appears in the column. Thus the requirement that the machine be asynchronous is readily checked on the flow table.

We assume that the inputs of the machine are specified as $n$-tuples of binary signals so that if the machine is in some stable state under some input combination, the next input combinations must be adjacent ones; that is, only a single input variable change is allowed. This restriction specifies some subset of columns of the flow table that can be input combinations directly following any given input combination.

We now concentrate on the problem of assigning binary $k$-tuples to the states of a machine so that no critical race conditions can arise. As discussed in Chapter 8, for any state assignment we know that the minimum value for $k$ is $k_m = \lceil \log_2 p \rceil$, where $p$ is the number of states of the machine. Thus for the machine of Figure 9.5.1 we need at least two variables $y_1$, $y_2$ to represent the states. For this example it is immediately evident from the structure of the state diagram that we can assign values of $y_1$, $y_2$ to the states so that no race conditions arise. For example, if we have the assignment

|       | $y_1$ | $y_2$ |
|-------|-------|-------|
| $q_1$ | 0     | 0     |
| $q_2$ | 0     | 1     |
| $q_3$ | 1     | 1     |
| $q_4$ | 1     | 0     |

each transition from one state to another of the state diagram occurs along the edge of the 2-cube representing the $y_1$, $y_2$ variables. The state diagram is said to be *embedded* in the 2-cube. Since any transition from one state to another thereby changes only one $y_i$ variable, no races occur.

---

* See Section 6.4.

The state assignment completes the specification for the design of the combinational circuits. These specifications are given in tabular form (truth tables) by simply replacing each occurrence of $q_i$ in the flow table by its assigned $k$-tuple. Thus, for our example, we obtain the table shown in Figure 9.5.3. This tabular form for the $y'$ variables is also called the "excitation matrix" or "$Y$-matrix," and that for the $z$ variables the "output matrix" or "Z-matrix." From the switching functions for each $y_i'$ and $z_j$ specified by this tabular form, the techniques for designing hazard-free networks discussed in Section 9.4 can be applied to complete the design of the asynchronous network.

|  | Inputs | |
| States | 0 | 1 |
| --- | --- | --- |
| 0   0 | 0 0/0 | 0 1/0 |
| 0   1 | 1 1/0 | 0 1/0 |
| 1   1 | 1 1/1 | 1 0/1 |
| 1   0 | 0 0/1 | 1 0/1 |

Figure 9.5.3   Combinational circuit specifications for $y_1'y_2'/z_1$.

For more complex flow charts it is not usually apparent how to embed the state diagram into a $k$-cube. It will be often impossible without adding states to the state diagram, where one or more states of this machine correspond to each state of the original machine and where this process of adding the states does not change the machine behavior. To illustrate this adding or *splitting* of states, consider the example of Figure 9.5.4.

Obviously, this state diagram cannot be embedded in any $k$-cube since it has a cycle of transitions from $q_1$ to $q_2$ to $q_3$ and back to $q_1$; also, a similar cycle exists for states $q_1$, $q_4$, and $q_5$. If $q_1$ is split into two states $q_1'$ and $q_1''$ so that each of these cycles is of length 4 rather than 3, as shown in Figure 9.5.5, a suitable embedding is possible.

The flow table, with states represented by an assignment on the 3-cube, is shown in Figure 9.5.6; from this table the required combinational networks are readily designed.

Note that state $q_1''$ is not a stable state. It is *transient*, that is, it serves simply as a route from states $q_3$ and $q_5$ to state $q_1'$. In the operation of this network, if the present state is $q_5$ and input 0 0 is given, the sequence of state transitions is $101 \rightarrow 001 \rightarrow 000$. It is important here that $y_1$ changes to 0 before $y_3$ is allowed to change, for if a race were allowed to occur between $y_1$ and $y_3$, state 1 0 0 ($q_4$) might be reached giving a critical

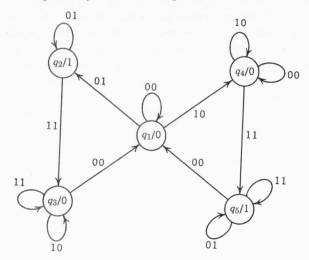

State diagram

Inputs $x_1 x_2$

| States | 0 0 | 0 1 | 1 0 | 1 1 |
|--------|-----|-----|-----|-----|
| $q_1$ | $\textcircled{q_1}/0$ | $q_2/0$ | $q_4/0$ | $-/0$ |
| $q_2$ | $-/1$ | $\textcircled{q_2}/1$ | $-/1$ | $q_3/1$ |
| $q_3$ | $q_1/0$ | $-/0$ | $\textcircled{q_3}/0$ | $\textcircled{q_3}/0$ |
| $q_4$ | $\textcircled{q_4}/0$ | $-/0$ | $\textcircled{q_4}/0$ | $q_5/0$ |
| $q_5$ | $q_1/1$ | $\textcircled{q_5}/1$ | $-/1$ | $\textcircled{q_5}/1$ |

Flow table

Figure 9.5.4.  Example for splitting of states.

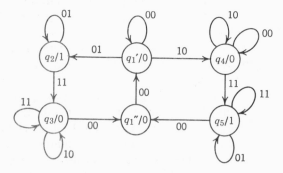

Figure 9.5.5  State $q_1$ of Figure 9.5.4 split.

race. Since the network must reach $q_1'$ before it becomes stable, the time between input changes must be sufficiently long to allow for the sequence of state changes from $q_5$ to $q_1''$ to $q_1'$. The reader may check that a similar situation occurs when the network is in state $q_3$ and an input of 0 0 is applied.

A general technique is unknown for splitting states so that the resulting machine can be embedded in a $k$-cube of minimum dimension. This general problem appears to be very difficult. The following general technique that uses $p$ state variables, where $p$ is the number of states, provides a simple means for implementing an asynchronous network which has no race conditions.

For a machine with states $q_1, q_2, \ldots, q_p$ let $y_1, y_2, \ldots, y_p$ represent the state variables and assign the $p$-tuple $E_i = (e_1, e_2, \ldots, e_p)$, where $e_i = 1$

Inputs $x_1 x_2$

| States | $y_1$ | $y_2$ | $y_3$ | 0 0 | 0 1 | 1 0 | 1 1 |
|---|---|---|---|---|---|---|---|
| $q_1'$ | 0 | 0 | 0 | ⟨000⟩/0 | 010/0 | 100/0 | –/0 |
| $q_1''$ | 0 | 0 | 1 | 000/0 | –/0 | –/0 | –/0 |
| $q_2$ | 0 | 1 | 0 | –/1 | ⟨010⟩/1 | –/1 | 011/1 |
| $q_3$ | 0 | 1 | 1 | 001/0 | –/0 | ⟨011⟩/0 | ⟨011⟩/0 |
| $q_4$ | 1 | 0 | 0 | ⟨100⟩/0 | –/0 | ⟨100⟩/0 | 101/0 |
| $q_5$ | 1 | 0 | 1 | 001/1 | ⟨101⟩/1 | –/1 | ⟨101⟩/1 |

Figure 9.5.6   Flow table with state assignment specified.

and $e_j = 0$ for $i \neq j$, to state $q_i$ for $1 \leq i \leq p$. For a transition of the machine from state $q_j$ to $q_k$ under an input $i$, if $j = k$, then no state variable changes are necessary; if $j \neq k$, the state variable $y_k$ is changed first to 1, giving a $p$-tuple $E_{jk}$ with $e_j = e_k = 1$ and other values 0. Then $y_j$ is changed from 1 to 0. With this operation no race conditions occur in the state variable changes. Furthermore, since $q_k$ must be stable for input $i$, when we reach the combination of state variable values in which $e_j = e_k = 1$, it is clear that the next part of the operation is to change $y_j$ to 0. Note that this operation corresponds to splitting state $q_j$ into two states $q_j'$ and $q_j$, where $q_j'$ is assigned $E_{jk}$, $q_j$ is assigned $E_j$, $q_k$ is assigned $E_k$, and $q_j'$ serves as a transient state during the transition from $q_j$ to $q_k$. For the machine of Figure 9.5.4 this assignment results in the excitation- and output-matrices shown in Figure 9.5.7. In addition, for any transient state from $q_j$ to $q_k$ we have specified that the output remains constant at the value of $q_j$ until $q_k$ is actually reached. (Alternatively, one might specify that the output change to that of $q_k$ as soon as the transient state is reached.)

Although this type of assignment uses many more variables than needed, it shows that an asynchronous network can be obtained for any asynchronous machine, no more than $p$ internal variables are required, and the rate of changing the inputs need only be sufficient to allow for two successive changes of state, no matter what transition is taking place. Also, the combinational networks to implement this assignment are usually quite simple.

Inputs $x_1 x_2$

| State | $y_1$ | $y_2$ | $y_3$ | $y_4$ | $y_5$ | 0 0 | 0 1 | 1 0 | 1 1 |
|-------|-------|-------|-------|-------|-------|------|------|------|------|
| $q_1$      | 1 | 0 | 0 | 0 | 0 | ⭘10000/0 | 11000/0 | 10010/0 | –/0 |
| $q_1'$     | 1 | 1 | 0 | 0 | 0 | – | 01000/0 | – | – |
| $q_1''$    | 1 | 0 | 0 | 1 | 0 | – | – | 00010/0 | – |
| $q_2$      | 0 | 1 | 0 | 0 | 0 | –/1 | ⭘01000/1 | –/1 | 01100/1 |
| $q_2'$     | 0 | 1 | 1 | 0 | 0 | – | – | – | 00100/1 |
| $q_3$      | 0 | 0 | 1 | 0 | 0 | 10100/0 | –/0 | ⭘00100/0 | ⭘00100/0 |
| $q_3'$     | 1 | 0 | 1 | 0 | 0 | 10000/0 | – | – | – |
| $q_4$      | 0 | 0 | 0 | 1 | 0 | ⭘00010/0 | –/0 | ⭘00010/0 | 00011/0 |
| $q_4'$     | 0 | 0 | 0 | 1 | 1 | – | – | – | 00001/0 |
| $q_5$      | 0 | 0 | 0 | 0 | 1 | 10001/1 | ⭘00001/1 | –/1 | ⭘00001/1 |
| $q_5'$     | 1 | 0 | 0 | 0 | 1 | 10000/1 | – | – | – |

Figure 9.5.7   One variable per state assignment for Figure 9.5.4.

We shall next describe a more complex type of assignment which uses $2k_m - 1$ variables and can be applied to any asynchronous machine. In the previous state assignments exactly one $k$-tuple was associated with each state. The adding of states to the machine to attain a suitable assignment, however, could also be viewed as associating a set of $k$-tuples to each state. For example, in the assignment of Figure 9.5.7 we could view this as an assignment with the following sets of $k$-tuples associated with each state.

$q_1$     $\{(1\ 0\ 0\ 0\ 0), (1\ 1\ 0\ 0\ 0), (1\ 0\ 0\ 1\ 0)\}$,

$q_2$     $\{(0\ 1\ 0\ 0\ 0), (0\ 1\ 1\ 0\ 0)\}$,

$q_3$     $\{(0\ 0\ 1\ 0\ 0), (1\ 0\ 1\ 0\ 0)\}$,

$q_4$     $\{(0\ 0\ 0\ 1\ 0), (0\ 0\ 0\ 1\ 1)\}$,

$q_5$     $\{(0\ 0\ 0\ 0\ 1), (1\ 0\ 0\ 0\ 1)\}$.

The following definitions for a set $S$ of $k$-tuples are useful.

**Definition 9.5.2**   A pair $(s_1, s_2)$ of $k$-tuples $s_1, s_2 \in S$ is called *connected* if there is a sequence of adjacent $k$-tuples of $S$ that starts with $s_1$ and ends with $s_2$.

**Definition 9.5.3** A set $S$ is called a *connected set* if each pair of elements $s_i, s_j \in S$ is connected. Also, if a set contains only one $k$-tuple, we shall call it a *connected set*.

Note that each set associated with a state in the preceding example is a connected set.

**Definition 9.5.4** Two connected sets $S_1$ and $S_2$ are called *adjacent* if there is an $s_1 \in S_1$ and an $s_2 \in S_2$ such that $s_1$ and $s_2$ are adjacent $k$-tuples.

If we let $R_j$ designate a set of $k$-tuples associated with a state $q_j$ of a machine, $R_j$ may be partitioned into one or more connected sets $R_{j1}$, $R_{j2}, \ldots$, in which no $R_{jr}$ is adjacent to any $R_{js}$. For this example each $R_j$ was composed of exactly one connected set; among the many adjacencies we find that $R_1$ is adjacent to $R_2$ and $R_4$.

**Definition 9.5.5** Let $R_j$ and $R_k$ be sets associated with $q_j$ and $q_k$ of a machine $\mathcal{M}$. $R_j$ is said to be *coupled* with $R_k$ if each connected set $R_{jr}$ of $R_j$ is adjacent to at least one connected set $R_{ks}$ of $R_k$.

Thus, if there is a transition from $q_j$ to $q_k$ of $\mathcal{M}$, for any $R_j$ it is possible to generate a sequence of adjacent $k$-tuples such that each $k$-tuple is a member of a single connected set of $R_j$ and the last element of this sequence is adjacent to some element of $R_k$.

If in an assignment of $R_j$ to each $q_j$ of $\mathcal{M}$ we find that $R_j$ is coupled to $R_k$ whenever there is a transition from $q_j$ to $q_k$, the changes in the $y_i$ variables may be restricted to single changes of the type described and no race conditions will arise in changing from one state to the next if sufficient time is allowed between input changes for the sequence of $y_i$ changes to be completed.

For a general assignment technique, we must allow for the possibility of a transition from any state to any other state; that is, we want the $R_j$ assigned to the states to satisfy the following definition.

**Definition 9.5.6** The sets $R_1, R_2, \ldots, R_p$ associated with $q_1, q_2, \ldots, q_p$ of a machine $\mathcal{M}$ are called *intermeshed* if $R_j$ is coupled to $R_k$ for $1 \leq j, k \leq p$.

Two different assignments of 3-tuples to form intermeshed sets for four-state machines are shown in Figure 9.5.8. For 9.5.8a $R_i$ consists of a single connected set of two 3-tuples for each state $q_i$, $1 \leq i \leq 4$; whereas for 9.5.8b each $R_i$ consists of two 3-tuples, where each 3-tuple is a single element connected set. The reader may readily verify that each of these $R_i$ is actually intermeshed. A tabular form for representing intermeshed row sets using five variables, which can be used for machine having up to

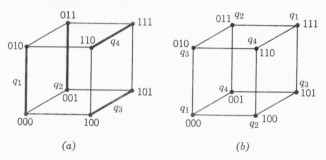

Figure 9.5.8    Intermeshed sets with three variables.

eight states ($k = 2k_m - 1$), is shown in Figure 9.5.9, where numbers in the table indicate the state to which a given 5-tuple is assigned.

If we start with $q_1$ we see that $R_1 = \{(0\,0\,0\,0\,0), (0\,0\,1\,0\,0), (0\,1\,0\,0\,0),$ $(0\,1\,0\,0\,1)\}$ is a single connected set. The reader may check that this is true for each $R_i$. Set $R_1$ is adjacent to each other set, for example, the transition from $R_1$ to $R_6$ is obtained by going from $(0\,0\,1\,0\,0)$ to $(1\,0\,1\,0\,0)$. If, however, we had started the transition with $k$-tuple $(0\,1\,0\,0\,1)$ of $R_1$, the sequence of four changes $(0\,1\,0\,0\,1) \rightarrow (0\,1\,0\,0\,0) \rightarrow (0\,0\,0\,0\,0) \rightarrow$ $(0\,0\,1\,0\,0) \rightarrow (1\,0\,1\,0\,0)$ would be required to complete the desired transition.

The dashed lines in Figure 9.5.9 depict a general configuration from which $2k_m - 1$ intermeshed set assignments can be obtained for larger machines. We show the case for seven variables, which handles machines from nine to sixteen states, in Figure 9.5.10. As in Figure 9.5.9 each $R_i$ contains a single connected set, but now each set contains eight rather

|  |  |  | $y_4$ | 0 | 0 | 1 | 1 |
|  |  |  | $y_5$ | 0 | 1 | 0 | 1 |
| $y_1$ | $y_2$ | $y_3$ |  |  |  |  |  |
| 0 | 0 | 0 |  | 1 | 2 | 3 | 3 |
| 0 | 0 | 1 |  | 1 | 2 | 4 | 4 |
| 0 | 1 | 0 |  | 1 | 1 | 3 | 4 |
| 0 | 1 | 1 |  | 2 | 2 | 3 | 4 |
| 1 | 0 | 0 |  | 5 | 5 | 5 | 6 |
| 1 | 0 | 1 |  | 6 | 6 | 5 | 6 |
| 1 | 1 | 0 |  | 7 | 8 | 7 | 7 |
| 1 | 1 | 1 |  | 7 | 8 | 8 | 8 |

Figure 9.5.9    Intermeshed sets with five variables.

than four elements. The general construction of an intermeshed set table is to have $k_m$ variables to indicate rows and $k_m - 1$ variables to indicate columns, and then to split the table into four blocks of rows where $y_1$ and $y_2$ are constant over each block, and into two blocks of columns where $y_{k_m+1}$ is constant over each block. The states are then filled into the table in

| $y_1$ $y_2$ $y_3$ $y_4$ \ $y_5$ $y_6$ $y_7$ | 0 0 0 | 0 0 1 | 0 1 0 | 0 1 1 | 1 0 0 | 1 0 1 | 1 1 0 | 1 1 1 |
|---|---|---|---|---|---|---|---|---|
| 0 0 0 0 | 1 | 2 | 3 | 4 | 5 | 5 | 5 | 5 |
| 0 0 0 1 | 1 | 2 | 3 | 4 | 6 | 6 | 6 | 6 |
| 0 0 1 0 | 1 | 2 | 3 | 4 | 7 | 7 | 7 | 7 |
| 0 0 1 1 | 1 | 2 | 3 | 4 | 8 | 8 | 8 | 8 |
| 0 1 0 0 | 1 | 1 | 1 | 1 | 5 | 6 | 7 | 8 |
| 0 1 0 1 | 2 | 2 | 2 | 2 | 5 | 6 | 7 | 8 |
| 0 1 1 0 | 3 | 3 | 3 | 3 | 5 | 6 | 7 | 8 |
| 0 1 1 1 | 4 | 4 | 4 | 4 | 5 | 6 | 7 | 8 |
| 1 0 0 0 | 9 | 9 | 9 | 9 | 9 | 10 | 11 | 12 |
| 1 0 0 1 | 10 | 10 | 10 | 10 | 9 | 10 | 11 | 12 |
| 1 0 1 0 | 11 | 11 | 11 | 11 | 9 | 10 | 11 | 12 |
| 1 0 1 1 | 12 | 12 | 12 | 12 | 9 | 10 | 11 | 12 |
| 1 1 0 0 | 13 | 14 | 15 | 16 | 13 | 13 | 13 | 13 |
| 1 1 0 1 | 13 | 14 | 15 | 16 | 14 | 14 | 14 | 14 |
| 1 1 1 0 | 13 | 14 | 15 | 16 | 15 | 15 | 15 | 15 |
| 1 1 1 1 | 13 | 14 | 15 | 16 | 16 | 16 | 16 | 16 |

Figure 9.5.10 Intermeshed sets with seven variables.

rows and columns within these blocks as shown in Figures 9.5.9 and 9.5.10.

Because more than four elements appear in each $R_i$, one may think that a sequence of more than four variable changes would be required in some state transitions. Actually, however, certain race conditions can be allowed so that the time required for a sequence of four variable changes is sufficient for any transition. The races which are allowed (and are noncritical) correspond to the changes along a half of a row (or one-quarter of a column) of the table for which all the $k$-tuples are assigned to the same state. For example, if we started in (0 1 0 0 0 1 1) of $R_1$ and wanted to reach $R_{12}$, we could first change to (0 1 0 0 0 0 0) letting $y_6$ and $y_7$ change simultaneously (that is, race) since (0 1 0 0 0 1 0) and (0 1 0 0 0 0 1) are also elements of $R_1$. After (0 1 0 0 0 0 0) is reached, we would change $y_2$

to 0, giving $(0\,0\,0\,0\,0\,0\,0)$. This could be followed by a race of $y_3$ and $y_4$ changing to 1, giving $(0\,0\,1\,1\,0\,0\,0)$, which is then followed by a final change of $y_1$, giving $(1\,0\,1\,1\,0\,0\,0)$, which is an element of $R_{12}$.

The first general assignment scheme which we discussed requires $p$-state variables for a $p$-state machine and a sequence of two state variable changes to accomplish a change of state as specified by the machine. Although the $2k_m - 1$ variable assignment requires fewer state variables than this first method, it requires sequences of up to four changes in state variables to accomplish a change of state. To increase network speed, or for other reasons, it may be desirable to minimize the length of the sequence of state variable changes necessary to produce a change of state.

We now describe a general assignment scheme that allows any transition from one state to another to be realized by a single state variable change, which of course, is the minimum possible change. For such an assignment we require that if $R_i$ is assigned to $q_i$ and a $k$-tuple $s \in R_i$, then for each $q_j$, $j \neq i$, there is a $k$-tuple assigned to $q_j$ which is adjacent to $s$. Thus, from the properties of a $k$-cube if the machine has $p$-states $k \geq p - 1$, and if $k = p - 1$ then each connected set consists of a single vertex. Figure 9.5.8b is an example of such an assignment, where $p = 4$ and $k = 3$. This assignment could also be used for a three state machine by leaving unassigned those vertices assigned to $q_4$. The scheme we describe gives an assignment for power of 2 values of $p$ and uses $k = p - 1$ variables. If $p$ is not a power of 2 and $2^{r-1} < p < 2^r$, the $2^r$ assignment can be used for the $p$-state machine, assigning only those vertices which would be assigned to the first $p$-states of a $2^r$-state machine.

Assume $p = 2^t$ and let the states be numbered $q_0, q_1, \ldots, q_{p-1}$. To determine how the $(p - 1)$-tuples of values for the $y_1, y_2, \ldots, y_{p-1}$ variables are to be assigned to the states, consider the $t$-tuples $(r_1, r_2, \ldots, r_t)$ defined as follows. Each $r_j$ is the modulo two sum of certain $y_i$ variables, where $y_i$ enters into the $r_t$ sum if and only if the binary representation of $i$ has a 1 in the least significant place; $y_i$ enters into the $r_{t-1}$ sum if and only if the binary representation of $i$ has a 1 in the second place from the right, etc. The form of the $r_j$ is

$$r_t = y_1 \oplus y_3 \oplus y_5 \oplus y_7 \oplus \cdots$$

$$r_{t-1} = y_2 \oplus y_3 \oplus y_6 \oplus y_7 \oplus \cdots$$

$$r_{t-2} = y_4 \oplus y_5 \oplus y_6 \oplus y_7 \oplus \cdots$$

(9.5.1)

$$\cdot$$
$$\cdot$$
$$\cdot$$

$$r_1 = y_{p/2} \oplus \cdots \oplus y_{p-2} \oplus y_{p-1}.$$

| | | | $y_1$ | 0 | 0 | 0 | 0 | 1 | 1 | 1 | 1 |
|---|---|---|---|---|---|---|---|---|---|---|---|
| | | | $y_2$ | 0 | 0 | 1 | 1 | 0 | 0 | 1 | 1 |
| | | | $y_3$ | 0 | 1 | 0 | 1 | 0 | 1 | 0 | 1 |
| $y_4$ | $y_5$ | $y_6$ | $y_7$ | | | | | | | | |
| 0 | 0 | 0 | 0 | 0 | 3 | 2 | 1 | 1 | 2 | 3 | 0 |
| 0 | 0 | 0 | 1 | 7 | 4 | 5 | 6 | 6 | 5 | 4 | 7 |
| 0 | 0 | 1 | 0 | 6 | 5 | 4 | 7 | 7 | 4 | 5 | 6 |
| 0 | 0 | 1 | 1 | 1 | 2 | 3 | 0 | 0 | 3 | 2 | 1 |
| 0 | 1 | 0 | 0 | 5 | 6 | 7 | 4 | 4 | 7 | 6 | 5 |
| 0 | 1 | 0 | 1 | 2 | 1 | 0 | 3 | 3 | 0 | 1 | 2 |
| 0 | 1 | 1 | 0 | 3 | 0 | 1 | 2 | 2 | 1 | 0 | 3 |
| 0 | 1 | 1 | 1 | 4 | 7 | 6 | 5 | 5 | 6 | 7 | 4 |
| 1 | 0 | 0 | 0 | 4 | 7 | 6 | 5 | 5 | 6 | 7 | 4 |
| 1 | 0 | 0 | 1 | 3 | 0 | 1 | 2 | 2 | 1 | 0 | 3 |
| 1 | 0 | 1 | 0 | 2 | 1 | 0 | 3 | 3 | 0 | 1 | 2 |
| 1 | 0 | 1 | 1 | 5 | 6 | 7 | 4 | 4 | 7 | 6 | 5 |
| 1 | 1 | 0 | 0 | 1 | 2 | 3 | 0 | 0 | 3 | 2 | 1 |
| 1 | 1 | 0 | 1 | 6 | 5 | 4 | 7 | 7 | 4 | 5 | 6 |
| 1 | 1 | 1 | 0 | 7 | 4 | 5 | 6 | 6 | 5 | 4 | 7 |
| 1 | 1 | 1 | 1 | 0 | 3 | 2 | 1 | 1 | 2 | 3 | 0 |

Figure 9.5.11 Assignment for an eight-state machine using $2^{k_m} - 1$ variables.

Now if we consider the $t$-tuples $(r_1, r_2, \ldots, r_t)$ as binary numbers, these numbers can range over the value 0 through $p - 1$. We form the set $R_i$ by assigning to $R_i$ all the $(p - 1)$-tuples which give a binary value of $i$ to the $t$-tuple $(r_1, r_2, \ldots, r_t)$. The set $R_i$ is then assigned to state $q_i$.

With this assignment we see that $(0, 0, \ldots, 0)$ is assigned to $q_0$; similarly, the unit $(p - 1)$-tuple having the $j$th coordinate equal to 1 and all other coordinates equal to 0 is assigned to $q_j$. Each set of vertices $R_j$ assigned to $q_j$ contains $2^{p-1-t}$ vertices. It can be shown that $R_0$ is a subgroup of the group of $(p-1)$-tuples, where the group operation is the coordinate by coordinate modulo two sum. For, if $s$ and $s'$ belong to $R_0$, from the equations for $(r_1, r_2, \ldots, r_t)$ we readily see that $s \oplus s'$ is a $(p-1)$-tuple that also belongs to $R_0$. In addition, it follows that $R_j$, $j \neq 0$, is a coset of $R_0$*. The $R_j$ can be seen to be intermeshed as follows. Vertex $s_0 = (0, 0, \ldots, 0)$ is adjacent to the unit vertices, one of which belongs to each $R_j$, $j \neq 0$. From the properties of the subgroup $R_0$ and cosets $R_1, R_2, \ldots, R_{p-1}$, if $s \in R_i$ is some $(p-1)$-tuple, $s$ can be transformed into $s_0$ by the operation $s \oplus s$. If $s$ is added to all other elements of each $R_j$, a unit $(p-1)$-tuple appears in each set $\{R_j \oplus s\}$, where $j \neq i$. Since the adjacency properties of $(p-1)$-tuples are unchanged by the modulo two-sum operation, this shows that each $s$ is adjacent to a $(p-1)$-tuple assigned to each of the other states, thereby showing that the sets are intermeshed.

As an example of the scheme, Figure 9.5.11 depicts the assignment for an eight-state machine, where states are indicated simply by their subscript number in the table.

This assignment shows that it is possible to attain any transition by changing a single state variable. However, the number of variables required is somewhat excessive, especially when the number of states of the machine is not close to a power of 2, since $2^{k_m} - 1$ variables are required.

In this section we have shown three general approaches to state assignment for asynchronous operation. The first method requires $p$-state variables for a machine with $p$-states, and a sequence of two changes of state variables is sufficient to accomplish any transition. The second method uses $2k_m - 1$ state variables (the minimum known for a general method) but requires up to a sequence of four changes to complete certain transitions. For specific examples, it may be possible to embed the machine in a $k$-cube, possibly by adding states, so that fewer than $2k_m - 1$ state variables are required, but no general methods are known for carrying out such an embedding process. The third scheme requires $2^{k_m} - 1$ state variables. Since it requires only a single state variable change to realize any transition, however, the number of state variables changes is minimized by this technique.

### 9.6 ESSENTIAL HAZARDS OF SEQUENTIAL NETWORKS

One of the basic assumptions about the operation of the sequential network designs discussed in Section 9.5 is that delay elements are placed

---

* The set $R_0$ is identical to the set of code words for a Hamming single-error correcting code.

in each feedback line and that these delays are sufficiently long to allow the combinational network to become stable before the state variables change. To attain fast network response, considerable effort is expended to design fast decision elements; thus it is usually undesirable to slow down the response by inserting unnecessary delay elements into the network. In this section we are concerned with determining when delay elements are necessary for realizing an asynchronous machine. We show under what conditions asynchronous networks can be designed without using delay elements in the feedback lines. When delay elements are necessary, we shall also see that no more than one delay element is required.

**Definition 9.6.1** Let $q$ be a state of an asynchronous machine $\mathcal{M}$, and $i$ be an input such that $\tau(q, i) = q$. If $i'$ is adjacent to $i$ and $\tau(q, i') = q'$, $\tau(q', i) = q''$, and $\tau(q'', i') = q'''$, where $q''' \neq q'$, $\mathcal{M}$ is said to contain an *essential hazard*. We designate this by the triple $(q, i, i')$.

An example is shown in Figure 9.6.1. In this figure $(q_1, 0, 1)$ designates an essential hazard, since

$$\tau(q_1, 0) = q_1, \ \tau(q_1, 1) = q_2, \ \tau(q_2, 0) = q_3, \quad \text{and} \quad \tau(q_3, 1) = q_3 \neq q_2.$$

| | Input $x$ | |
|---|---|---|
| State | 0 | 1 |
| $q_1$ | $\textcircled{q_1}$ | $q_2$ |
| $q_2$ | $q_3$ | $\textcircled{q_2}$ |
| $q_3$ | $\textcircled{q_3}$ | $\textcircled{q_3}$ |

Figure 9.6.1  Flow table with essential hazard.

In general, an essential hazard as illustrated by Figure 9.6.1 would consist of only a small portion of a machine, but we can illustrate how a hazard in the operation can actually arise by considering a network for realizing this flow chart.

If we use two state variables $y_1$ and $y_2$ and make the following state assignment, each transition can be accomplished by changing a single state variable.

| | State Assignment | |
|---|---|---|
| State | $y_1$ | $y_2$ |
| $q_1$ | 0 | 0 |
| $q_2$ | 0 | 1 |
| $q_3$ | 1 | 1 |

The combinational network is then described by the next state equations

$$y_1' = y_2(\bar{x} \vee y_1),$$
$$y_2' = \bar{y}_1 x \vee y_2.$$

Since outputs of the network do not enter into the definition of an essential hazard in any way, we need not be concerned with the output

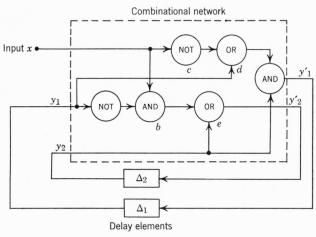

Figure 9.6.2   Network realizing Figure 9.6.1 flow table.

networks in this discussion. A network realizing these next state equations is shown in Figure 9.6.2. If we assume that we start in state $q_1$ represented by $(0, 0)$ and input $x = 0$, the network is stable. On a change to $x = 1$ the value of $y_2'$ will tend to change to a 1 when the AND-element labeled $b$ and the OR-element labeled $e$ react to the input change. With our assumption that the delay time of $\Delta_2$ is sufficiently long, both the NOT-element $c$ and the OR-element $d$ will have turned to 0 before $y_2$ changes from 0 to 1. Thus the network will reach the stable state $q_2$ represented by $(0, 1)$. Now assume, however, that we remove the delay elements $\Delta_1$ and $\Delta_2$ from the feedback lines. If we start in state $(0, 0)$ as before and change $x$ to 1, the $y_2'$ circuit will react to the change of input causing $y_2$ to change to 1. If the stray delays associated with the $y_1'$ circuit are such that the OR-element $d$ has not changed to 0 before $y_2$ has changed to 1, then $y_1'$, and subsequently $y_1$, may change to 1. If this occurs, we reach the erroneous stable state $q_3$ represented by $(1, 1)$. Thus a steady-state hazard arises if the delay elements $\Delta_1$ and $\Delta_2$ are eliminated.

This simple example demonstrates that if no delay elements are used in the network and the machine contains an essential hazard, certain values of the stray delays may create a steady-state hazard. This behavior is generally true as stated in the next theorem.

**Theorem 9.6.1** If an asynchronous sequential machine contains an essential hazard, then any asynchronous network which contains no steady-state hazard and realizes this machine must contain at least one delay element.

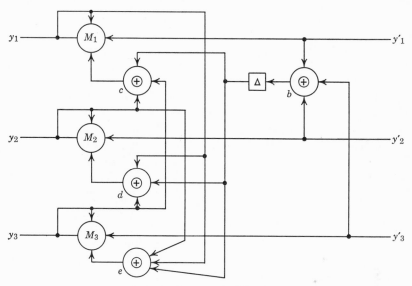

Figure 9.6.3   Unger's delay box.

This theorem may be proved by demonstrating that values of stray delays may always be chosen in a network having no delay elements such that a steady-state hazard occurs. We do not include a detailed proof here.

This theorem raises the natural question of whether more than one delay element is ever required. Figure 9.6.3 shows how the delay elements in the feedback lines of the basic sequential network (Figure 9.5.1) can be replaced by a network containing a single delay element. The figure shows a network to replace the delay elements in a sequential network containing three feedback lines. It illustrates the general structure of the $\oplus$-elements, majority elements, and their interconnection. It should be clear how to extend the network to treat any number of feedback lines.

This delay box will give the same behavior as having a delay element in each feedback line as long as only one state variable changes at a time and there is a sufficient time between changes for the delay box to become stable. The network designs discussed in Section 9.5, of course, provide network operation in which only one state variable changes at a time. Thus these restrictions on the operation of the delay box incur no essential restrictions on the asynchronous machines which can be realized by networks using the delay box.

To see how the delay box network operates, suppose the network is stable and $y_1 = y_1' = y_2 = y_2' = y_3 = y_3' = 0$. If $y_1'$ changes to 1, the only element of the network that will tend to change is the $\oplus$-element $b$. After this element changes to 1, the delay element $\Delta$ is affected and will eventually provide an output of 1. Through some stray delays, element $c$ will provide an output of 1. Note that elements $d$ and $e$ may also change to 1 at this time, but since $y_2 = y_2' = 0$ and $y_3 = y_3' = 0$ the majority elements $M_2$ and $M_3$ will not tend to change. Only after the output of element $c$ changes to 1 can further signal changes occur. The majority element $M_1$ will change to 1 after the 1-signals from the input $y_1'$ and the output element $c$ are sensed. Thus the behavior, which would be obtained by having a delay element between $y_1$ and $y_1'$, is simulated and the network outputs are $y_1 = 1$, $y_2 = 0$, $y_3 = 0$. Before another change on a $y_i'$ occurs, however, we must allow the changed output signal from $M_1$ to be sensed by elements $d$ and $e$ so that the output signals of elements $d$ and $e$ return to 0. Similar behavior of the delay box results for any stable input and output values.

Although the delay box network is somewhat complex and would probably not actually be used as a replacement for the feedback delay elements, it does show that from a theoretical viewpoint one delay element is sufficient for realizing an asynchronous machine that contains essential hazards. Thus with Theorem 9.6.1 we conclude that one delay element is both necessary and sufficient.

In conclusion, we show that when an asynchronous machine contains no essential hazards, it can be realized by an asynchronous network which contains no delay elements.

**Theorem 9.6.2** If an asynchronous machine contains no essential hazards, it can be realized by an asynchronous network containing no delay elements.

PROOF. To prove the theorem we describe a state assignment that results in a network that contains no steady-state hazards and is similar to the basic sequential network model of Figure 9.5.1, except that no delay elements are used in the feedback lines. A variety of the last type of state assignment discussed in Section 9.5 [as illustrated by Equations (9.5.1) and Figure 9.5.11] is used so that only a single state variable change is required for any transition. Since we restrict input changes

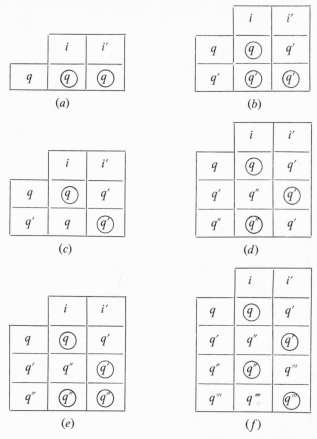

Figure 9.6.4   Transition cases for single input change.

to be between adjacent input combinations, say $i$ and $i'$, we need concern ourselves only with the possible state changes which might arise when changing from $i$ to $i'$. Suppose state $q$ is stable under input $i$ and $\tau(q,i') = q'$. The transition from $q$ to $q'$ is accomplished by a single state variable change, say $y_j$. Because of stray delays the input change from $i$ to $i'$ may not have been sensed by some other $y_s{'}$ networks, $s \neq j$, by the time $y_j$ has changed. In this case, we must insure that $\tau(q',i)$ will not cause a change of some such $y_s{'}$ by which the network could reach a new state and create a steady-state hazard. All the cases which may arise for a machine when starting in a stable state $q$ and changing the input from $i$ to $i'$ are depicted in flow chart form in Figure 9.6.4. Both $(e)$ and $(f)$ correspond to an essential hazard represented by the triple $(q, i, i')$; thus we need consider only $(a)$ through $(d)$ to prove the theorem.

For ($a$) no state variables will change. Thus no steady-state hazard can occur no matter how the state assignment is made.

For ($b$) assume that the single state variable $y_j$ changes to accomplish the transition from $q$ to $q'$. Since $\tau(q', i) = q'$, no other state variables will tend to change even if the input change from $i$ to $i'$ has not yet been sensed. Note that $\tau(q', i)$ could also be undefined in the asynchronous machine; by defining it as $\tau(q', i) = q'$ we obtain ($b$), which causes no difficulty.

For ($c$), when the single state variable senses the change in input to accomplish the transition from $q$ to $q'$, no further state variables will tend to change since $\tau(q', i) = q$. Thus no steady-state hazard can occur for ($b$) or ($c$) as long as a state assignment is used for which any transition between states can be made by changing only a single state variable.

For ($d$) the entry $\tau(q', i) = q''$ can cause added difficulties. Let $y_j$ be the single variable that changes for the $q$ to $q'$ transition. If after $y_j$ changes, because of stray delays, some of the other state variable networks may not yet have sensed the input change $i$ to $i'$. If the state variable that changes for the $q'$ to $q''$ transition (call it $y_f$) is one of these state variables, $y_f$ may also change. The network for some state variable $y_g$, where $j \neq f \neq g$, may now sense the $y_j$, $y_f$, and input changes in any order whatsoever. If the $y_f$ change is sensed before the $y_j$ change, the state of the network may be some state $q_r$, which is not equal to $q$, $q'$, or $q''$. Furthermore, $q_r$ may be stable under input $i'$, which would cause a steady-state hazard. To guard against this hazard we add a state $q'''$ to the machine and make $\tau(q''', i) = q'''$ and $\tau(q''', i') = q'$. This additional $q'''$ is called a *trap state*. If the state variable combination, in which $y_f$ is changed but $y_j$ is unchanged from the combination representing $q$, is assigned to state $q'''$, then if $y_f$ is sensed as changing before $y_j$, no further state variable changes can occur. That is, no variable $y_g$ as discussed previously can exist. Eventually, the $y_j$ and input changes will be sensed by the network and the stable state $q'$ will be obtained so that no steady-state hazard would occur.

We now describe a state assignment requiring only one state variable change to accomplish any transition, enabling us to assign the desired state variable combinations to as many added trap states as could occur. Let the original asynchronous machine $\mathcal{M}$ have $p$ states, $q_0, q_1, \ldots, q_{p-1}$, where $\mathcal{M}$ contains no essential hazards. Let $R_0, R_1, \ldots, R_{2^p-1}$ be those sets of $(2^p - 1)$-tuples which would be assigned to a $2^p$ state machine by the method of Section 9.5 as given in Equations (9.5.1) and Figure 9.5.11. Assign $R_{2i}$ to state $q_i$ of $\mathcal{M}$. If states $q_a$, $q_b$, and $q_c$ are $q$, $q'$, and $q''$, respectively, which have transitions of the form of Figure 9.6.4$d$, then the trap state which is added for these three states is assigned set $R_s$, where $s = 2^a + 2^b + 2^c$. Note that $s \leq 2^p - 1$, so that such an $R_s$ exists; $R_s$ is not assigned to any of the states $q_0$ through $q_{p-1}$ since $s \neq 2^d$ for any integer $d$; and finally if $(q_{a'}, q_{b'}, q_{c'})$ correspond to a triple of states not equal to $(q_a, q_b, q_c)$ which satisfy $d$, $s' = 2^{a'} + 2^{b'} + 2^{c'} \neq s$, and thus the same set $R_s$ is not assigned to two different trap states.

Finally, we want to show that $R_s$ contains the state variable combination that is adjacent to the combination for $q_a$ where the value differs in variable $y_f$. Denoting the combination for $q_a$ as $(y_1, \ldots, y_j, \ldots, y_f, \ldots, y_{2^p-1})$, we have an adjacent combination for $q_b$ which differs only in $y_j$, giving $(y_1, \ldots, \bar{y}_j, \ldots, y_f, \ldots, y_{2^p-1})$, and a combination for $q_c$

Inputs $x_1 x_2$

| States | 0 0 | 0 1 | 1 1 | 1 0 |
|--------|-----|-----|-----|-----|
| $q_0$ | $q_1 \xleftarrow{a}$ | $(q_0) \xrightarrow{c}$ | $q_3$ | $q_1$ |
| $q_1$ | $(q_1)$ | $q_2 \xleftarrow{d}$ | $(q_1)$ | $(q_1)$ |
| $q_2$ | $q_1$ | $(q_2)$ | $q_3$ | $q_1$ |
| $q_3$ | $(q_3) \xrightarrow{\;\;b\;\;}$ | $q_2$ | $(q_3)$ | $q_1$ |

Figure 9.6.5   A machine with no essential hazards.

which differs from the $q_b$ assignment only in $y_f$, giving $(y_1, \ldots, \bar{y}_j, \ldots, \bar{y}_f, \ldots, y_{2^p-1})$. Taking the modulo two sum of these three combinations gives $(y_1, \ldots, y_j, \ldots, \bar{y}_f, \ldots, y_{2^p-1})$, which is to be assigned to the trap state. But since in Equations (9.5.1) a single and different $r_k = 1$ for each state $q_a$, $q_b$ and $q_c$, the modulo two sum of these three vectors on the $r$'s is $2^a + 2^b + 2^c$ which equals $s$. The desired assignment is thus shown to hold and the theorem is proved.

An example of a machine having no essential hazards is shown in Figure 9.6.5. This machine has four transitions of the type in Figure 9.6.4d, which are indicated by the arrows labeled $a$, $b$, $c$, and $d$ on the flow table. The states $(q_0, q_1, q_2)$ are involved for the change labeled $a$, $(q_1, q_2, q_3)$ for $b$, $(q_0, q_2, q_3)$ labeled $c$, and $(q_1, q_2, q_3)$ for $d$. Since $b$ and $d$ involve the same triple of states $(q_1, q_2, q_3)$, a single trap state is used for both these changes. Thus three trap states are added. They are $q_4$ for $a$, $q_5$ for $b$ and $d$, and $q_6$ for $c$. The resulting machine, with the state assignment derived from the proof of Theorem 9.6.2, is shown in Figure 9.6.6.

To illustrate that the assignment to trap states actually gives the property required in the proof of Theorem 9.6.2, suppose we start in $q_0$ with assignment $y_1 = 1$, $y_2$ through $y_{15} = 0$, and change the input from 0 1 to 0 0. The desired transition is to state $q_1$; the reader may check that the assignment $y_1 = y_3 = 1$ and all other state variables equal to 0 is assigned to $q_1$ and requires only a change of a single state variable. If the network

| State Assignment | States | Inputs $x_1x_2$ | | | |
|---|---|---|---|---|---|
| | | 0 0 | 0 1 | 1 1 | 1 0 |
| $R_1$ | $q_0$ | $q_1$ | $(q_0)$ | $q_3$ | $q_1$ |
| $R_2$ | $q_1$ | $(q_1)$ | $q_2$ | $(q_1)$ | $(q_1)$ |
| $R_4$ | $q_2$ | $q_1$ | $(q_2)$ | $q_3$ | $q_1$ |
| $R_8$ | $q_3$ | $(q_3)$ | $q_2$ | $(q_3)$ | $q_1$ |
| $R_7$ | $q_4$ | $q_1$ | $(q_4)$ | – | – |
| $R_{14}$ | $q_5$ | $(q_5)$ | $q_2$ | $(q_5)$ | – |
| $R_{13}$ | $q_6$ | – | $(q_6)$ | $q_3$ | – |

Figure 9.6.6  Trap states and assignment for Figure 9.6.5.

for the $y_6$ state variable senses the $y_3$ change before the input change, the $y_6$ variable may change since the assignment $y_1 = y_3 = y_6 = 1$ with other state variables 0 is assigned to $q_2$. The assignment $y_1 = y_6 = 1$ with other state variables 0 is a member of $R_7$, however, and since $R_7$ is assigned to the trap state $q_4$, no other state variables can change so that no steady-state hazard will occur. The equations which the reader may use to check this illustration are

$$r_4 = y_1 \oplus y_3 \oplus y_5 \oplus y_7 \oplus y_9 \oplus y_{11} \oplus y_{13} \oplus y_{15},$$

$$r_3 = y_2 \oplus y_3 \oplus y_6 \oplus y_7 \oplus y_{10} \oplus y_{11} \oplus y_{14} \oplus y_{15},$$

$$r_2 = y_4 \oplus y_5 \oplus y_6 \oplus y_7 \oplus y_{12} \oplus y_{13} \oplus y_{14} \oplus y_{15},$$

$$r_1 = y_8 \oplus y_9 \oplus y_{10} \oplus y_{11} \oplus y_{12} \oplus y_{13} \oplus y_{14} \oplus y_{15}.$$

Note that fifteen state variables are required for this assignment even though the original machine has only four states. In special instances it may be possible to form assignments which do not require such an excessive number of variables but which still result in a network having no delay elements and no steady-state hazards. Unfortunately, however, no general assignment technique is known which requires fewer than $2^p - 1$ state variables.

Finally, we should mention that a network, as described in the proof of Theorem 9.6.2, may contain transient hazards in the output networks. For example, for Figure 9.6.4$d$, if the output associated with $(q'', i)$ is different from that of $(q, i)$ or $(q', i')$, transient hazards may occur on the output lines since the state variables may actually change to indicate temporarily $q''$. Similarly, a transient hazard could exist for Figure 9.6.4$b$ if the output under $(q', i)$ differed from that of $(q, i)$ and $(q', i')$.

## 9.7 COMPLIANT ASYNCHRONOUS NETWORKS

In the design of asynchronous networks for which the stray delays are bounded, we restricted the operation of the external environment only in (1) the rate of changing inputs to the network and (2) requiring only one input variable to change at a time. No extra signals between the external environment and the network were required to assure proper operation. For unbounded stray delays, however, an example in Section 9.3 was given for which an a priori rate for changing inputs could not be predetermined.

In this section we shall assume that the stray delays are unbounded, each decision element in the network has an associated element delay, and no line delays occur in the network. The assumption of no line delays should be appropriate in practical cases for which the reaction time of the decision elements overbalances significantly the time required for transmission of signals along a line. We also require the assumption of no line delays since if unbounded line delays occur, there are no known techniques for network design. Under the assumptions, if the output of a decision element is connected to inputs of several decision elements, any signal change on the output will simultaneously appear on the inputs to these elements as soon as the element delay has reacted to the change.

Suppose that we specify the behavior of the desired network by a sequential machine, where the external environment supplies inputs to and receives outputs from the network which realizes the machine. Since the delays within the network cannot be predetermined, after an input has been supplied to the network the external environment will not, in general, be able to determine when the network has responded to this input; for example, the output may not be required to change, and if the network supplies no extra signals to the external environment there is no indication that the network has responded to the input. Suppose an extra input signal $G$ is supplied to the network from the external environment designating when the signals on inputs to the network may be read, and an extra signal $R$ is supplied to the external environment from the network designating when the network has responded to an input and the outputs of the network are stable. A block diagram of this system is shown in Figure 9.7.1. The signal $G$ can be viewed as a "go" signal for the network and signal $R$ as a "reply" signal.

Assume that the sequence of steps in the communication between the network and external environment can proceed as follows. Let us start with network $N$ being stable, signal $G = 0$, and signal $R = 1$, indicating that the outputs may be read. The external environment may then read the outputs and change the input signal values to the next desired input. When the inputs have attained the desired values and the outputs have been read, the signal $G$ is changed to a 1. The network will then accept the input signals and on recognizing the inputs will change signal $R$ to 0. The changing of $R$ to 0 indicates to the external environment that the inputs have been accepted by the network, so signal $G$ will be set back to

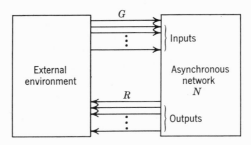

Figure 9.7.1    Extra signals between external environment and asynchronous network.

0. When $G = 0$, network $N$ can proceed to complete its reaction to the input and generate the desired outputs. When these outputs have been generated, then signal $R$ is changed to 1.

This completes the acceptance of an input to the network and the generation of outputs and a reply signal. The signals $G = 0$ and $R = 1$ indicate that another input may be supplied. Later we describe a general network structure for realizing such behavior.

First, however, we note that nowhere in the described sequence of steps did we require that two successive inputs to the network be different. Rather, the sequencing of the $G$ signal specifies when an input is being supplied to $N$. Thus the sequential machine specifying the behavior of $N$ need not be asynchronous; therefore we shall not restrict our attention to asynchronous machines in this section. Second, while $R = 1$ and $G = 0$ the inputs to $N$ are not being read; thus they may change in any desired way. This allows us to have any input combination succeed a given input. No restriction to adjacent input combinations is required.

Requiring the two extra binary signals $G$ and $R$ is actually the minimum possible number of signals necessary for realizing general sequential machines by asynchronous networks with unbounded element delays.

This can be seen as follows. For each input $i$ of a machine $\mathcal{M}$ there may be a state $q$ such that $\tau(q, i) = q'$ and $\tau(q', i) = q''$, where states $q'$ and $q''$ are not compatible states. Thus, if we start in state $q$ and apply a single input of $i$, we wish to end in state $q'$ rather than $q''$. To indicate a second input of $i$, another representation of input $i$ is required. Since $i$ was chosen arbitrarily, this means that we need two times the number of inputs of the original machine. If the inputs are encoded by the minimum number of binary signals, then one extra binary signal is required to represent the doubled number of inputs. A similar argument can be applied to the outputs to show that at least one extra signal is needed to represent the outputs, and the minimality of the go and reply signals is verified.

We now describe a gate element realization which gives the desired performance. An outline of the network for changing states is shown in Figure 9.7.2 and that for generating outputs in Figure 9.7.3. We have shown the elements which pertain to a change of state from a state $q_m$ to a state $q_n$ under an input $i$, and also those elements for making no state change when in state $q_m$ given input $j$. If machine $\mathcal{M}$ has $p$ states, the network includes two sets of $p + 1$ flip-flops $F^1 = \{f_1^1, f_2^1, \ldots, f_p^1, h^1\}$ and $F^2 = \{f_1^2, f_2^2, \ldots, f_p^2, h^2\}$, as well as other flip-flops labeled $S_1$, $S_2$, $R$, $N$, $Z$, and $A$. The flip-flops are logically equivalent to the network

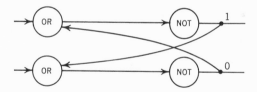

This is depicted by the symbol

$$\rightarrow \boxed{\begin{array}{c} 1 \\ \hline 0 \end{array}} \!\!-$$

where the output labeled 1 is set to a 1 by the signal entering the 1-side of the box, and similarly for the 0-output. With this flip-flop the outputs are never both equal to 1, and thus if one output equals 1 it is assured that the other output equals 0.

This network provides a general structure for realizing any sequential machine $\mathcal{M}$ of the Moore type. Although we have assumed that $\mathcal{M}$ has only a single output $Z$ for the network shown in Figure 9.7.3, this structure

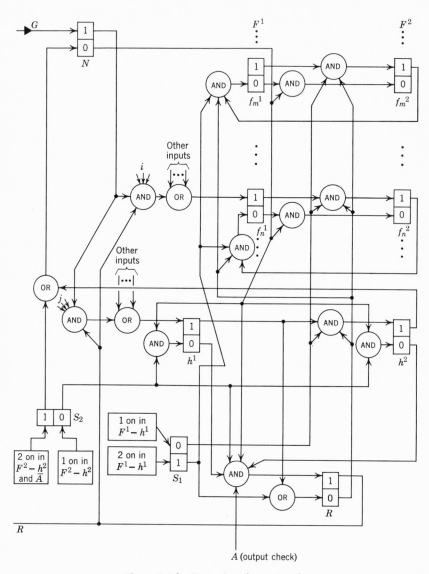

Figure 9.7.2  State changing network.

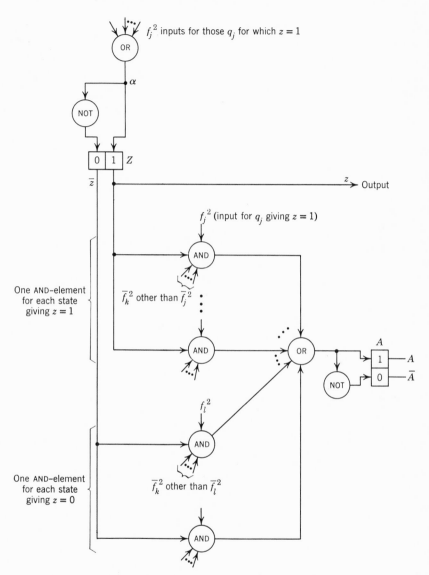

Figure 9.7.3   Output and output check network.

is readily extended to more outputs. For the operation of the network of Figure 9.7.2 we assume that $f_m^1 = f_m^2 = 1$ and all other flip-flops in $F^1$ and $F^2$ equal 0 for representing a state $q_m$. When changing from $q_m$ to $q_n$, the flip-flop $f_n^1$ is turned on first and later in the operation $f_m^1$ is turned off. Thus the operation is similar to the $p$-variable assignment discussed in Section 9.5.

To describe the sequence of operation in more detail, assume that $f_m^1 = f_m^2 = 1$ and all other flip-flops in $F^1$ and $F^2$ are 0. Assume also that $S_1 = 0$, $S_2 = 0$, $R = 1$, $N = 0$, and $A = 1$. When the input is ready (assume either input $i$ or $j$ is given), $G$ changes to 1. We proceed as follows:

1. When $G = 1$, turn $N$ to 1.
2. (a) When $N = 1$, input equals $i$, and $R = 1$, set $f_n^1$ to 1.
   (b) When $N = 1$, input equals $j$, and $R = 1$, set $h^1$ to 1.
3. When $S_1 = 1$ or $h^1 = 1$, set $R$ to 0.
4. If $R = 0$, $S_1 = 1$, and $f_m^2 = 1$, set $f_m^1$ to 0.
5. (a) If $S_1 = 0$, $R = 0$, and $f_n^1 = 1$, set $f_n^2$ to 1.
   (b) If $S_1 = 0$, $R = 0$, and $h^1 = 1$, set $h^2$ to 1.
6. When $S_2 = 1$ or $h^2 = 1$, set $N$ to 0.
7. When $N = 0$ and $f_m^1 = 0$, set $f_m^2$ to 0.
8. When $S_2 = 0$ and $N = 0$, set $h^1$ to 0 and $h^2$ to 0.
9. When $h^1 = h^2 = S_2 = N = 0$ and $A = 1$, set $R$ to 1.

In Figure 9.7.2 the boxes labeled "1 on in $F^1 - h^1$," "2 on in $F^1 - h^1$," "1 on in $F^2 - h^2$," and "2 on in $F^2 - h^2$ and $\bar{A}$" represent hazard-free networks. The input signals for $i$ and $j$ are represented symbolically rather than in the required encoded form. Each of the binary input signals is assumed to be supplied on a pair of lines from the external environment.

In the network of Figure 9.7.3 the outputs of flip-flop $Z$ are used to produce the network output $z$. Two sets of AND-elements, one set for states which produce an output of $z = 1$ and the other for $z = 0$, feed an OR-element to set flip-flop $A$ for signaling that the output value is correct. Note that when two flip-flops equal 1 in $F^2$ as produced by Step 5($a$) of the operation sequence, before $S_2$ is set to 1 flip-flop $A$ must be set to 0. This insures that in a change of state all the AND-elements of the network must be 0 before the operation is allowed to continue and the output produced by the next state is checked as correct.

In the design of the network of Figures 9.7.2 and 9.7.3 no attempt has been made to minimize the number of elements, particularly flip-flops, which are required. It is quite likely that a simpler circuit could be designed using the same basic sequencing of the $G$ and $R$ signals with the external environment. Other type decision elements might be used also. These networks simply illustrate that it is possible to realize the desired properties. If the network to be designed is simply a combinational network, a different type of network with or without $G$ and $R$ signals may be possible. Of course, the network just described can be used in this case by representing the combinational network as a simple sequential machine, which for a single output circuit would have two states.

Suppose that in addition to interconnecting an asynchronous network to an external environment as shown in Figure 9.7.1, we are interested in interconnecting two or more asynchronous networks, where the outputs

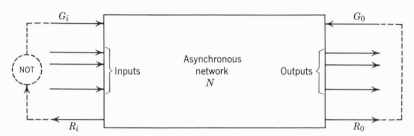

Figure. 9.7.4   Extra signals for interconnecting asynchronous networks.

of some of these networks serve as inputs to other networks. The sequence of $G$ and $R$ signals described for the operation of the network of Figures 9.7.2 and 9.7.3 does not suffice if the external environment is itself another asynchronous network. This can be readily verified by the reader by assuming that the external environment is an asynchronous network $N'$ with signal $G'$ entering the network and $R'$ leaving the network such that $G'$ and $R$ are one line, and $R'$ and $G$ are one line. For example, in our original operation the external environment changes inputs to $N$ when $G = 0$ and $R = 1$, whereas the asynchronous network starts to accept new inputs and generate new outputs when $G = R = 1$.

Consider the modified network of Figure 9.7.4, however, where $G_i$ indicates that the inputs to $N$ are ready, $R_i$ indicates acceptance of inputs, $R_0$ indicates that the outputs of $N$ are ready, and $G_0$ indicates that the outputs are accepted.

An approach similar to that described in this section can be applied to the configuration shown in Figure 9.7.4 such that signal $R_0$ acts as a $G_i'$ signal and $G_0$ as an $R_i'$ for a network $N'$ whenever the outputs of $N$ are connected as inputs to $N'$. The dotted connections indicate the sequencing of $G_i$, $R_i$, $G_0$, and $R_0$ signals and also indicate a strong similarity of this approach with the interconnection results described in Section 10.5.

**Exercises**

**1.** Find all static and dynamic hazards for the following networks.

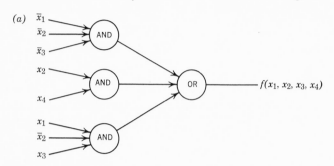

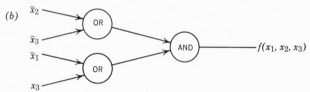

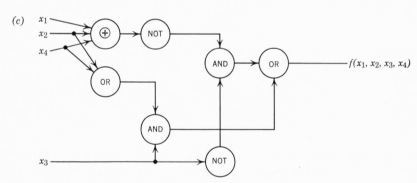

**2.** Design hazard-free networks for the Boolean functions represented by the networks of Exercise 1.

**3.** Design hazard-free networks for the following switching functions.

(a)

|  | $x_3$ | | |
|---|---|---|---|
| 1 | 1 | 0 | $d$ |
| 0 | 1 | 0 | 0 |
| 0 | 0 | $d$ | $d$ |
| 1 | 0 | 0 | $d$ |

(b)

|  | $x_3$ | | |
|---|---|---|---|
| $d$ |  |  |  |
| 1 | $d$ | 1 | $d$ |
| 1 | $d$ |  | 1 |
| $d$ |  | $d$ | 1 |

(c) $f = x_1x_2 \lor x_1x_3 \lor x_2x_3$.

(d) $f = \bar{x}_1(x_2x_3 \lor x_4)$.

(e) $f = x_1 \oplus x_2 \oplus x_3 \oplus x_4$.

(f) $f = x_1 \oplus [x_1x_2 \lor (x_3 \oplus x_4)]$.

**4.** Find the race conditions and steady-state hazards which can arise from adjacent input combination changes in the following sequential networks.

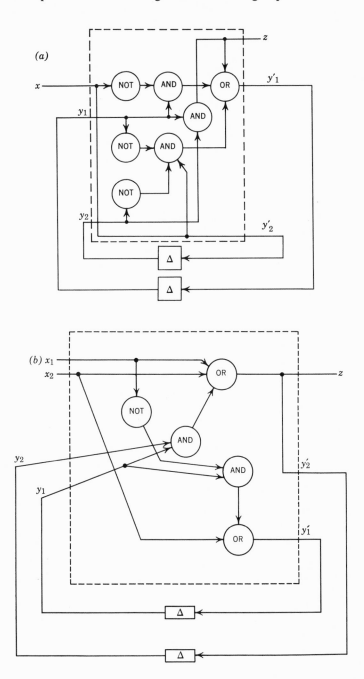

5. Design asynchronous networks having no steady-state hazards to replace the two networks of Exercise 4. Assume bounded stray delays.
6. Develop necessary and sufficient conditions for a two-level OR-AND network to be hazard-free.
7. Let $N$ be a two-level AND-OR network so that at most one input to any AND-element is associated with a single variable. Prove that $N$ contains no dynamic hazards.
8. Prove either that a gate-type network which contains no static hazards also contains no dynamic hazards or give a counterexample.
9. Find state assignments of each of the three types described in Section 9.5 for the following sequential machines.

($a$)

|  | Inputs | |
| --- | --- | --- |
|  | $\bar{x}$ | $x$ |
| States | 0 | 1 |
| $q_1$ | $\textcircled{$q_1$}$ | $q_3$ |
| $q_2$ | $q_1$ | $\textcircled{$q_2$}$ |
| $q_3$ | $q_4$ | $\textcircled{$q_3$}$ |
| $q_4$ | $\textcircled{$q_4$}$ | $q_2$ |

($b$)

|  | Inputs $x_1x_2$ | | | |
| --- | --- | --- | --- | --- |
| States | 0 0 | 0 1 | 1 0 | 1 1 |
| $q_1$ | $\textcircled{$q_1$}$ | $q_3$ | $\textcircled{$q_1$}$ | $q_4$ |
| $q_2$ | $q_1$ | $\textcircled{$q_2$}$ | – | $\textcircled{$q_2$}$ |
| $q_3$ | $\textcircled{$q_3$}$ | $\textcircled{$q_3$}$ | $q_1$ | $q_2$ |
| $q_4$ | $q_3$ | $q_2$ | – | $\textcircled{$q_4$}$ |

($c$)

|  | Inputs $x_1x_2$ | | | |
| --- | --- | --- | --- | --- |
| States | 0 0 | 0 1 | 1 0 | 1 1 |
| $q_1$ | $q_5/0$ | $\textcircled{$q_1$}/0$ | $\textcircled{$q_1$}/1$ | – |
| $q_2$ | $q_3/0$ | $\textcircled{$q_2$}/1$ | $q_1/1$ | $q_4/0$ |
| $q_3$ | $\textcircled{$q_3$}/0$ | $q_1/0$ | $\textcircled{$q_3$}/1$ | – |
| $q_4$ | – | $q_1/0$ | $q_3/1$ | $\textcircled{$q_4$}/0$ |
| $q_5$ | $q_5/0$ | $q_2/1$ | – | – |

10. For the machine of Exercise 9$a$ find a state assignment by embedding the machine in a $k$-cube, where $k$ is minimized.
11. Determine the essential hazards, if any, in each of the machines of Exercises 4 and 9.

**12.** Determine the trap states and a state assignment, for a network requiring no delay elements, for each of the following machines.

(*a*)

|        | Inputs $x_1 x_2$ | | | |
|--------|-----|-----|-----|-----|
| States | 0 0 | 0 1 | 1 1 | 1 0 |
| $q_0$ | $\textcircled{$q_0$}$ | $q_1$ | $q_2$ | $\textcircled{$q_0$}$ |
| $q_1$ | $\textcircled{$q_1$}$ | $\textcircled{$q_1$}$ | $q_2$ | $q_0$ |
| $q_2$ | $q_3$ | $q_1$ | $\textcircled{$q_2$}$ | $\textcircled{$q_2$}$ |
| $q_3$ | $\textcircled{$q_3$}$ | $\textcircled{$q_3$}$ | $q_2$ | $q_2$ |

(*b*)

|        | Inputs $x_1 x_2$ | | | |
|--------|-----|-----|-----|-----|
| States | 0 0 | 1 0 | 0 1 | 1 1 |
| $q_0$ | $q_3$ | $\textcircled{$q_0$}$ | $q_4$ | $\textcircled{$q_0$}$ |
| $q_1$ | $\textcircled{$q_1$}$ | $q_2$ | $q_3$ | – |
| $q_2$ | $q_1$ | $\textcircled{$q_2$}$ | – | $\textcircled{$q_2$}$ |
| $q_3$ | $\textcircled{$q_3$}$ | $q_5$ | $\textcircled{$q_3$}$ | – |
| $q_4$ | $\textcircled{$q_4$}$ | $q_2$ | $\textcircled{$q_4$}$ | $q_0$ |
| $q_5$ | $q_3$ | $\textcircled{$q_5$}$ | – | $q_2$ |

REFERENCE NOTATIONS

The design of hazard-free combinational networks as discussed in Section 9.4 was first treated by Huffman [9]. A detailed study of necessary and sufficient conditions and a technique for testing for transient hazards have been developed by McCluskey [13]. Various algebraic techniques for treating transient conditions have been devised; for example, see [17, 19, 22]. The different types of assumptions which are made for delays and the operation of asynchronous networks have been previously discussed by McCluskey [14] and Miller [18]. Much of Section 9.5 was derived from the pioneering work of Huffman [7, 8] on sequential network design. Some other types of state assignments are discussed by Liu [10], Eichelberger [3], and Hazeltine [6]. Section 9.6 is based on the work of Unger [21], in which proofs and further techniques for designing networks having no delay elements can be found. Interconnection of asynchronous networks and their communication with an external environment has been considered by several authors [1, 4, 5, 15, 16, 20]. Arden [1] and McNaughton [15, 16] consider networks having perfect delays. The discussion in Section 9.7 is based on some current work of Miller and Winograd.

**REFERENCES**

**1.** Arden, D. N., "Delayed Logic and Finite State Machines," *Proceedings of the AIEE Second Annual Symposium on Switching Circuit Theory and Logical Design,* Vol. S-134, pp. 133–151, September 1961.

**2.** Caldwell, S. H., *Switching Circuits and Logical Design,* John Wiley and Sons, New York, 1958.

3. Eichelberger, E. B., "Sequential Circuit Synthesis Using Input Delays," *Proceedings of the IEEE Fourth Annual Symposium on Switching Circuit Theory and Logical Design*, Vol. S-156, pp. 105–116, September 1963.

4. Goldberg, J. and R. A. Short, "Antiparallel Control Logic." *Proceedings of the IEEE Fifth Annual Symposium on Switching Circuit Theory and Logical Design*, pp. 30–43, November, 1964.

5. Hammel, D., "Ideas on Asynchronous Feedback Networks." *Proceedings of the IEEE Fifth Annual Symposium on Switching Circuit Theory and Logical Design*, pp. 4–11, November 1964.

6. Hazeltine, B., "A Procedure for Obtaining an Economical Asynchronous Sequential Circuit Directly from a Set of Regular Expressions," *Proceedings of the AIEE Third Annual Symposium on Switching Circuit Theory and Logical Design*, Vol. S-141, pp. 72–79, September 1962.

7. Huffman, D. A., "The Synthesis of Sequential Switching Circuits," *Journal of the Franklin Institute*, Vol. 257, No. 3, pp. 161–190, March 1954, and No. 4, pp. 275–303, April 1954.

8. Huffman, D. A., "A Study of the Memory Requirements of Sequential Switching Circuits," Massachusetts Institute of Technology, Research Laboratory of Electronics, Technical Report No. 293, March 1955.

9. Huffman, D. A., "The Design and Use of Hazard-Free Switching Networks," *Journal of the ACM*, Vol. 4, No. 1, pp. 47–62, January 1957.

10. Liu, C. N., "A State Variable Assignment Method for Asynchronous Sequential Switching Circuits," *ACM Journal*, Vol. 10, No. 2, pp. 209–216, April 1963.

11. Maley, G. A. and J. Earle, *The Logic Design of Transistor Digital Computers*, Prentice-Hall, Englewood Cliffs, New Jersey, 1963, Chapters 8-11.

12. Marcus, M. P., *Switching Circuits for Engineers*, Prentice-Hall, Englewood Cliffs, New Jersey, 1962, Chapter 13-18.

13. McCluskey, E. J., Jr., "Transient Behavior of Combinational Logic Networks," Princeton University, Dept. of Electrical Engineering, Digital Systems Laboratory, Technical Report No. 13, January 1962; also *Redundancy Techniques for Computing Systems*, Spartan Books, 1962, pp. 9–46.

14. McCluskey, E. J., Jr., "Fundamental Mode and Pulse Mode Sequential Circuits," *Proceedings of the IFIP Congress*, 1962, Information Processing, Munich, Germany, North-Holland Publishing Co., Amsterdam, pp. 725–730.

15. McNaughton, R. F., "Finite Automata and Badly Timed Elements," *Proceedings of the IEEE Fourth Annual Symposium on Switching Circuit Theory and Logical Design*, Vol. S-156, pp. 117–130, September 1963.

16. McNaughton, R. F., "Badly Timed Elements and Well Timed Nets," Technical Report No. 65-02, University of Pennsylvania, The Moore School of Electrical Engineering, Philadelphia, Pennsylvania, June 10, 1964.

17. Metze, G. A., "Many-Valued Logic and the Design of Switching Circuits," Master's thesis, University of Illinois, Urbana, Illinois, 1955.

18. Miller, R. E., "A Survey of Asynchronous Logic Comparing Various Definitions and Models for Asynchronous Switching Networks," *Presented at the Fourth Annual IEEE Symposium for Switching Circuit Theory and Logical Design*, Vol. S-156, Chicago, Illinois, October 28-30, 1963.

19. Muller, D. E., "Treatment of Transition Signals in Electronic Switching Circuits by Algebraic Methods," *IRE Transactions on Electronic Computers*, Vol. EC-8, No. 3, p. 401, September 1959.

20. Muller, D. E., "Asynchronous Logics and Application to Information Processing," *Proceedings of a Symposium on the Application of Switching Theory in Space Technology*, Stanford University Press, March 1962.
21. Unger, S. H., "Hazards and Delays in Asynchronous Sequential Switching Circuits," *IRE Transactions on Circuit Theory*, Vol. CT-6, No. 1, pp. 12–25, March 1959.
22. Yoeli, M. and S. Rinon, "Application of Ternary Algebra to the Study of Static Hazards," *Journal of the ACM*, Vol. 11, No. 1, pp. 84-97.

# 10

## Speed Independent Switching Circuit Theory

### 10.1 INTRODUCTION

In discussing combinational and sequential switching networks in the chapters preceding Chapter 9, we usually assumed that the decision elements of the network either acted instantaneously, so that the output of each element could be represented by a Boolean function of its inputs, or we assumed that the element required some fixed and known interval of time $\Delta$ to react, so that the output at time $t + \Delta$ was a function of the element inputs plus the element output at time $t$. Such assumptions on the reaction times of the decision elements of a switching circuit are convenient because one can give rather simple functional expressions for the behavior of a switching circuit. Quite often, however, the reaction times of the decision elements do not completely match these assumptions. For example, because of tolerances in the components from which a decision element is made, the reaction time of one two-input AND-element may be somewhat different from that of another two-input AND-element. Furthermore, the reaction times of one type of element may be different from those of another type of element. Other factors, such as aging of the components, number of inputs to which the element output is attached, and other characteristics of the elements may cause the reaction time to change with time or be a complex function of the manner in which the decision elements are interconnected. Thus, when the simplifying assumptions about reaction times are not actually met by the circuit, some unexpected results may occur. This was seen in Chapter 9 where the effects of stray delays were studied and various design techniques described.

In this chapter, we present a theoretical approach for describing circuits whose behavior is independent of the relative reaction times of the circuit elements. That is, the element delays are unbounded and we assume that no line delays are present. In this theory the treatment of hazards and race conditions is implicit and, in contrast to the development of Chapter 9, does not require particular emphasis or special consideration.

To develop a general approach, we restrict our attention to networks that have no inputs. Later in the chapter we shall see that certain interpretations of these networks allow us to think of them as having certain inputs and outputs, where the desired behavior is given as a relation between the inputs and outputs. Finally, combining the approaches of Sections 9.7 and 10.5 leads to methods of interconnecting asynchronous realizations of sequential machines.

## 10.2  COMPLETE CIRCUITS AND SPEED INDEPENDENT CIRCUITS

In this section we give an abstract definition of a circuit and then develop precisely the concept of a circuit having speed independent behavior.

**Definition 10.2.1**  A *complete circuit* $C$ is defined as a finite set $S$ of $N$ objects, $a, b, c, \ldots$, where each of these objects is called a *state* of $C$, and where, at any time, $C$ is said to be in one of these states.

We shall often call a complete circuit simply "a circuit." We think of the state of a circuit to be a measurable quantity of $C$. For example, a state may consist of signal values, perhaps voltages or currents, on several signal lines.

**Definition 10.2.2**  The *behavior* of $C$ is defined by a set of sequences of states, where each sequence in the set is called an *allowed sequence*.

We depict a set of allowed sequences as

$$\left\{ \begin{matrix} a(1), a(2), \ldots \\ b(1), b(2), \ldots \\ \cdot \quad \cdot, \ldots \end{matrix} \right\},$$

where each allowed sequence may be either finite of infinite, and similarly, the set of allowed sequences for a given circuit may also be either finite or infinite.

The allowed sequences describe how the states of the circuit change with time. Thus for the sequence $a(1), a(2), a(3), \ldots$ state $a(2)$ would follow $a(1)$, state $a(3)$ would follow $a(2)$, etc., but the exact time that state $a(i + 1)$ follows state $a(i)$ is not specified. Since the time that a circuit remains in a state is unspecified, we can consider only allowed sequences in which consecutive states are not equal.

Note that since $S$ is defined as finite, we are considering only digital circuits. For the theory, we assume that there is no continuous variation or transient between states in $C$, but rather that at any time the circuit is in exactly one state from the set $S$. If a state is measured by certain signals, then by finiteness, each of these signals takes on a finite number of values and there is no transition range between these different values.

The following four properties are imposed on allowed sequences.

***Property 10.2.1*** In an allowed sequence $a(1)$, $a(2)$, ... for any pair of consecutive states $a(i) \neq a(i + 1)$.

***Property 10.2.2*** Each state $a$ of $S$ is the initial state of at least one allowed sequence.

***Property 10.2.3*** If $a(1)$, $a(2)$, $a(3)$, ... is an allowed sequence, so is $a(2)$, $a(3)$, ....

***Property 10.2.4*** If $a(1)$, $a(2)$, ... and $b(1)$, $b(2)$, ... are allowed sequences and $a(2) = b(1)$, then $a(1)$, $b(1)$, $b(2)$, ... is an allowed sequence.

Property 10.2.1 formalizes the concept that the exact timing of the circuit is unknown and thus only the state changes are of concern in an allowed sequence. Property 10.2.2 means that all the possible states of a circuit $C$ are known and are elements of the finite set $S$ and that each element of $S$ is a state of the circuit. Thus, if the circuit is initially set to any state $a \in S$, then an allowed sequence with $a$ as the first member of the sequence will result. Properties 10.2.3 and 10.2.4 mean that if a circuit is in a state $a(2)$, then the next possible states in allowed sequences of states depend only on $a(2)$ and not on any previous states, such as $a(1)$ or $b(1)$, which could have occurred in the allowed sequence. Thus Properties 10.2.3 and 10.2.4 imply that the state of a circuit describes completely the possible action of the circuit at any moment.

Property 10.2.4 gives a method of combining two allowed sequences into a new allowed sequence. This is extended in the following theorem.

**Theorem 10.2.1** A sequence of states $a(1)$, $a(2)$, ..., $a(i)$, $a(i + 1)$, ... is an allowed sequence if and only if $a(i)$, $a(i + 1)$, ... is an allowed sequence and $a(1)$, $a(2)$, ..., $a(i)$ is part of some allowed sequence.

PROOF. Let $a(1)$, $a(2)$, ..., $a(i)$, $a(i + 1)$, ... be an allowed sequence. Then by Property 10.2.3, $a(2)$, ..., $a(i)$, $a(i + 1)$, ... is an allowed sequence. Now assume that $a(k)$, ..., $a(i)$, $a(i + 1)$, ... is an allowed sequence for some $k \leq i$, then $a(k + 1)$, ..., $a(i)$, $a(i + 1)$, ... is an allowed sequence by Property 10.2.3. Therefore $a(r)$, $a(r + 1)$, ... is an allowed sequence for any $r \leq i + 1$. In particular, $a(i)$, $a(i + 1)$, ... is an allowed sequence. Furthermore, since $a(1)$, $a(2)$, ..., $a(i)$, $a(i + 1)$, ...

is an allowed sequence by assumption, it follows that $a(1), a(2), \ldots, a(i)$ is part of some allowed sequence. Thus the "only if" part of the theorem is proved. Now assume that $a(i), a(i + 1), \ldots$ is an allowed sequence and $a(1), \ldots, a(i)$ is part of some allowed sequence, $b(1), \ldots, b(j)$, $a(1), \ldots, a(i), b(k), \ldots$ As done previously by iteratively applying Property 10.2.3, we find that $a(1), \ldots, a(i), b(k), \ldots$ is an allowed sequence and also that each of the following sequences is an allowed sequence:

$$a(2), \ldots \ldots \ldots \ldots, a(i), b(k), \ldots$$
$$a(3), \ldots \ldots \ldots, a(i), b(k), \ldots$$

$$\cdot$$
$$\cdot$$
$$\cdot$$

$$a(i - 1), a(i), b(k), \ldots.$$

By Property 10.2.4, we combine this last allowed sequence with the allowed sequence $a(i), a(i + 1), \ldots$, obtaining $a(i - 1), a(i), a(i + 1), \ldots$ as an allowed sequence. Using induction, suppose $a(j), \ldots, a(i)$, $a(i + 1), \ldots$ is an allowed sequence for some $j \leq i - 1$. Then we have that $a(j - 1), a(j), \ldots, a(i), a(i + 1), \ldots$ is an allowed sequence by Property 10.2.4 since one of the preceding allowed sequences is $a(j - 1)$ $a(j), \ldots, a(i), b(k), \ldots.$ Thus, it follows that $a(1), a(2), \ldots, a(i)$, $a(i + 1), \ldots$ is an allowed sequence, and the theorem is proved.

As an example of a complete circuit $G$, let $S$ be a finite set of four states $S = \{a, b, c, d\}$. Also let the following two sequences be allowed sequences:

(1)  $a, b, a, b, \ldots$,

(2)  $a, c, d,$

where sequence (1) is an infinite sequence in which state $a$ is always directly followed by state $b$, and state $b$ is always directly followed by state $a$ and sequence (2) is a finite length sequence of three states. Since no two consecutive states in (1) or (2) are equal, both of these sequences satisfy Property 10.2.1.

Applying Property 10.2.3 to allowed sequences (1) and (2), we obtain the additional allowed sequences

$$b, a, b, a, \ldots,$$
$$c, d,$$

and

$$d.$$

We see that with these additional allowed sequences in the set of all allowed sequences, the requirement of Property 10.2.2 is satisfied by the set of all allowed sequences, since there exists at least one allowed sequence which starts in each of the four states $a$, $b$, $c$, and $d$. Applying Property 10.2.4 and Theorem 10.2.1 to the allowed sequences gives an infinite number of additional finite length allowed sequences of the following two varieties:

$$a, b, a, c, d \qquad\qquad b, a, c, d$$

$$a, b, a, b, a, c, d \qquad\qquad b, a, b, a, c, d$$

$$a, b, a, b, a, b, a, c, d \qquad b, a, b, a, b, a, c, d.$$

$$\cdot \qquad\qquad\qquad\qquad \cdot$$
$$\cdot \qquad\qquad\qquad\qquad \cdot$$
$$\cdot \qquad\qquad\qquad\qquad \cdot$$

Thus with this simple example we see that by specifying initially only two allowed sequences (1) and (2), the Properties 10.2.1 through 10.2.4 generate additional allowed sequences for the circuit so that the set of all allowed sequences for this circuit becomes an infinite set of sequences.

From the allowed sequences of a circuit, various relations between the states are defined.

**Definition 10.2.3**   Two states $a \in S$ and $b \in S$ are defined to be $\mathscr{R}$-*related*, $a \, \mathscr{R} \, b$, when either:

   1. $a = b$
or
   2. $a, b$ appears as a consecutive pair of states in some allowed sequence.

This $\mathscr{R}$-relation can be thought of as defining the states $b$ that can "directly follow" any given state $a$. Thus the $\mathscr{R}$-relation gives a mapping of each state $a \in S$ onto a subset $Q(a)$ of $S$, such that $b \in Q(a)$ if and only if $a \, \mathscr{R} \, b$. Since the exact timing of the sequences is unknown, there may be several states which can directly follow any state $a$; that is, the state diagram representing such a state, where transitions between states are given by the $\mathscr{R}$-relation, is a nondeterministic state diagram.

The subsets of states defined by the $\mathscr{R}$-relation for our previous example are

$$Q(a) = \{a, b, c\},$$
$$Q(b) = \{a, b\},$$
$$Q(c) = \{c, d\},$$
$$Q(d) = \{d\}.$$

The resulting state diagram for this example is shown in Figure 10.2.1, where the self-loops to each state are omitted for simplicity.

Although the state diagram for such circuits is nondeterministic, we shall not consider the possibility of assigning probabilities to the transitions in this theory. Instead, we shall be concerned in finding circuits that will give a desired behavior for any possible transitions which can occur in the nondeterministic state diagram.

The $\mathcal{R}$-relation is quite important in describing circuit properties, but the $\mathcal{R}$-relation alone does not determine the set of all allowed sequences. To see this, let us first define an $\mathcal{R}$-sequence.

**Definition 10.2.4** $a(1)$, $a(2)$, ..., $a(m)$ is called an $\mathcal{R}$-*sequence* if $a(i) \mathcal{R} a(i + 1)$ for $1 \leq i \leq m - 1$.

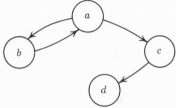

Figure 10.2.1 State diagram for four-state circuit.

If we assume that the states and the $\mathcal{R}$-relations between states are given, it would seem that all allowed sequences could be defined from the $\mathcal{R}$-sequences. Certainly, the set of all $\mathcal{R}$-sequences includes the set of all allowed sequences. Several difficulties arise which prevent these allowed sequences from being determined. Since an allowed sequence cannot have equal consecutive states, these must be removed from an $\mathcal{R}$-sequence to obtain an allowed sequence. However, if a finite $\mathcal{R}$-sequence has no equal adjacent states, we cannot conclude that this is an allowed sequence. It may only be a part of a longer, possibly infinite, one. For example, the finite sequence $a$, $b$ is an $\mathcal{R}$-sequence for the four-state example, but it is not an allowed sequence. Also, some infinite $\mathcal{R}$-sequences may not be allowed sequences, but this will not become clear until the next section.

The precise interrelationship between allowed sequences and $\mathcal{R}$-sequences is given in the next theorem.

**Theorem 10.2.2** If $a(1)$, $a(2)$, ..., $a(m)$ is an $\mathcal{R}$-sequence with no two equal consecutive states, and $a(m)$, $a(m + 1)$, ... is an allowed sequence, then $a(1)$, $a(2)$, ..., $a(m)$, $a(m + 1)$, ... is an allowed sequence.

PROOF. We have $a(m - 1) \mathcal{R} a(m)$ and $a(m - 1) \neq a(m)$ by hypothesis. Thus by definition of the $\mathcal{R}$-relation there exists some allowed sequence $r, \ldots, s, a(m - 1), a(m), b, c, \ldots$ so that $a(m - 1), a(m)$ is part of some allowed sequence. Then by Theorem 10.2.1, $a(m - 1)$, $a(m), a(m + 1), \ldots$ is an allowed sequence. By a simple inductive argument, it follows that $a(1), a(2), \ldots, a(m - 1), a(m), a(m + 1), \ldots$ is an allowed sequence.

**Definition 10.2.5**  For a circuit $C$, we say that a state $a$ is *followed* by a state $b$, denoting this by $a \mathscr{F} b$, if there exists an $\mathscr{R}$-sequence $a, \ldots, b$.

It follows immediately from this definition that the $\mathscr{F}$-relation is reflexive since $a, a$ is an $\mathscr{R}$-sequence for any state $a$. Furthermore, the $\mathscr{F}$-relation is transitive, for if $a \mathscr{F} b$ and $b \mathscr{F} c$, there exist $\mathscr{R}$-sequences $a, \ldots, b$ and $b, \ldots, c$ so that $a, \ldots, b, \ldots, c$ is also an $\mathscr{R}$-sequence and $a \mathscr{F} c$.

The $\mathscr{F}$-relation and allowed sequences are also closely interrelated, as shown by the following theorem.

**Theorem 10.2.3**  If $a$ and $b$ are two states of a circuit $C$ and $a \neq b$, $a$ and $b$ will appear in some allowed sequence, with $b$ appearing after $a$, if and only if $a \mathscr{F} b$.

PROOF.  Assume $a \neq b$ and $a \mathscr{F} b$, then there exists an $\mathscr{R}$-sequence $a, \ldots, b$. Then an $\mathscr{R}$-sequence with no equal consecutive states can be obtained from the first $\mathscr{R}$-sequence by deleting consecutive repetitions of equal states. By Property 10.2.2 there exists an allowed sequence $b, \ldots,$ and thus by Theorem 10.2.2, $a, \ldots, b, \ldots$ is an allowed sequence. This proves half the theorem; to prove the other half, let $\ldots, a, \ldots, b, \ldots$ be an allowed sequence. The part of the allowed sequence $a, \ldots, b$ is thus an $\mathscr{R}$-sequence and it follows directly from Definition 10.2.5 that $a \mathscr{F} b$.

Although the $\mathscr{F}$-relation is transitive and reflexive, it is not, in general, symmetric. For example, in the four-state example, the reader can check that $a \mathscr{F} d$, but we do not have $d \mathscr{F} a$. In certain cases, however, such as for states $a$ and $b$ of our example, we have both $a \mathscr{F} b$ and $b \mathscr{F} a$. When this is true, we have an equivalence relation between states of the circuit. We define this equivalence relation as follows.

**Definition 10.2.6**  Two states $a$ and $b$ are called *equivalent*, and denoted by $a \mathscr{E} b$, if $a \mathscr{F} b$ and $b \mathscr{F} a$.

The equivalence relation $\mathscr{E}$ thus partitions the finite set of states $S$ of any circuit into equivalence classes of states, which we denote by letters $A, B, C, \ldots$.

The $\mathscr{F}$-relation can then be extended to these equivalence classes by the following definition.

**Definition 10.2.7**  If $A$ and $B$ are two equivalence classes, then we write $A \mathscr{F} B$ if there are states $a^*$ in $A$, and $b^*$ in $B$ such that $a^* \mathscr{F} b^*$.

The next theorem shows that the $\mathscr{F}$-relation holds for any states of $A$ and $B$ if $A \mathscr{F} B$.

**Theorem 10.2.4**  If $a$ is in $A$, $b$ is in $B$, and $A \mathscr{F} B$, then $a \mathscr{F} b$.

PROOF.  By Definition 10.2.7, if $A \mathscr{F} B$, there exists states $a^* \in A$ and $b^* \in B$ such that $a^* \mathscr{F} b^*$. By Definition 10.2.6, if $a \in A$ and $a^* \in A$, then $a \mathcal{F} a^*$. Similarly, if $b \in B$, then $b^* \mathcal{F} b$. Thus $a \mathcal{F} a^*$, $a^* \mathcal{F} b^*$, and $b^* \mathcal{F} b$ so that by transitivity of the $\mathcal{F}$-relation $a \mathcal{F} b$, proving the theorem.

One should also note that it follows directly from this theorem that if $A \mathcal{F} B$ and $B \mathcal{F} A$, $A$ is the same equivalence class as $B$.

The $\mathcal{F}$-relation between equivalence classes can be seen to setup a partial ordering between classes. This ordering is also chronological. For any allowed sequence $a(1), a(2), \ldots$ a unique sequence of equivalence classes $A(1), A(2), \ldots, A(m)$ can be obtained with $A(i) \neq A(i + 1)$. Since there are finite numbers of states and equivalence classes of states, and since the $\mathcal{E}$-relation is symmetric, there is a definite last class $A(m)$, called a *terminal class*, for any allowed sequence. Thus we can express any finite or infinite allowed sequence as a finite sequence of equivalence classes. Also, since the set of equivalence classes is partially ordered, there is one or more maximal elements, where any maximal element is a terminal class for some allowed sequence. When a terminal class is not maximal under the partial ordering, it is called *pseudo-maximal*.

A terminal class is thus either maximal or pseudo-maximal.

Returning to the four-state example shown in Figure 10.2.1, we see that $a \mathcal{E} b$ and states $c$ and $d$ are not equivalent to any other states. Thus the equivalence classes forming the partition of $S$ for this example are

$$\{\{a, b\}, \{c\}, \{d\}\}$$

and if we let $A = \{a, b\}$, $B = \{c\}$, and $C = \{d\}$, the $\mathcal{F}$-relation extended to the equivalence classes is $A \mathcal{F} A$, $A \mathcal{F} B$, $A \mathcal{F} C$, $B \mathcal{F} B$, $B \mathcal{F} C$, and $C \mathcal{F} C$. This relation can be depicted in a diagram, where self-loops and arrows which follow by transitivity are omitted, as

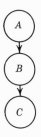

which, in this case, is a total ordering.

Note that the finite allowed sequence $a, c, d$ is now replaced by the finite sequence $A, B, C$ of equivalence classes, and the infinite allowed sequences $a, b, a, b, \ldots$ and $b, a, b, a, \ldots$ are both replaced by the finite sequence $A$, a single equivalence class. The reader should determine the sequences of equivalence classes which replace the other allowed sequences for this example.

Note that equivalence class $A$ is terminal for allowed sequence $a, b, a, b, \ldots$, but since $A \mathcal{F} B$, $A$ is not maximal. Therefore $A$ is pseudo-maximal. For this example, it is easy to see that $C$ is the only maximal equivalence class.

The formal definition of speed independence can now be given.

**Definition 10.2.8**  A circuit $C$ is called *speed independent with respect to a state u* if all allowed sequences starting with state $u$ have the same terminal class.

Note that this definition assumes a certain starting state $u$ for the circuit and that from this state $u$ any allowed sequence will eventually lead to a unique terminal class $T$. It is this uniqueness in the terminal behavior of $C$ that characterizes speed independence.

Thus, for the four-state example circuit, we see that the circuit is *not* speed independent with respect to state $a$, since there are allowed sequences starting with state $a$ that end in terminal class $A$ and also there are allowed sequences starting in state $a$ that end in terminal class $C$. However, this circuit is speed independent with respect to either state $c$ or state $d$ since all allowed sequences starting in either state $c$ or state $d$ end in terminal class $C$.

**Theorem 10.2.5**  Circuit $C$ is speed independent with respect to $u$ if and only if $U$, the equivalence class of $u$, is followed by only one maximal class $K$ and no pseudo-maximal classes.

This theorem follows from the fact that if some other maximal class, or pseudo-maximal class existed, an allowed sequence terminating in this class could be constructed.

In the next section we shall introduce some further structure into the definition of a circuit so that we can define certain subclasses of speed independent circuits for which further results of analysis and synthesis can be developed.

## 10.3  SIGNALS TO REPRESENT STATES

We now inject further structure into the definition of a complete circuit. We consider only circuits constructed from a certain kind of decision element and the states of these circuits represented by $n$-tuples of signal values. The states of a circuit thus satisfy the following definition.

**Definition 10.3.1** Each state $a$ of $S$ is determined by $n$ signals $a_1, a_2, \ldots,$ $a_n$; and each signal $a_i$ has range $S_i = \{0, 1, \ldots, k_i - 1\}$. The state $a$ is then written as an $n$-tuple $a = (a_1, a_2, \ldots, a_n)$, and the set $S$ of states are all possible $n$-tuples $S = S_1 \times S_2 \times \cdots \times S_n$.

The number of states $N$ is again finite, with $N = \prod_{i=1}^{n} k_i$. Since all possible $n$-tuples are used as states, this implies independent signals. We are usually interested in networks of interconnected logical elements. In such a case $k_i = 2$ for all $i$ and the states are $n$-tuples of binary signals.

A decision element is shown in Figure 10.3.1. For such a decision element the output value on line $z_4$ depends on the values of $z_1, z_2, z_3$ and possibly $z_4$ itself, and we can express the value to which $z_4$ is tending by a function

$$z_4' = f(z_1, z_2, z_3, z_4),$$

Figure 10.3.1 A decision element.

where $z_4'$ indicates the functional value which signal line $z_4$ is tending to attain. If $z_4 = z_4'$, then we say that the decision element is in *equilibrium*, whereas if $z_4 \neq z_4'$ we say that the decision element is *excited*. In any case, the $z_4'$ value is called the *implied value*. For this type of element we assume that if it is excited, the time for the element to react and attain its implied value is not exactly known; it is only known to be in the range $0 \leq \tau < \infty$, where $\tau$ represents the reaction time of the element. This delay corresponds to an unbounded stray element delay, as discussed in Chapter 9.

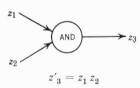

$$z_3' = z_1 z_2$$

Figure 10.3.2 AND-element.

For example, Figure 10.3.2 shows an AND-element. For this element if $z_1 = z_2 = 1$ and $z_3 = 0$, then the implied value is $z_3' = 1 \cdot 1 = 1$, so the element is excited. If both the signals $z_1$ and $z_2$ remain 1 for a sufficient length of time, then at some time $\tau$, $0 \leq \tau < \infty$, the output $z_3$ of the AND-element will change from 0 to 1. What are the other combinations of values on $z_1$, $z_2$, and $z_3$ for which the element is excited?

For a complete circuit constructed from decision elements, the decision elements must be interconnected according to certain rules. A circuit is thus defined as follows.

**Definition 10.3.2** A *circuit* is an interconnection of $n$ decision elements, where each input to a decision element is connected to exactly one output, and no two outputs are interconnected.

An example of a simple circuit is shown in Figure 10.3.3, where two elements are interconnected. One of the elements is a 1-element, that is, an element whose output is tending toward a 1 at all times. This is represented by the equation $z_1' = 1$. The second element is an AND-element and is represented by the equation $z_2' = z_1 z_2$. The states for this circuit are $(0, 0)$, $(0, 1)$, $(1, 0)$, and $(1, 1)$.

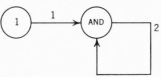

Figure 10.3.3  A simple circuit.

In general, with signals defined, a circuit and its allowed sequences can be defined by a set of switching functions as follows.

**Definition 10.3.3**   A set of $n$ functions

$$z_i' = f_i(z_1, z_2, \ldots, z_n); \qquad i = 1, 2, \ldots, n$$

defines a mapping of $S$ into $S$, where $z_j$ has range $S_j$ and $z_i'$ has range within $S_i$.

We can then call $a' = f(a)$ the *implied state* for $a$ and $a_i' = f_i(a)$ the *implied signal*. The set of functions $z' = f(z)$ defines the logical structure of the circuit, and the $i = 1, 2, \ldots, n$ are called *nodes* of the circuit. Thus for Figure 10.3.3 we obtain

$$z_1' = 1,$$

$$z_2' = z_1 z_2.$$

It should be noted that the only delay in this type of circuit is in the decision element; that is, element delays, and no delay is assumed along the interconnection lines of the circuit. Thus, if an output of some decision element in a circuit is connected to inputs of two other decision elements, the signal values on this output line and on the two input lines are assumed to be identical at all times. If the delay along an interconnection line is of interest, however, then a delay element may be used to simulate the delay of the line.

In the next definition we redefine what is meant by an allowed sequence in terms of the signals and implied signals. Following this definition we show the relationship of this new type of allowed sequence with the previous definition of an allowed sequence.

**Definition 10.3.4**   An *allowed sequence* $a(1)$, $a(2)$, ... is any sequence of states satisfying these three conditions

1. No two consecutive states $a(i)$ and $a(i + 1)$ are equal.
2. Each signal $a_i(j + 1)$ for any $a(j + 1)$ satisfies either

$$a_i(j + 1) = a_i(j)$$

or

$$a_i(j + 1) = a_i'(j).$$

3. If there exists a node $i$ and a state $a(j)$ such that $a_i(j) = a_i(r)$ and $a_i'(j) = a_i'(r)$ for all $a(r)$ in the sequence following $a(j)$, then

$$a_i(j) = a_i'(j).$$

The second condition means that a signal need not change at every step, but that it either stays constant or changes directly to its implied value. Since in practice we have continuously varying signals this assumption only can be approximated. Condition (3) means that if a signal is tending to some constant value for all states in an allowed sequence, eventually this signal must attain its implied value. Thus one can say that the time for a signal to attain its implied value is greater than or equal to zero, but less than infinity. This assumption may also have to be approximated in practice.

We shall now show that those sequences satisfying Definition 10.3.4 also satisfy Properties 10.2.1 through 10.2.4, and thus any sequence which is an allowed sequence under Definition 10.3.4 is also an allowed sequence in terms of the previous section.

Since condition (1) of Definition 10.3.4 is identical to Property 10.2.1, any sequence satisfying Definition 10.3.4 also satisfies Property 10.2.1. Let $a(1)$ be any state of a circuit; then Property 10.2.2 can be satisfied by constructing a sequence starting with $a(1)$ which satisfies Definition 10.3.4. This is done as follows. Let $a(1)$ be the first state of the sequence. If $a'(1) \neq a(1)$. Then let $a'(1) = a(2)$ be the second state of the sequence. If $a'(1) = a(1)$, then $a(1)$ alone is a sequence satisfying Definition 10.3.4. By induction if $a(i) \neq a'(i)$, let $a(i + 1) = a'(i)$ in the sequence, and if $a(i) = a'(i)$, terminate the sequence. It is easily seen that this sequence satisfies Definition 10.3.4. Property 10.2.3 states that if $a(1), a(2), \ldots$ is an allowed sequence, $a(2), \ldots$ is also an allowed sequence. Thus if $a(1), a(2), \ldots$ is a sequence satisfying Definition 10.3.4, it follows immediately that $a(2), \ldots$ is also a sequence satisfying Definition 10.3.4 and thus $a(2), \ldots$ is also an allowed sequence. Finally, Property 10.2.4 states that if $a(1), a(2), \ldots$ and $b(1), b(2), \ldots$ are allowed sequences and $a(2) = b(1)$, then $a(1), b(1), b(2), \ldots$ is an allowed sequence. In this case it follows immediately that $a(1), b(1), b(2), \ldots$ satisfies Definition 10.3.4; hence Property 10.2.4 is implied by Definition 10.3.4.

Reconsidering the circuit of Figure 10.3.3, we can thus see that the set of allowed sequences for this circuit is

$$\left\{ \begin{array}{l} (1, 0) \\ (1, 1) \\ (0, 0), (1, 0) \\ (0, 1) \, (0, 0) \, (1, 0) \\ (0, 1) \, (1, 1) \end{array} \right\}$$

and the state diagram for the circuit is

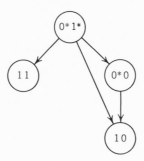

In this state diagram, we use a * to indicate that the element, corresponding to the given node and state, is excited. Since for this circuit there are no two states $a$ and $b$ such that both $a \, \mathscr{F} \, b$ and $b \, \mathscr{F} \, a$, each state of the circuit is also its own equivalence class and $(1, 1)$ and $(1, 0)$ are maximal classes. Thus the circuit is speed independent with respect to states $(0, 0)$, $(1, 0)$, and $(1, 1)$, but it is not speed independent with respect to state $(0, 1)$ since one allowed sequence starting with $(0, 1)$ ends in the equilibrium state $(1, 0)$ and the other allowed sequence starting with $(0, 1)$ ends in state $(1, 1)$.

Several other concepts defined for the more abstract circuits in the previous section can now be further extended by using the concept of signals representing states.

**Theorem 10.3.1**    For states $a$ and $b$ of a circuit $a \, \mathscr{R} \, b$ if and only if either $b_i = a_i$ or $b_i = a_i'$ for each node $i$.

PROOF.    By Definition 10.2.3, if $a \, \mathscr{R} \, b$, then either $a = b$ or $a, b$ appears as a consecutive pair of states in some allowed sequence. If $a = b$, $b_i = a_i$ for each node $i$. If $a, b$ appears as a consecutive pair in some allowed sequence, by (2) of Definition 10.3.4 either $b_i = a_i$ or $b_i = a_i'$ for each node $i$ and thus the "only if" part of the theorem is proved. Now if $b_i = a_i$ for each node $i$, $a = b$ and $a \, \mathscr{R} \, b$ by Definition 10.2.3. If $b_i = a_i' \neq a_i$ for some $i$, and for each $j$, $i \neq j$ either $b_j = a_j$ or $b_j = a_j'$, we can construct a sequence $a, b, \ldots$ satisfying Definition 10.3.4 by using $b'$ for the state in the sequence directly following $b$, if $b' \neq b$, as was done to show that Property 10.2.2 was implied by Definition 10.3.4. Then since $a, b, \ldots$ is an allowed sequence, it follows that $a \mathcal{R} b$, completing the proof of the theorem.

The next theorem characterizes a terminal class of a circuit in terms of the signal values appearing in the set of states comprising the class.

**Theorem 10.3.2**  An equivalence class of states $T = \{b(1), b(2), \ldots, b(k)\}$ is a terminal class if and only if for any node $i$ such that $b_i(1) = b_i(2) = \cdots = b_i(k)$ and $b_i'(i) = b_i'(2) = \cdots = b_i'(k)$, then $b_i(j) = b_i'(j)$ for $j = 1, 2, \ldots, k$.

PROOF.  Suppose $T$ is a terminal class. Then let $a(1), a(2), \ldots$ be an allowed sequence with terminal class $T$. Thus there exists some $a(m)$ of the allowed sequence such that $a(m), a(m + 1), \ldots$ are all members of $T$. Thus, if $b_i(1) = b_i(2) = \cdots = b_i(k)$ and $b_i'(1) = b_i'(2) = \cdots = b_i'(k)$, $a_i(m) = a_i(m + 1) = \cdots$ and $a_i'(m) = a_i'(m + 1) = \cdots$. By condition (3) of Definition 10.3.4 it follows that $a_i(m) = a_i'(m)$ and thus $b_i(j) = b_i'(j)$ for some $j$. It follows then that $b_i(j) = b_i'(j)$ for all $j = 1, 2, \ldots, k$.

Now the converse must be proved; that is, if $T = \{b(1), b(2), \ldots, b(k)\}$ is an equivalence class and for any node $i$ such that $b_i(1) = b_i(2) = \cdots = b_i(k)$ and $b_i'(1) = b_i'(2) = \cdots = b_i'(k)$, we have $b_i(j) = b_i'(j)$ for $j = 1, 2, \ldots, k$, then $T$ is a terminal class. To prove this we construct an allowed sequence having $T$ as its terminal class. If $T = \{b(1)\}$, for any node $i$, the conditions $b_i(1) = b_i(2) = \cdots = b_i(k)$ and $b_i'(1) = b_i'(2) = \cdots = b_i'(k)$ are trivially satisfied, since $k = 1$. Thus, for any node $i$, we must have $b_i(1) = b_i'(1)$. Therefore the state $b(1)$ is itself a sequence satisfying Definition 10.3.4, so $b(1)$ is an allowed sequence and $T$ is the terminal class for this sequence. Now suppose $T$ contains two or more states. Then starting with $b(1)$ form the following infinite sequence

$$b(1), \ldots, b(2), \ldots, \ldots, b(k), \ldots, b(1), \ldots,$$

where after returning to $b(1)$ the sequence repeats itself indefinitely. Each pair $b(j), \ldots, b(j + 1)$ is joined by an $\mathcal{R}$-sequence with no two equal consecutive states, and each state in the sequence is an element of $T$. Such a sequence is possible since $T$ is an equivalence class. Obviously, conditions (1) and (2) of Definition 10.3.4 are satisfied for this sequence. Also condition (3) is satisfied since the sequence is infinite and for any node with $b_i(1) = b_i(2) = \cdots = b_i(k)$ and $b_i'(1) = b_i'(2) = \cdots = b_i'(k)$, the conditions of the theorem insure that $b_i(j) = b_i'(j)$, which is exactly what is required by condition (3). Thus this sequence is an allowed sequence and $T$ is its terminal class, proving the theorem.

A terminal equivalence class $T$ of states $\{b(1), b(2), \ldots, b(k)\}$ is thus characterized by either

1. There is no node $i$ such that $b_i(r) = b_i(s)$ and $b_i'(r) = b_i'(s)$ for all $r$ and $s$ in the range $1 \leq r, s \leq k$.
2. For any node $i$ with $b_i(r) = b_i(s)$ and $b_i'(r) = b_i'(s)$ for all $r$ and $s$ in the range $1 \leq r, s \leq k$, we must also have $b_i(r) = b_i'(r)$.

Conversely, any nonterminal equivalence class $A$ of states $\{a(1), a(2), \ldots, a(q)\}$ is characterized by the existence of node $i$ which has $a_i(r) = a_i(s)$ and $a_i'(r) = a_i'(s)$ for all $r$ and $s$, $1 \leq r, s \leq q$, and $a_i(r) \neq a_i'(r)$.

If $a_i = a_i'$, the signal on node $i$ is said to be in *equilibrium*. If a signal is not in equilibrium, it is called *excited*. If all the signals of a state are in equilibrium, it is an *equilibrium state*. Any equilibrium state is a single-state equivalence class that is maximal. Conversely, the state of any single-state equivalence class which is a terminal class is an equilibrium state.

Although Definition 10.3.4 has been shown to imply Properties 10.2.1 through 10.2.4, it does not follow that the behavior of a circuit as defined by Section 10.2 can be realized by a circuit with signals representing states, particularly if each signal is binary. For example, we cannot obtain a four-state circuit using binary signals to represent states for the circuit (Figure 10.2.1) discussed in Section 10.2. This can be seen as follows. If binary signals are to represent the four states, exactly two binary signals must be used. Without any loss of generality we can let $a = (0, 0)$. For state $b$ we can use $(0, 1)$, $(1, 0)$, or $(1, 1)$. If $b = (1, 1)$, the implied state of $a$ is $a' = (1, 1)$, since $a, b, \ldots$ is an allowed sequence. But then $(0, 0)$, $(0, 1), \ldots$ and $(0, 0), (1, 0), \ldots$ are also allowed sequences, and this means that both $a, c, \ldots$ and $a, d, \ldots$ are allowed sequences. This is not possible since $a, d, \ldots$ is not an allowed sequence in the abstract circuit. If $b = (1, 0)$, $c$ is either $(0, 1)$ or $(1, 1)$. In either case we obtain $a' = (1, 1)$ implying that $a \mathcal{R} d$, which does not correspond to the behavior of the abstract circuit. Similarly, if $b = (0, 1)$ we again obtain $a \mathcal{R} d$, proving that the abstract circuit behavior cannot be realized by a circuit with binary signals.

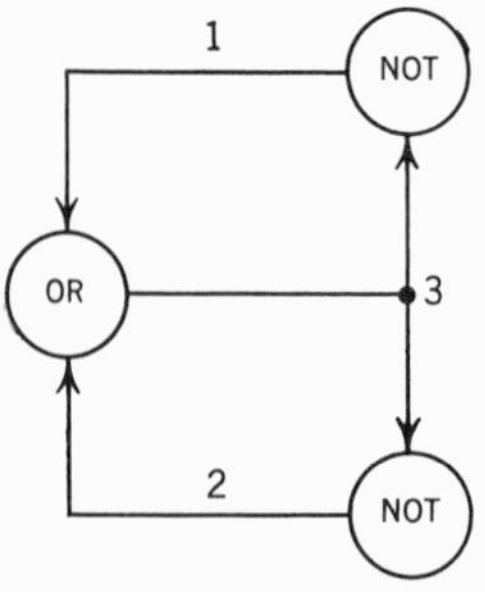

This example thus illustrates that introducing signals to represent states gives an essential restriction on the types of circuits which will be studied. More precisely, it follows from (2) of Definition 10.3.4 that the number of states in $Q(a)$ [where $Q(a)$ is that set of states $b$ such that $b \in Q(a)$ if and only if $a \mathcal{R} b$] for any state $a$ must be equal to some power of 2, if the states of the circuit are to be represented by binary signals.

Figure 10.3.4 A three element circuit.

A final example of a circuit for this section is shown in Figure 10.3.4. The state diagram for this circuit, again using an * to indicate excited nodes, is the following.

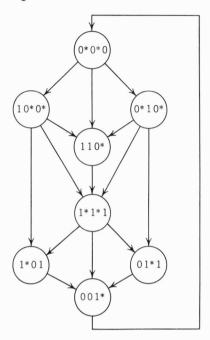

Since any state of this circuit can follow any other state in some $\mathcal{R}$-sequence, all states of this circuit belong to the same equivalence class. Thus, this circuit, very simply, is speed independent with respect to any state of the circuit.

## 10.4 SEVERAL SUBCLASSES OF SPEED INDEPENDENT CIRCUITS

Even with the introduction of signals to represent states, the general concept of speed independence eludes detailed analysis and synthesis. Several subclasses of speed independent circuits enable one to provide a more adequate description.

**Definition 10.4.1** A circuit is called *totally sequential* with respect to a state $u$ if there is only one allowed sequence starting with $u$.

An example of a totally sequential circuit with respect to a state $(0, 0)$ and its state diagram is shown in Figure 10.4.1.

Every allowed sequence of states of a circuit was shown previously to terminate in some equivalence class of states called a *terminal class*.

Since there is only one allowed sequence starting with $u$ for a circuit totally sequential with respect to $u$, it is obvious that all allowed sequences starting with $u$ have the same terminal class, proving the following theorem.

**Theorem 10.4.1**  A circuit totally sequential with respect to $u$ is also speed independent with respect to $u$.

Note that the state diagram for this circuit has at most one transition leaving each state $a$, where $u \mathcal{F} a$. Thus the state diagram of all states

Circuit

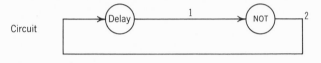

State
Diagram

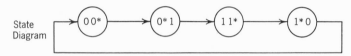

Figure 10.4.1    A totally sequential circuit.

which follow $u$ is deterministic. Also, if $a$ is any state of a circuit totally sequential with respect to $u$, where $u \mathcal{F} a$, only one signal of state $a$ can be excited. This means that there are no "race conditions" in a totally sequential circuit. Although this restriction simplifies materially the behavior of a circuit, it may often be desirable to allow two or more signals to be excited simultaneously, thus allowing a type of "parallel operation" in the circuit. In fact, to attain high-speed operation it may be essential to allow such parallelism. For this reason we consider a more general type of speed independent circuit, called a semi-modular circuit, which allows parallelism.

**Definition 10.4.2**  A circuit is *semi-modular* with respect to $u$ if every pair of states $a$, $b$ satisfying $u \mathcal{F} a$ and $a \mathcal{R} b$ also satisfies $b \mathcal{R} a'$.

An alternate definition for semi-modularity, equivalent to Definition 10.4.2, is as follows. A circuit is semi-modular with respect to $u$ if every pair of states $a$, $b$ satisfying $u \mathcal{F} a$ and $a \mathcal{R} b$ has $b_i' = a_i'$ for each node $i$ satisfying $b_i = a_i \neq a_i'$. Thus, in a semi-modular circuit, if a node $i$ is excited in state $a$, but node $i$ does not change to $a_i'$ when the circuit goes to state $b$, then node $i$ must still be excited in state $b$ and to the same value as in state $a$.

In a circuit that is totally sequential with respect to a state $u$ if $u \mathcal{F} a$

and $a \mathscr{R} b$, $b$ differs from $a$ only in the one signal value which is excited in state $a$. Thus $b = a'$, so it immediately follows from the definition of the $\mathscr{R}$-relation that $b \mathscr{R} a'$. This proves the following theorem.

**Theorem 10.4.2** A circuit totally sequential with respect to $u$ is also semi-modular with respect to $u$.

The definition of semi-modularity gives a rather strong interrelationship between pairs of allowed sequences starting from any state $u$; if we have two allowed sequences $u, a(2), \ldots, a(j), a(j+1), \ldots$ and $u, b(2), \ldots, b(k), b(k+1), \ldots$ for a circuit which is semi-modular with respect to $u$, where $a(j) = b(k)$, then both $a(j+1) \mathscr{R} a'(j)$ and $b(k+1) \mathscr{R} a'(j)$, so that the sequences $u, a(2), \ldots, a(j), a'(j), \ldots$ and $u, b(2), \ldots, b(k)$, $a'(j), \ldots$ are also allowed sequences for the circuit. By using this property, a rather long sequence of results can be obtained for semi-modular circuits, which concludes with the following result [9, 11].

**Theorem 10.4.3** A circuit semi-modular with respect to a state $u$ is also speed independent with respect to $u$.

The converse of this theorem is not generally true as can be demonstrated by the circuit of Figure 10.3.4 in the previous section. The following state diagram for this circuit is shown again.

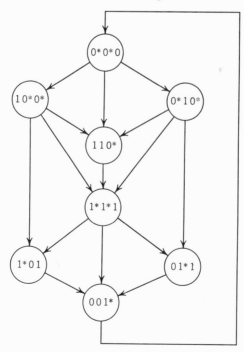

For this circuit if $u = (0, 0, 0)$, the circuit is speed independent with respect to $u$. It is not semi-modular with respect to $u$, however, for if $a = 100$ and $b = 101$, we have that $u \mathscr{F} a$ and $a \mathscr{R} b$; but $a' = 111$ and $b' = 001$, so that $b$ is not related to $a'$ by $b \mathscr{R} a'$, thus violating the definition of semi-modularity. It can also be seen that semi-modularity is violated by the states $a$ and $b$ of the circuit because in state $a$ we have both signals $a_2$ and $a_3$ excited. On going to state $b$, however, only signal $a_3$ changes from 0 to 1, but even though signal $a_2$ does not change it does become unexcited in state $b$. This was seen earlier to violate the alternate method of defining semi-modularity.

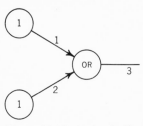

Figure 10.4.2 A circuit displaying semi-modularity.

As another example, consider the circuit of Figure 10.4.2. The state diagram for this circuit is

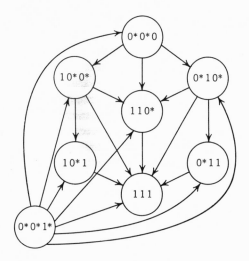

This circuit is semi-modular with respect to state $(0, 0, 0)$ since once any node is excited to a 1, it remains excited until it changes to a 1. Obviously, this circuit is not totally sequential with respect to $(0, 0, 0)$, thus showing that the converse of Theorem 10.4.2 is not true. Also this circuit is not semi-modular with respect to state $(0, 0, 1)$ since in state $(0, 0, 1)$ node 3 is excited, but $(0, 0, 1) \mathscr{R} (1, 0, 1)$ and node 3 does not change for this transition but returns to equilibrium in state $(1, 0, 1)$. Is the circuit speed independent with respect to state $(0, 0, 1)$?

Although this example does not display cyclic behavior, it is possible to have cycles in a circuit which is semi-modular but not totally sequential

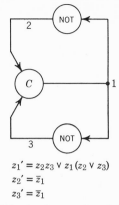

$$z_1' = z_2 z_3 \lor z_1 (z_2 \lor z_3)$$
$$z_2' = \bar{z}_1$$
$$z_3' = \bar{z}_1$$

Figure 10.4.3 Another semi-modular circuit.

with respect to some state. A circuit displaying such behavior is shown in Figure 10.4.3. The state diagram for this circuit is

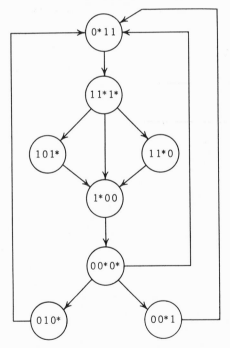

As can be seen from the state diagram each state is followed by each other state in some allowed sequence, and if a node becomes excited, it must change in order to go to equilibrium. Therefore this circuit is semi-modular with respect to any state of the circuit.

Since the behavior of circuits has been described rather abstractly through a set of allowed sequences, it may be difficult to visualize any operation that a speed independent circuit might perform. A simple example of a scale of two counter, which is totally sequential, is given in Figure 10.4.4.

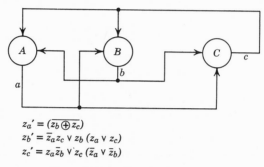

$$z_a' = (\overline{z_b \oplus z_c})$$
$$z_b' = \overline{z}_a z_c \vee z_b (z_a \vee z_c)$$
$$z_c' = z_a \overline{z}_b \vee z_c (\overline{z}_a \vee \overline{z}_b)$$

Figure 10.4.4   A scale of two counter.

The state diagram for the circuit is shown, where the circles are omitted from the states for convenience.

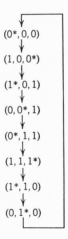

Obviously, this circuit is totally sequential with respect to any state of the circuit.

To visualize the operation of this counter think of signal line $a$ being broken at the output of element $A$; call the output of element $A$ signal $a_1$, and call the resulting input to $B$ and $C$ signal $a_2$. Starting in condition $a_1 = a_2 = 0$, $b = c = 0$, eventually $a_1$ will change from 0 to 1. When this change occurs, we say that the circuit is "ready" to receive an input of 1 on signal $a_2$. When $a_2$ changes to a 1, element $C$ is excited and will change from 0 to 1 after this element $A$ is again excited so that $a_1$ changes from 1 to 0. The signal $a_1$ going from 1 to 0 indicates that the circuit is "ready" to accept an input change on $a_2$ of 1 to 0. The changes on $a_1$ thus indicate when the circuit is ready to accept a change on the input line $a_2$, and the signal $a_1$ is thus called a *reply back* signal of the circuit. Note that signals $a_2$ and $a_1$ are similar to the $G$ and $R$ signals of Section 9.7. If the changes on node $b$ are related to the changes on node $a$, we see that node $a$ changes twice for every single change on node $b$. Thus from node $a$ to node $b$ we have a scale of two counter.

One reason that semi-modular circuits are more convenient to describe than general speed independent circuits is that it is possible to construct sets of "cumulative" states for semi-modular circuits which describe the *number of changes* which have occurred on the respective nodes.

**Definition 10.4.3** For a semi-modular circuit with respect to state $a(1)$ and any $\mathscr{R}$-sequence $a(1), a(2), \ldots, a(m)$, a sequence of $C$-*states* (cumulative states) $\alpha(1), \alpha(2), \ldots, \alpha(m)$ is defined as follows:

1. Each $C$-state is an $n$-vector $\alpha(j) = [\alpha_1(j), \alpha_2(j), \ldots, \alpha_n(j)]$ with integer components $\alpha_i(j)$.
2. $\alpha(1) = (0, 0, \ldots, 0)$.
3. $\alpha(j)$ is defined recursively by

$$\alpha_i(j) = \alpha_i(j-1) \qquad \text{if} \quad a_i(j) = a_i(j-1)$$
$$\alpha_i(j) = \alpha_i(j-1) + 1 \qquad \text{if} \quad a_i(j) \neq a_i(j-1).$$

Thus $\alpha_i(j)$ is the number of changes which have occurred on node $i$ in the partial $\mathscr{R}$-sequence $a(1), a(2), \ldots, a(j)$. Letting $a(1) = u$, one can define a function $t(u; \theta, i)$ on all pairs $(\theta, i)$, where $\alpha_i(j) = \theta$ for some $C$-state $\alpha(j)$ of the sequence, such that $t(u; \theta, i) = a_i(r)$ whenever $\alpha_i(r) = \theta$. Similarly, we let $t[u; \alpha(j)]$ represent an $n$-vector $t[u; \alpha(j)] = [t[u; \alpha_1(j), 1]$, $t[u; \alpha_2(j), 2] \cdots t[u; \alpha_n(j), n]]$. These $C$-states and the function $t(u; \theta, i)$ have been shown to depend on only the first state $u$ of the $\mathscr{R}$-sequence. Thus from the $C$-states of a semi-modular circuit the mapping $t[u; \alpha(j)]$ gives the exact state of the circuit which corresponds to $C$-state $\alpha(j)$. Also, it is not possible to construct a similar result for more general speed independent circuits. Because of these mappings it is useful to define several sets.

**Definition 10.4.4** For a semi-modular circuit with respect to $u$, let $B[u]$ represent the set of all states $a$ such that $u \mathscr{F} a$. Let $C[u]$ be the set of $C$-states such that $\alpha \in C[u]$ if and only if $\alpha$ appears in some $C$-state sequence starting with state $u$. Let $\Sigma[u]$ represent the set of all integer pairs $(\theta, i)$ such that $\theta = \alpha_i$ for some $\alpha$ of $C[u]$.

With these definitions, it follows that $t(u; \theta, i)$ provides a mapping of the set $\Sigma[u]$ onto the set of signals in states of $B[u]$. Also, the function $t(u; \alpha)$ provides a mapping from $C[u]$ onto $B[u]$. Thus any $C$-state from $C[u]$ represents only one state which can be reached from state $u$. In fact, suppose we impose a partial ordering on $C[u]$ as follows.

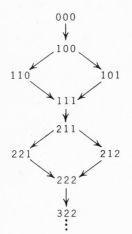

**Definition 10.4.5**   Let $\alpha$ and $\beta$ be elements of $C[u]$. Then $\alpha \leq \beta$ if $\alpha_i \leq \beta_i$, $1 \leq i \leq n$.

Then it is possible to show that if $\alpha \leq \beta$ there is an $\mathcal{R}$-sequence starting with $u$ such that the corresponding $C$-state sequence contains $\alpha$ followed by $\beta$.

We refer back to the circuit of Figure 10.4.3 to illustrate some of these results. If $u = (0, 1, 1)$ for this circuit, then

$$B[u] = \{(0, 0, 0), (0, 0, 1), (0, 1, 0),$$
$$(0, 1, 1), (1, 0, 0), (1, 0, 1), (1, 1, 0), (1, 1, 1)\}.$$

Figure 10.4.5   Diagram of $C$-states for circuit of Figure 10.4.3.

The set $C[u]$ of $C$-states is an infinite set, and we illustrate it by Figure 10.4.5, which corresponds rather closely to the state diagram of the circuit.

The function $t(u, \theta, i)$ for this example can be seen to be

$$t[(0, 1, 1), \theta, 1] \equiv \theta \bmod 2$$
$$t[(0, 1, 1), \theta, 2] \equiv (\theta + 1) \bmod 2$$
$$t[(0, 1, 1), \theta, 3] \equiv (\theta + 1) \bmod 2$$

Thus, for example, the $C$-state $(2, 2, 2)$ corresponds to the state $(0, 1, 1)$ of the circuit, and the $C$-state $(1, 1, 0)$ corresponds to the state $(1, 0, 1)$ of the circuit. Also, if $\alpha = (1, 0, 1)$ and $\beta = (2, 2, 1)$, then $\alpha \leq \beta$ by Definition 10.4.5; and there is a $C$-state sequence $(1, 0, 1)$, $(1, 1, 1)$, $(2, 1, 1)$, $(2, 2, 1)$ from $\alpha$ to $\beta$, and this corresponds to the $\mathcal{R}$-sequence $(1, 1, 0)$, $(1, 0, 0)$, $(0, 0, 0)$, $(0, 1, 0)$.

On the set $C[u]$ a component maximizing operation $\alpha \vee \beta$ and a component minimizing operation $\alpha \wedge \beta$ for $\alpha$ and $\beta$ in $C[u]$ can be defined as follows.

**Definition 10.4.6**   Let $\alpha$ and $\beta$ be elements of $C[u]$; then define the components of $\gamma = \alpha \vee \beta$ as

$$\gamma_i = \max(\alpha_i, \beta_i).$$

Also define the components of $\delta = \alpha \wedge \beta$ as

$$\delta_i = \min(\alpha_i, \beta_i).$$

With this definition on pairs of $C$-states it can be proved that $\gamma = \alpha \vee \beta$ is an element of $C[u]$ whenever $\alpha$ and $\beta$ are elements of $C[u]$; that is, $C[u]$ is closed under the $\vee$-operation.

**Theorem 10.4.4** The set $C[u]$ is a semi-modular lattice with a zero under the componentwise ordering of Definition 10.4.5.

PROOF. To outline the proof, we show first that $C[u]$ is a lattice (see Definition 2.8.11 of Volume I) under the partial ordering $\alpha \leq \beta$. This can be accomplished by proving that there exists a g.l.b. $\alpha \cap \beta$ and a l.u.b. $\alpha \cup \beta$ for each pair of elements $\alpha$ and $\beta$ in $C[u]$. For any two elements $\alpha$ and $\beta$ if we let $\gamma = \alpha \vee \beta$, then $\gamma \in C[u]$ and obviously $\alpha \leq \gamma$ and $\beta \leq \gamma$. Also, no other $\gamma^* \leq \gamma$ can exist with both $\alpha \leq \gamma^*$ and $\beta \leq \gamma^*$ since if $\gamma^* \neq \gamma$, there must be some component of $\gamma^*$ such that $\gamma_i{}^* < \gamma_i$, but then either $\gamma_i{}^* < \beta_i$ or $\gamma_i{}^* < \alpha_i$, so that $\gamma^*$ does not have both $\alpha \leq \gamma^*$ and $\beta \leq \gamma^*$. Therefore $\gamma$ is the l.u.b. of $\alpha$ and $\beta$. Since $C[u]$ is not necessarily closed under $\alpha \wedge \beta$, the greatest lower bound $\alpha \cap \beta$ of the semi-modular lattice may not equal $\alpha \wedge \beta$. However, $C[u]$ contains a zero equal to $(0, 0, \ldots, 0)$ which is a lower bound for $\alpha \cap \beta$. Thus there are a finite number of elements of $C[u]$ which are $\leq$ both $\alpha$ and $\beta$, since the components of elements in $C[u]$ are integers. Let $\lambda(1), \lambda(2), \ldots, \lambda(m)$ be all these lower bounds for $\alpha$ and $\beta$. Then $\lambda = \lambda(1) \vee \lambda(2) \vee \cdots \vee \lambda(m)$ is a lower bound for $(\alpha, \beta)$ and since $\lambda \geq \lambda(j)$ for $1 \leq j \leq m$, it follows that $\lambda$ is the g.l.b. for $(\alpha, \beta)$. Thus $C[u]$ is a lattice with zero $(0, 0, \ldots, 0)$.

For semi-modularity of the lattice, one must show that if two distinct elements $\alpha$ and $\beta$ both cover an element $\lambda$, then both are covered by $\alpha \cup \beta$. By covering, we mean that $\alpha$ covers $\lambda$ if $\lambda < \alpha$ and there is no element $\gamma$ such that $\lambda < \gamma < \alpha$. In $C[u]$ it can be shown that $\alpha$ covers $\lambda$ if and only if there is one node $j$ such that $\alpha_j = \lambda_j + 1$ and $\alpha_i = \lambda_i$ for all other nodes.

Let $\alpha = (\alpha_1, \alpha_2, \ldots, \alpha_n)$ and $\beta = (\beta_1, \beta_2, \ldots, \beta_n)$, where $\alpha \neq \beta$. Since $\lambda$ is covered by both $\alpha$ and $\beta$, we have that $\lambda$ differs from $\alpha$ in just one component, say $\alpha_i \neq \lambda_i$; and similarly $\beta$ differs from $\lambda$ in just one component, say $\beta_j \neq \lambda_j$. Note that $j \neq i$. Thus $\lambda$ can be expressed as

$$\lambda = (\alpha_1, \ldots, \alpha_{i-1}, \lambda_i, \alpha_{i+1}, \ldots, \alpha_{j-1}, \lambda_j, \alpha_{j+1}, \ldots, \alpha_n),$$

where

$$\lambda_j = \alpha_j \neq \beta_j \quad \text{and} \quad \lambda_i = \beta_i \neq \alpha_i.$$

Also, $\beta_j = \lambda_j + 1$ and $\alpha_i = \lambda_i + 1$. Thus

$$\alpha \cup \beta = (\alpha_1, \ldots, \alpha_{i-1}, \alpha_i, \alpha_{i+1}, \ldots, \alpha_{j-1}, \beta_j, \alpha_{j+1}, \ldots, \alpha_n)$$
$$= (\beta_1, \ldots, \beta_{i-1}, \alpha_i, \beta_{i+1}, \ldots, \beta_{j-1}, \beta_j, \beta_{j+1}, \ldots, \beta_n),$$

so that $\alpha \cup \beta$ differs from both $\alpha$ and $\beta$ by only one component, which is, in each case, greater than the corresponding component of $\alpha$ or $\beta$. Thus $\alpha \cup \beta$ covers both $\alpha$ and $\beta$, and we have proved the semi-modularity of the lattice $C[u]$.

The structure of the semi-modularity is defined by Figure 10.4.6, where arrows are now used only to indicate the covering relation.

Figure 10.4.6  Semi-modularity condition.

The term *semi-modular circuit* is used simply because $C[u]$ for this type of circuit is a semi-modular lattice. More general types of semi-modular lattices exist, however, than those created by $C[u]$. For example, the reader may check that the following lattice is semi-modular but does not correspond to any $C[u]$.

Note that the componentwise ordering of $C$-states also represents a chronological ordering of the changes occurring in the circuit. We consider this ordering in more detail. With the covering relation on $C$-states one can describe a sequence of $C$-states in which consecutive $C$-states $\alpha$, $\beta$ are all of the type that $\beta$ covers $\alpha$. Such a sequence is called a *covering sequence*. Each covering sequence with two or more elements has a corresponding unique sequence of elements from $\Sigma[u]$ called a *sequence of changes*. The set of elements appearing in sequences of changes we call $\Sigma_1[u]$; and $\Sigma_1[u] = \Sigma[u] - \{(0, 1)(0, 2) \cdots (0, n)\}$.

We can define a partial ordering over $\Sigma_1[u]$ by writing $(\theta, i) \leq (\phi, j)$ whenever $(\theta, i)$ and $(\phi, j)$ are in $\Sigma_1[u]$ and all states $\alpha$ of $C[u]$ satisfying $\alpha_i < \theta$ also have $\alpha_j < \phi$. $\Sigma_1[u]$ with this partial ordering is called a *change chart* for the circuit. This change chart is useful for synthesis, since all change sequences of a circuit must conform to the partial ordering of $\Sigma_1[u]$. It may be viewed as a description of the precedence relation on changes which are to occur in a circuit.

To illustrate change charts, we consider several examples. First we look at the circuit of Figure 10.4.2 which is repeated in Figure 10.4.7. This circuit was seen previously to be semi-modular with respect to state $(0, 0, 0)$. Thus, if $u = (0, 0, 0)$, we have

$C[u] = \{(0, 0, 0), (1, 0, 0), (0, 1, 0), (0, 1, 1), (1, 0, 1), (1, 1, 0), (1, 1, 1)\},$

$\Sigma[u] = \{(0, 1), (1, 1), (0, 2), (1, 2), (0, 3), (1, 3)\},$

and

$\Sigma_1[u] = \{(1, 1), (1, 2), (1, 3)\}.$

To define the change chart for this circuit we must describe the partial ordering between elements in $\Sigma_1[u]$. We check to find possible orderings on $\Sigma_1[u]$ by checking over the elements of $C[u]$.

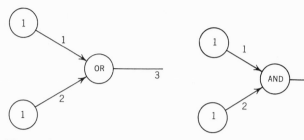

Figure 10.4.7. Figure 10.4.2 repeated.

Figure 10.4.8 Another circuit example.

For example, is $(1, 3) \leq (1, 2)$? If $(1, 3)$ were $\leq (1, 2)$, then all elements of $C[u]$ which have $\alpha_3 < 1$ must also have $\alpha_2 < 1$; this, however, is not true since for $\alpha = (1, 1, 0)$, which is an element of $C[u]$, we have $\alpha_3 < 1$ but $\alpha_2 \not< 1$. Thus $(1, 3) \not\leq (1, 2)$. For this circuit no element of $\Sigma_1[u]$ is $\leq$ any other element of $\Sigma_1[u]$, as may be checked by the reader.

A second example is the circuit of Figure 10.4.8, which is different from Figure 10.4.7 only in that the OR-element has been replaced with an AND-element. The partial state diagram for this circuit, comprising the states which can be reached from state $(0, 0, 0)$, is

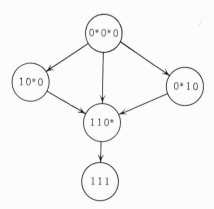

Obviously, this circuit is semi-modular with respect to state $(0, 0, 0)$.

The reader may find it instructive to construct the state diagram of all

states for this circuit and determine for which of the three missing states the circuit is semi-modular or speed independent.

If $u = (0, 0, 0)$ for this circuit, we obtain

$$C[u] = \{(0, 0, 0), (1, 0, 0), (0, 1, 0), (1, 1, 0), (1, 1, 1)\},$$
$$\Sigma[u] = \{(0, 1), (1, 1), (0, 2), (1, 2), (0, 3), (1, 3)\},$$

and

$$\Sigma_1[u] = \{(1, 1), (1, 2), (1, 3)\}.$$

In this case, however, we find that for the change chart we obtain the partial ordering

$$(1, 3) \leq (1, 1)$$

and

$$(1, 3) \leq (1, 2),$$

since whenever $\alpha_1 < 1$ or $\alpha_2 < 1$ we also have $\alpha_3 < 1$ for any element of $C[u]$. This means that both nodes 1 and 2 must change to a 1 before node 3 can change to a 1, which, of course, is quite obvious for the circuit in Figure 10.4.8.

As a final example we reconsider the totally sequential circuit of Figure 10.4.1, and repeat this circuit and state diagram in Figure 10.4.9. For

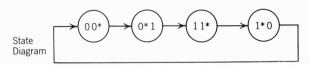

Figure 10.4.9    Figure 10.4.1 repeated.

this circuit if $u = (0, 0)$, then $C[u]$, $\Sigma[u]$, and $\Sigma_1[u]$ are infinite sets.

$$C[u] = \{(0, 0), (0, 1), (1, 1), (1, 2), (2, 2), (2, 3), (3, 3) \ldots\},$$
$$\Sigma[u] = \{(0, 1), (0, 2), (1, 1), (1, 2), (2, 1), (2, 2) \ldots\},$$

and

$$\Sigma_1[u] = \{(1, 1), (1, 2), (2, 1), (2, 2), \ldots\}.$$

The partial ordering on the change chart is a total ordering $(1, 2) \leq (1, 1) \leq (2, 2) \leq (2, 1) \ldots$, where, in general, $(j, 2) \leq (j, 1)$ and $(j, 1) \leq (j + 1, 2)$ for $j = 1, 2, \ldots$. For change charts for a circuit totally sequential with respect to some states, the following theorem is easily proved.

**Theorem 10.4.5** The change chart of $\Sigma_1[u]$ of a circuit is a total ordering if and only if the circuit is totally sequential with respect to $u$.

The change chart is not sufficient for predicting all change sequences in a semi-modular circuit, since some sequences of elements satisfying the partial ordering on $\Sigma_1[u]$ may not be change sequences. For example, the sequence $(1, 3)$, $(1, 2)$, $(1, 1)$ is not a change sequence for the circuit of Figure 10.4.7. Similarly, not all numerical vectors consistent with the ordering relations need be members of $C[u]$. For the circuit of Figure 10.4.7 the numerical vector $(0, 0, 1)$ is consistent with the partial ordering, but it is not an element of $C[u]$. A further restriction to "distributive" circuits eliminates this complication.

**Definition 10.4.7** A semi-modular circuit with respect to $u$ is *distributive* with respect to $u$ if every total ordering of $\Sigma_1[u]$ consistent with its partial ordering yields a change sequence of $C$-states.

In a distributive circuit, $\Sigma_1[u]$ uniquely determines $C[u]$. Also a circuit is distributive if and only if $C[u]$ is closed under $\alpha \wedge \beta$. Then $\alpha \wedge \beta = \alpha \cap \beta$ for the greatest lower bound of the lattice. Since $\alpha \wedge \beta = \alpha \cap \beta$, the distributive laws

$$\alpha \wedge (\beta \vee \gamma) = (\alpha \wedge \beta) \vee (\alpha \wedge \gamma)$$

and

$$\alpha \vee (\beta \wedge \gamma) = (\alpha \vee \beta) \wedge (\alpha \vee \gamma)$$

can be verified by simply the component properties of numerical vectors, and the lattice $C[u]$ is a distributive lattice for distributive circuits.

Since $\Sigma_1[u]$ determines uniquely $C[u]$ for distributive circuits, synthesis from the change chart to a distributive circuit can be accomplished. That is, if the change chart $\Sigma_1[u]$ is assumed given, one can determine $C[u]$ and the lattice ordering of $C[u]$. From $C[u]$ the states $B[u]$ can be obtained by the function $t[u, \alpha(j)]$, and the ordering of $C[u]$ gives the state diagram of the circuit. Finally, from the state diagram the $z_i'$ equations can be obtained immediately.

For synthesis several other considerations are crucial. First, it would be desirable to have one circuit perform several different but similar operations under the control of some inputs which were held constant during any one of these operations. Thus one would like to represent on one chart several different but similar change charts, and obtain one circuit for all of them. Second, one might desire to specify the sequences of changes on some of the nodes of the circuit, but not all the nodes, so that during synthesis additional nodes might be required to attain the desired sequencing. Both these objectives are attained in a *flow chart* for a circuit. On flow charts, the different change chart behavior is noted by conditions on the arrows, and the entries corresponding to states in a change chart may describe sequencing only on some of the nodes. A flow chart method of design is described in Section 10.6, and is an

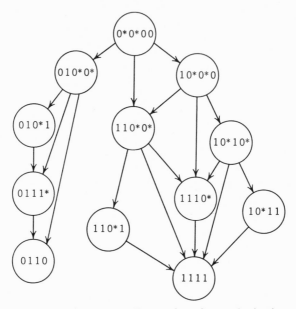

Figure 10.4.10   A state diagram for a four node circuit.

extremely convenient notation for the synthesis of distributive and semi-modular circuits.

As a final example in this section, consider the state diagram of Figure 10.4.10 for a circuit having four nodes. This circuit is not speed independent with respect to state 0000. It is speed independent, but not semi-modular with respect to state 0100. It is semi-modular, but not distributive with respect to state 1000. It is distributive, but not totally sequential with respect to state 1100. It is totally sequential with respect to state 0101 and it has equilibrium states 0110 and 1111.

### 10.5   AN INTERCONNECTION THEOREM FOR SEMI-MODULAR CIRCUITS

One of the problems in the design of a large digital system is the interconnection of several switching networks, each of which performs certain special operations required of the system. Normally this is done by interconnecting the outputs of one network to the inputs of another network, often by using memory elements to store the information between network output and network input. In complete circuits, however, there are no inputs or outputs of the circuits. Thus a different approach to the interconnection of complete circuits is required. In this section we discuss two theorems for the interconnection of semi-modular circuits that preserve semi-modularity and enable one to produce either series or parallel operation of semi-modular circuits. Finally, we show the effect of applying these results to simple counters like the scale of two counter of Figure 10.4.4.

**Theorem 10.5.1** Let $C$ be a circuit which is semi-modular with respect to a state $u$ and let $i$ be a node of $C$. If node $i$ is broken to form an input branch $i_1$ and an output branch $i_0$, and the signal of branch $i_1$ is held as the constant value $u_i$, with $C$ starting in state $u$, then the output branch $i_0$ can change value at most once.

PROOF. Assume $i_0$ can change twice or more. The break of node $i$ prevents the changes on $i_0$ from affecting the circuit elements in any way. Let element $I$ be the one having the output which corresponds to node $i$, and thus $I$ has output $i_0$.

Each change of node $i_0$ must occur by first having element $I$ excited and then changing to its implied value. Now to start with $i_0 = u_i$. For the first change on $i_0$ let the implied value be $a_i'$, and for the second change on $i_0$ let the implied value be $a_i''$. Since these are two changes on node $i_0$, $u_i \neq a_i'$ and $a_i' \neq a_i''$. Assume element $I$ acted slower so that the first change did not occur; then we reach a state such that $i_0 = u_i$ and the implied value is $a_i'$, but the implied value changes to $a_i''$ in the next state. That is, we have a state $a$ such that $u \mathscr{F} a$ and $a \mathscr{R} b$, where $u_i = a_i = b_i \neq a_i'$ but $b_i' = a_i'' \neq a_i'$. This latter condition contradicts the alternate definition of semi-modularity (Definition 10.4.2) and thus the theorem is proved.

Note that the single change on signal line $i_0$ can be considered to be a "reply" or external indication that the semi-modular circuit has recognized or accepted the signal value on $i_1$. If signal line $i_1$ is then changed to the value on $i_0$, as·would normally be the situation in the semi-modular circuit if node $i$ had not been broken, at some later time the signal value on $i_0$ may again change once. Each such change is a reply indicating acceptance of the signal on line $i_1$, where the signal on line $i_1$ can be thought of as a circuit input. This interpretation of line $i_0$ gives the basis for calling such a signal a "reply back signal." We shall see later in this section and the following section how these reply back signals can be used in the interconnection of circuits.

Since any node of a semi-modular circuit, once broken as in Theorem 10.5.1, can change at most once, we can interconnect semi-modular circuits as described in the next theorem.

**Theorem 10.5.2    (Interconnection Theorem)**    Let $A$ and $B$ be two circuits which are semi-modular with respect to state $a$ of $A$ and state $b$ of $B$, respectively, where node $i$ of circuit $B$ is the output of a NOT-element. Let node $j$ of circuit $A$ be broken as in Theorem 10.5.1 and replace the NOT-element of circuit $B$ where the NOT-element input is connected to $j_1$ and node $i$ is connected to $j_0$. If this replacement is made when the states of the circuit are $a(m)$ and $b(n)$, respectively, where $a \mathscr{F} a(m)$ and $b \mathscr{F} b(n)$, such that for states $a(m)$ and $b(n)$ the signal on $j_0$ equals that on $i_1$ and the signal on $j_1$ matches that on $i_0$. Then the resulting circuit is semi-modular with respect to the combined $[a(m), b(n)]$ state.

Note that since node $i$ of circuit $B$ corresponds to a NOT-element, the signal values on node $i$ of $B$, the input to the NOT-element and node $j$ of circuit $A$ must be binary-valued signals for this theorem to apply.

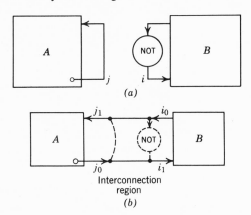

Figure 10.5.1    Illustration of interconnection theorem.

Figure 10.5.1 illustrates this interconnection theorem, where part $a$ shows circuits $A$ and $B$ before interconnection and part $b$ shows the resulting circuit after interconnection, where the NOT-element shown dotted has been removed and replaced with circuit $A$.

PROOF.    Theorem 10.5.2 can be shown by considering two cases:

1. When in state $b(n)$ the NOT-element is in equilibrium.
2. When in state $b(n)$ the NOT-element is excited.

1. The NOT-element is in equilibrium and thus for interconnection the signal on $j_0$ is not equal to that on $j_1$. This means that in state $a(m)$ for

circuit $A$, the element $J$, having output node $j$, has acted once since the break of node $j$. By Theorem 10.5.1 node $j$ will not act a second time provided the signal value on $j_1$ is not changed. The change of $j_1$ can occur only from circuit $B$, since it can change at most once for a change on $j_1$. Also circuit $B$ appears to circuit $A$ as if the element $J$ is acting slower than before the interconnection. Thus, since both $A$ and $B$ are semi-modular with respect to $a(m)$ and $b(n)$, respectively, it follows that the combined circuit is also semi-modular.

2. For this case the NOT-element is excited, so that for the interconnected signals to match we conclude that the signal on $j_0$ equals that on $j_1$, so that element $J$ has not acted since node $j$ was broken. If $j_0$ changes, this appears to circuit $B$ as if the NOT-element has acted. If $j_0$ does not change, this looks to circuit $B$ like the NOT-element is excited but has not acted. In other words, as if the output of the NOT-element had been broken. Thus circuit $B$ acts in a semi-modular fashion. Considering circuit $B$ with node $i$ broken, from Theorem 10.5.1 the resulting node $i_0$ can change at most once, so that the input signal to the NOT-element can change at most once. Thus, if $j_0$ changes, the signal $j_1$ can change at most once for circuit $A$. If $j_0$ changes, this appears to circuit $A$ as if element $J$ has acted slower than before interconnection; if $j_1$ does not change, this appears to circuit $A$ as if node $j$ is broken. Thus the combined circuit maintains semi-modularity in this case also, and the theorem is proved.

From Theorem 10.5.2, both series interconnection and parallel interconnection of semi-modular circuits are possible. Consider, for example,

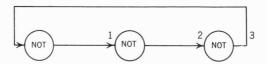

Figure 10.5.2   Basic circuit for series interconnection.

the circuit of Figure 10.5.2. This circuit is totally sequential, and thus semi-modular, with respect to any state $a$ in which we do not have $a_1 = a_2 = a_3$. For example, if $a = (010)$, then the state diagram of states following $a$ is

$$010 \rightarrow 110 \rightarrow 100$$
$$\uparrow \qquad\qquad \downarrow$$
$$011 \leftarrow 001 \leftarrow 101.$$

By Theorem 10.5.2 the NOT-elements 1 and 2 can each be replaced by semi-modular circuits by breaking a node in each circuit. This interconnection is shown in Figure 10.5.3.

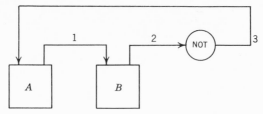

Figure 10.5.3   Series interconnection of circuits $A$ and $B$.

For the circuit of Figure 10.5.2 we see that the NOT-elements act in sequence, or series, as follows.  Starting with state 010, element 1 acts first, then element 2, then element 3, etc.  In the circuit of Figure 10.5.3 the circuits $A$ and $B$ replace NOT-elements 1 and 2 and if each is connected satisfying Theorem 10.5.2, the resulting circuit is semi-modular.  Also the operation of circuit $A$ mimicks the operation of NOT-element 1 in terms of the circuit action on the broken node of circuit $A$.  The same is true for circuit $B$.  Thus we find that the operation of circuits $A$ and $B$ are now serial.  If started in state 010 for the labeled 1, 2, and 3 nodes, then circuit $A$ is allowed to act first.  After circuit $A$ has acted and indicated its action by changing the signal value on node 1, then circuit $B$ is allowed to act.  Similarly, circuit $B$ may indicate its action by changing node 2; then NOT-element 3 reacts again allowing circuit $A$ to react, etc.

The circuit of Figure 10.5.4, which was also discussed earlier, is used as a basic circuit for interconnecting circuits to perform parallel operation.

This circuit is semi-modular with respect to any possible state;  in particular, if state (000) is used to start the circuit, then both the NOT-elements are excited and tend to act in parallel.  After both NOT-elements change to 1, the $C$-element changes to 1.  This again excites both NOT-elements to change from 0 to 1.  After both have changed, the $C$-element

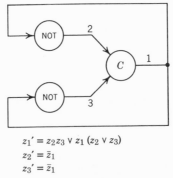

$z_1' = z_2 z_3 \vee z_1 (z_2 \vee z_3)$
$z_2' = \bar{z}_1$
$z_3' = \bar{z}_1$

Figure 10.5.4   Basic circuit for parallel interconnection.

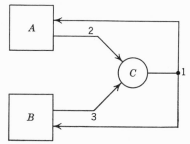

Figure 10.5.5 Parallel interconnection of circuits $A$ and $B$.

is excited and may change from 1 to 0, bringing us back to the original state (000), after which the operations are repeated.

Using Theorem 10.5.2, we can replace each NOT-element of the circuit shown in Figure 10.5.4 with a semi-modular circuit by breaking a node of each circuit for this interconnection. This interconnection of circuits is shown in Figure 10.5.5. As can be checked by the reader, circuits $A$ and $B$ replace NOT-elements 2 and 3 such that these two circuits operate in a parallel fashion as just described for their corresponding NOT-elements.

Figures 10.5.3 and 10.5.5 show the basic series and parallel interconnections of semi-modular circuits, respectively. It is evident that more complex series-parallel interconnections of semi-modular circuits are possible by using extensions of the basic circuits of Figures 10.5.2 and 10.5.4 for more circuits in series and more circuits in parallel, respectively, and also by interconnecting these basic circuits into desired series-parallel configurations before the NOT-elements are replaced with semi-modular circuits.

As an application of a simple interconnection of semi-modular circuits, consider two semi-modular counter circuits similar to Figure 10.4.4, where circuit $A$ is a "scale of $n$" counter from node $i$ to node $j$; and circuit $B$ is a "scale of $m$" counter from node $k$ to node $l$. Breaking node $j$ of circuit $A$ and node $k$ of circuit $B$, we can series interconnect these circuits as in Figure 10.5.3. For two counters this interconnection is shown in Figure 10.5.6.

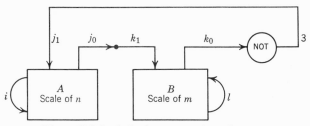

Figure 10.5.6 Series interconnection of counters.

Because of the series operation of $A$ and $B$, we can consider the counting action between nodes $i$ and $l$. For each set of $n$ changes on node $i$, there is one change on $j_0$. When $j_0$ changes by the interconnection, signal $k_1$ changes. When the change on $k_1$ is recognized by circuit $B$, signal $k_0$ will change to indicate this recognition. This signal change on $k_0$ is called a *reply back signal* since it indicates that the information of a change on $k_1$ has been accepted by circuit $B$. When $k_0$ changes, this forces the NOT-element to be excited; and when $j_1$ changes, this acts as a "reply back" signal to circuit $A$, noting that $B$ has accepted the signal change on $j_0$. After $n$ times $m$ changes on node $i$, there have been $m$ changes on node $k_1$, and thus node $l$ changes for the first time. Thus from node $i$ to node $l$ we have a "scale of $n \times m$" counter. Thus this series interconnection of counters has the effect of multiplying the scales of the two interconnected circuits.

## 10.6  A FLOW CHART APPROACH FOR CIRCUIT DESIGN

Although a synthesis procedure for distributive circuits has been briefly discussed in Section 10.4, which uses the change chart as a form of circuit specification, there are two main practical disadvantages to this procedure. First, in the change chart, its partial ordering requires the specification of the changes on each node of the circuit, whereas one is usually interested in the relative changes of only a few nodes of the circuit. For example, in the scale of two counter of Figure 10.4.4, the scale of two counting was accomplished by the interrelation of changes occurring on two nodes of the circuit, and the third node was simply an auxiliary node required for totally sequential operation. Ideally, it would be desirable to have a synthesis procedure that inserted nodes when required. Second, from the change chart specification, the synthesis procedure leads directly to a definite set of $z'$ equations, so that there is no choice in the type of elements to be used in the circuit. Thus some of the $z'$ equations may specify rather complex elements that are impractical to make. Furthermore, the theory does not allow such a complex element to be replaced by a switching network of elements, since such a replacement introduces additional nodes into the circuit that may change the circuit from a distributive circuit to a nonspeed independent circuit having erroneous operation.

A precise synthesis procedure, which overcomes these two difficulties, would be of considerable interest. Short of this, we discuss a rather practical method of specifying the general operation of certain types of circuits by a flow chart. We then present certain basic semi-modular circuits that perform the operations of the flow chart and the inter-connection of these basic circuits as specified by the structure of the flow chart. In particular, we describe the flow chart and circuits used in the design of the arithmetic control for Illiac II [4, 18].

Only a few basic operations are required for an arithmetic control: (1) gate information into an arithmetic register by energizing a gate driver circuit, (2) set a selector mechanism to open certain data paths and close other data paths, and (3) set a control flip-flop for temporary storage of information. Each gate driver, selector, and control flip-flop is named.

The flow chart consists of a block diagram interconnected by arrows. Each block or box designates one operation or several operations which are to be performed in parallel, and these are indicated in each box by their respective names. The arrows between blocks designate the sequencing of the oper-ations, that is, what operations are to be done next when those of any given block have just been completed. For example, the block diagram of Figure 10.6.1 illustrates a simple flow chart for performing two gates in parallel; gate *A*, labeled *gA*, and gate *B*, labeled *gB*, operate first, and after both *gA* and *gB* are completed, the two other gates *gC* and *gD* are to operate in parallel. This operation is to be performed cyclically, and thus the arrow from the *gC*, *gD* box returns to the first box *gA*, *gB*.

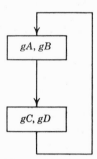

Figure 10.6.1 A simple flow chart.

Before giving a circuit realization for the flow chart of Figure 10.6.1, we specify in greater detail the sequences of operations performed for each of the basic operations of gating, selecting, and setting of flip-flops which are used to insure speed independent operation. The symbol *gY* indicates the operation of a gating signal. This operation consists of (1) the "turn on" of the signal, (2) a check that the gate driver is turned on, (3) the "turn off" of the signal, and (4) a check that the gate driver is turned off. This sequence of four operations is assumed to be completed before one is allowed to proceed to the next box of the flow chart. Steps (2) and (4) are essentially "reply back" signals required of the circuitry to indicate that the gate driver has been turned on and turned off, respectively.

For the selector mechanism, the following sequence of operations is required: (1) switch the selector to some desired state, (2) check that the selector has been switched, and (3) check that the decision elements used in the switching have returned to an equilibrium condition. The state of a selector circuit consists of a memory and associated logic which

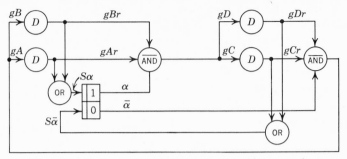

Figure 10.6.2   A circuit to perform parallel gating operations.

enables and disables certain gate drivers to be open or closed for a desired set of data paths.

The sequence of operations for setting a control flip-flop are similar to those for the selector: (1) set the flip-flop, (2) check to see if the flip-flop is set, and (3) check that the decision elements to set the flip-flop have returned to an equilibrium condition.

In all three of these sequences of operation, "reply back" signals are assumed to be formed immediately after the turning on or turning off of a signal, so that only after the reply signal is obtained will the next operation be allowed to be started. Although such replies provide a continuous check on semi-modular operation, they are signals not

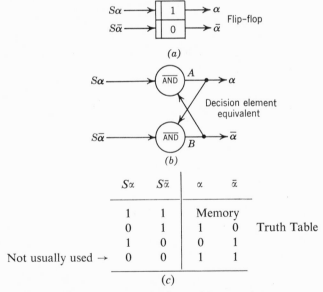

Figure 10.6.3   Flip-flop and its operation.

required in the general development of the theory. Whether the use of reply back signals is essential to semi-modular circuits or whether other methods of design not requiring generation of reply back signals at each step are possible are two problems deserving further study.

A circuit which performs the operations of the flow chart of Figure 10.6.1 is shown in Figure 10.6.2.

The $D$-elements are simply delay elements indicating that some delay is involved between the gate signals and the reply signals. The symbols $\overline{\text{AND}}$ are used to designate functions $\overline{(x_1 x_2 x_3)}$, and the symbol $\boxed{-\dfrac{1}{0}}$ is used to designate a special type of flip-flop. The operation and decision element equivalent of this flip-flop are shown in Figure 10.6.3.

Signals of 0 on either the $S\alpha$ or $S\bar{\alpha}$ lines are used to set the flip-flop to a desired state; thus both $S\alpha$ and $S\bar{\alpha}$ of 0 are not usually applied to the flip-flop. If $\alpha = 1$ and $\bar{\alpha} = 0$ with $S\alpha = S\bar{\alpha} = 1$ and we wish to reverse the setting of the flip-flop, we set $S\bar{\alpha}$ to 0. This excites $\overline{\text{AND}}$-element $B$ of Figure 10.6.3$b$, but leaves element $A$ in equilibrium. When element $B$ reacts, changing to a 1, element $A$ is excited and will eventually change to a 0, completing the resetting of the flip-flop.

Now the operation of the circuit of Figure 10.6.2 can be described. A slightly simplified state diagram for this circuit is shown in Table 10.6.1.

**Table 10.6.1**   Sequence of Operations for Figure 10.6.2

| $S\alpha$ | $S\bar{\alpha}$ | $\alpha$ | $\bar{\alpha}$ | $\begin{cases} gA \\ gB \end{cases}$ | $gAr$ | $gBr$ | $\begin{cases} gC \\ gD \end{cases}$ | $gCr$ | $gDr$ |
|---|---|---|---|---|---|---|---|---|---|
| →1 | 1 | 0 | 1 | 0 | 1* | 1* | 1 | 1 | 1 |
| 1* | 1 | 0 | 1 | 0 | 0 | 0 | 1 | 1 | 1 |
| 0 | 1 | 0* | 1 | 0 | 0 | 0 | 1 | 1 | 1 |
| 0 | 1 | 1 | 1* | 0 | 0 | 0 | 1 | 1 | 1 |
| 0 | 1 | 1 | 0 | 0* | 0 | 0 | 1 | 1 | 1 |
| 0 | 1 | 1 | 0 | 1 | 0* | 0* | 1 | 1 | 1 |
| 0* | 1 | 1 | 0 | 1 | 1 | 0* | 1 | 1 | 1 |
| 1 | 1 | 1 | 0 | 1 | 1 | 0* | 1 | 1 | 1 |
| 1 | 1 | 1 | 0 | 1 | 1 | 1 | 1* | 1 | 1 |
| 1 | 1 | 1 | 0 | 1 | 1 | 1 | 0 | 1* | 1* |
| 1 | 1* | 1 | 0 | 1 | 1 | 1 | 0 | 0 | 0 |
| 1 | 0 | 1 | 0* | 1 | 1 | 1 | 0 | 0 | 0 |
| 1 | 0 | 1* | 1 | 1 | 1 | 1 | 0 | 0 | 0 |
| 1 | 0 | 0 | 1 | 1 | 1 | 1 | 0* | 0 | 0 |
| 1 | 0 | 0 | 1 | 1 | 1 | 1 | 1 | 0* | 0* |
| 1 | 0* | 0 | 1 | 1 | 1 | 1 | 1 | 0* | 1 |
| └─1 | 1 | 0 | 1 | 1* | 1 | 1 | 1 | 1 | 1 |

In this table signals $gA$ and $gB$ are grouped together as one signal since they correspond to the output of only one element; similarly for $gC$ and $gD$.

Starting in state 1101011111 both gates $gA$ and $gB$ are 0, which we interpret as being on, and the reply signals $gAr$ and $gBr$ are not as yet on, being still equal to 1. Both $gAr$ and $gBr$ are tending to change, however, and after both change, the or-element for $S\alpha$ becomes excited, but all other signals remain in equilibrium. After the flip-flop changes, we arrive at state 0110000111 and signals $gA$ and $gB$ are excited to return to

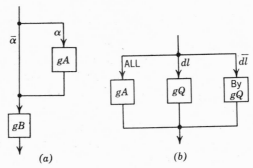

Figure 10.6.4   Conditional control labels in flow charts.

1 (that is, be turned off). When $gA$, $gB$ become 1, $gAr$ and $gBr$ tend to 1. As soon as either $gAr$ or $gBr$ changes to a 1, the signal $S\alpha$ is excited and can change to a 1. In the table we show $gAr$ operating first, then $S\alpha$; but at this point $gBr$ must change to a 1 before the $gC$, $gD$ signal is excited (that is, tends to be turned on from 1 to 0). Thus we see that so far in the sequence of operations we have obtained replies saying that $gA$ and $gB$ are turned on. Then we have "turned off" $gA$ and $gB$; whereupon replies are obtained saying that both $gA$ and $gB$ are turned off. After these replies are obtained, both $gC$ and $gD$ are "turned on" and the circuit sequences through a similar operation for $gC$ and $gD$ as explained for $gA$ and $gB$. When both replies indicating the turn off of $gC$ and $gD$ are obtained, that is, $gCr = gDr = 1$, gates $gA$ and $gB$ are again energized, returning to the original state 1101011111 so that cycling can commence.

For the circuit of Figure 10.6.2, gates $A$ and $B$ were to operate in parallel under all conditions whenever gates $C$ and $D$ were completed. Sometimes the operation of a gate, selector, or flip-flop is to be dependent on some other conditions in the network. This dependence or *conditional operation* may be expressed, for example, by some Boolean function of network signals. The conditional operation or setting is indicated on the flow chart by symbols on the arrow leading into a box of a flow chart; for example, two different conditional operations are shown in Figure 10.6.4. In both these flow charts each of the conditions $\alpha$, $\bar{\alpha}$, $dl$, and $\overline{dl}$

must be defined elsewhere by some signal of the circuit. Also the alternative conditions should be mutually exclusive and one must always be true. In (*a*) the gate *gA* is to be operated on reaching this part of the flow chart if condition α is present, and after this gate *gB* is to be operated. If condition α is not present, $\bar{\alpha}$ is true and gate *gB* is to be operated, bypassing the operation of gate *gA*. For (*b*) the gate *gA* is to be operated

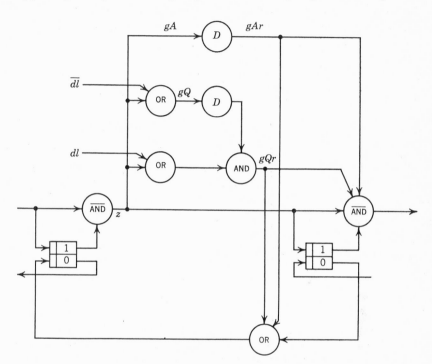

Figure 10.6.5    Circuit to realize flow chart of Figure 10.6.4*b*.

under all conditions, and for clarity the word "all" is written on this arrow. If condition *dl* is present, *gQ* is to be operated in parallel with *gA*; but if $\overline{dl}$ is true, gate *gQ* is not to be operated, but rather gate *gQ* is to be bypassed. A circuit for realizing this flow chart is shown in Figure 10.6.5.

The reader may note the similarity between this circuit and that in Figure 10.6.2. In both the operation and sensing of the flip-flops are performed by similar configurations of OR-elements and $\overline{\text{AND}}$-elements. This circuit, however, is not a complete circuit since the previous and next operations are not shown on the flow chart. Thus inputs and reply back signals emit from both the left and the right sides of the circuit to connect to the respective previous and next operations. Note that for this circuit, when signal $z$ goes from 1 to 0, gate $gA$ is turned on. In addition, if condition $dl = 1$, so that $\overline{dl} = 0$, gate $gQ$ is also turned on after the OR-element changes from 1 to 0. If $dl = 0$, however, $gQ$ is bypassed. In either case one of the inputs to the AND-element $gQr$ will change from 1 to 0. When both $gQr$ and $gAr$ are 0, the OR-element will change the state of the left-most flip-flop so that the gates will be turned off. By line $z$ feeding the right-hand $\overline{\text{AND}}$-element, the next operations cannot start until both $gAr$ and $gQr$ are returned to 1 and also $z = 1$.

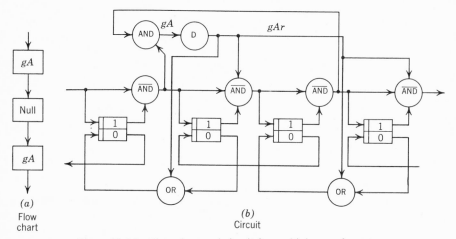

**Figure 10.6.6** Flow chart and circuit for multiple use of a gate.

Frequently, in a large flow chart one desires to use the same gate in more than one box of the flow chart. Furthermore, when a gate is to be operated immediately after operation, it may be necessary to insert a *null operation* between the successive gate operations in order to maintain speed independence. Such a flow chart and associated circuit are shown in Figure 10.6.6, again using a configuration similar to that of Figures 10.6.2 and 10.6.5.

This circuit operates similarly to the two previously discussed circuits, where, in this circuit, the upper left-hand AND-element serves the purpose of allowing gate $gA$ to be activated at each of the two points shown in the flow chart.

The operation of a selector requires a setting and a memory of the setting desired. A simplified circuit for a selector, which we call selector $X$ and denote by the symbol $sX$, is shown in Figure 10.6.7. This selector has three possible different settings labeled $AsX$, $BsX$, and $CsX$. The operation of this circuit can be described briefly as follows. Assume that the selector is set to have $AsX = 1$, $BsX = 0$, and $CsX = 0$. This corresponds to having the selector set in condition $AsX$. Normally, the set signals entering the left of this circuit are all ones, unless it is desired to change the setting of the selector. With the given values on $AsX$, $BsX$, and $CsX$, an equilibrium state of the circuit can be easily calculated. Now assume we wish to set $sX$ to condition $BsX$. One of the signals to set the selector to $BsX$

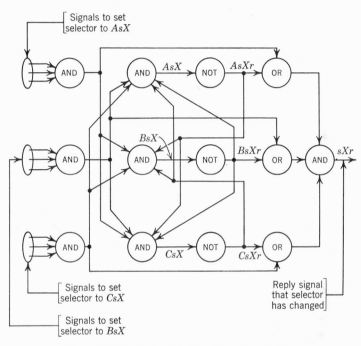

Figure 10.6.7   A simplified version of a selector.

indicates this by becoming 0. The AND-element thus becomes 0, causing the AND-element for $AsX$ to be excited to change from 1 to 0. Then the NOT-element $AsXr$ changes from 0 to 1. This change causes signal $BsX$ to tend to change from 0 to 1, as desired. Then $BsXr$ becomes 0, which allows the OR-element to change to 0, eventually giving a reply signal of $sXr = 0$. By symmetry of the circuit one can see that the selector can be set to any condition by similar changes. Furthermore, if more than three conditions are required of a selector, additional chains of AND-, NOT-, OR-elements can be added to the circuit with additional crosscoupling as required for the additional elements.

The setting of a control flip-flop and reply signal for the setting is attained by a circuit very similar to the selector circuit. This circuit is shown in Figure 10.6.8, where the AND-elements are crosscoupled to make a flip-flop as was done in Figure 10.6.3. When setting this flip-flop with a 0 signal on either $S\alpha$ or $S\bar{\alpha}$, the reader may check that a reply signal of $S\alpha r = 0$ will be attained after the flip-flop has been set.

The basic circuits to realize a flow chart have now been described. Minor extensions of the designs are possible to provide for variations in flow chart structure.

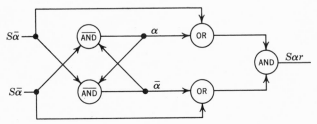

Figure 10.6.8    Control flip-flop circuit.

In general, the method of design using flow charts takes on the following pattern.

1. Create a flow chart for each sequence of operations to be performed.

2. Combine the various flow charts, when possible, for sections having similar sequences of operations.

3. Using the basic circuits, realize each section of the flow chart.

4. Interconnect basic circuits by the interconnection rules and reply back signals.

5. Check out circuits by an analysis program.

As indicated by these five steps, much of the success of the synthesis by flow chart depends on the skill of the person to attain good flow charts in Steps 1 and 2. Methods of analysis, based on the theory discussed in Sections 10.2 through 10.4, have been devised to perform the analysis for Step 5 by computer programs. The method of attaining the basic circuits discussed earlier in this section is also somewhat of an art, using trial and error in combination with the analysis programs of Step 5.

Several areas for further development of synthesis procedures should now be fairly apparent. First, no mention has been made of an equivalence between circuits or of any approach for obtaining an "economical" circuit to perform a given sequence of operations. In addition, further connections between the theory and flow chart method of design might lead to more direct methods of obtaining practical circuits to perform desired operations.

## 10.7 SOME PRACTICAL PROBLEMS IN THE PHYSICAL REALIZATION OF SPEED INDEPENDENT CIRCUITS

Several basic assumptions in the theory for speed independent circuits do not coincide perfectly with the physical realization of these circuits using electronic gate-type elements. In this section we discuss the effects of several of the differences between the abstract model and the actual circuits, and then show practical solutions to the problems arising from these differences.

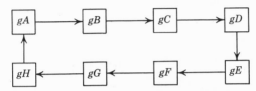

Figure 10.7.1   Flow chart for cycle of eight gates.

Each of the definitions for a circuit being speed independent, semi-modular, distributive, or totally sequential is made with respect to some initial state $u$ of the circuit. Thus for the circuit to have the desired behavior, it must be started in the initial state $u$. As an example of how this may create problems in a practical circuit, imagine a circuit to realize a cyclic sequence of eight gates as shown in the flow chart of Figure 10.7.1.

A circuit to realize this flow chart may be obtained easily by modifying the basic circuits of the previous section. The circuit will be semi-modular with respect to a state $u$, where $u$ is a state having one gate signal on and all other gate signals off. If, however, the circuit starts (or, by a transient malfunction, is placed) in a state in which two gates are simultaneously on—say $gA$ and $gE$—then the circuit is not speed independent with respect to this state. Notice that it may either keep cycling with two gates on, or one sequence of gates being on may catch up to the other sequence of gates being on. To remedy this difficulty in practical circuits, one must insure that the circuit is started in an appropriate state. Even so, however, if a transient malfunction causes one to go to an unexpected state, this malfunction may be very hard to detect, since it may cause a rather long and unpredicted sequence of operations to follow.

Another assumption of the theory is that a circuit may attain only a finite number of states. Thus, when signals are used to represent states, we assume that each signal line can attain only a finite number of values. In all the circuits discussed, we considered only binary-valued signal

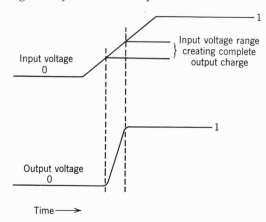

Figure 10.7.2   Input-output signals represented by voltages.

lines having values 0 or 1. In practice, this binary character of the signal value may be realized by a voltage $v_s$, such that if $v_s \geq v$, the signal value is interpreted as a 1 and if $v_s < v$, the signal value is interpreted as a 0. In practice, the voltage values on a line change in a continuous fashion rather than taking on only two values. Also, a small range of change on an input to a decision element may cause the output of the element to change through its entire range. This effect is illustrated in Figure 10.7.2.

Because of the tolerance of components in an element, the exact range that causes an output change may be different for different decision elements. Thus, if one signal is connected to inputs of several decision elements, one of these elements may sense the signal as changing at a different time from some other element. For example, consider signal $gAr$ of Figure 10.7.3, which acts as an input to an AND-element and as an input to flip-flop.

In the theory we assume that the $gAr$ signal changes from 0 to 1 and 1 to 0 at exactly the same moment for the AND-element and flip-flop $B$. If we assume that the AND-element and flip-flop have different sensing levels for the change of $gAr$, then either of two actions can occur: (1) for

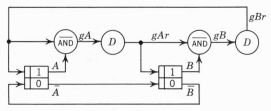

Figure 10.7.3   Circuit demonstrating difficulty with sensing of signal level.

$gAr$ changing from 1 to 0 the change is sensed on the flip-flop before on the $\overline{\text{AND}}$-element, and for $gAr$ changing from 0 to 1 the change is sensed on the $\overline{\text{AND}}$-element before on the flip-flop; or (2) for $gAr$ changing from 1 to 0 the change is sensed on the $\overline{\text{AND}}$-element before on the flip-flop, and for $gAr$ changing from 0 to 1 the change is sensed on the flip-flop before on the $\overline{\text{AND}}$-element.

We now see how the states of the circuit may change for cases (1) and (2) on the sensing of change of $gAr$. Assuming that case (1) holds, and we start in a state with $gA$ on, but $gAr$ not yet changed from 1 to 0, we obtain the following possible changes:

| $gBr$ | $A$ | $\bar{A}$ | $gA$ | $\bar{B}$ | $\overline{\text{AND}}$ | $B$ | $\bar{B}$ | $gB$ |
|-------|-----|-----------|------|-----------|-------------------------|-----|-----------|------|
| 1 | 1 | 0 | 0 | 1* | 1* | 0 | 1 | 1 |
| 1 | 1 | 0 | 0 | 0 | 1* | 0* | 1 | 1 |
| 1 | 1 | 0 | 0 | 0 | 1* | 1 | 1* | 1* |

(Column header group: $gAr$ spanning $\bar{B}$ and $\overline{\text{AND}}$)

Thus, if flip-flop $B$ starts changing with signal $B$ going from 0 to 1 before the $gAr$ input to the $\overline{\text{AND}}$-element is sensed as a 0 by the $\overline{\text{AND}}$-element, signal $gB$ can be energized to change from 1 to 0 (that is, be turned on) before signal $gA$ has been turned off. This gives incorrect operation of the circuit. To counteract this difficulty, one must insure that the sensing levels on the flip-flop and $\overline{\text{AND}}$-element satisfy case 2 rather than 1. The reader may check that the circuit operates correctly when the ordering of changes satisfies case 2, both for the 1 to 0 and 0 to 1 changes of signal $gAr$, where similar ordering of signal changes is also assumed for the elements with input $gBr$. In practice, it is quite simple to insure that the sensing levels satisfy case 2, say by changing the voltage level with a resistor voltage divider. Although it is simple, however, it is an important deviation from the theory.

The last difference between the basic theoretical model and practical circuits to be discussed here concerns the theoretical assumption that any delay of signals occurs in the decision elements and no delay occurs along the lines interconnecting the elements. Actually, there is a delay along each line in a physical electronic circuit. Thus, if the output of an element serves as the input to two or more elements and the delays along the different input lines are considerably different, then the abstract model does not faithfully represent the circuit. Indeed, delay elements may have to be added to the logical circuit description to simulate the delays of the line. If a delay is added, however, a circuit which was speed independent without the delay element may no longer be speed independent. Consider, for example, the circuit of Figure 10.6.6, redrawn in Figure 10.7.4, where a line delay has been inserted as shown in the *gAr* signal line.

Assume in this circuit that *gA* has just been turned off from 0 to 1. When *gAr* goes from 0 to 1, as a result of the added delay element, the *gAr* signal, marked *gAr'*, does not immediately change from 0 to 1. The

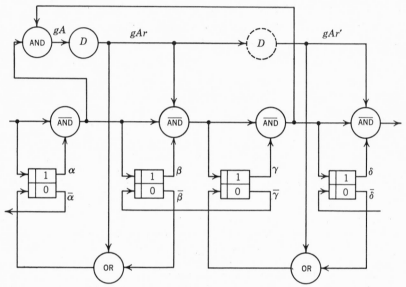

Figure 10.7.4.   Figure 10.6.6 redrawn with added delay element.

AND-element, fed by *gAr* and $\beta$, can now change from 1 to 0, which then sets $\gamma = 1$, $\bar{\gamma} = 0$, which then sets $\bar{\beta} = 1$, $\beta = 0$. When $\beta$ becomes 0, the $\overline{\text{AND}}$-element fed by $\beta$ changes back from 0 to 1 and now, since $\gamma = 1$, the $\overline{\text{AND}}$-element fed by $\gamma$ changes from 1 to 0, which then feeds the AND-element to again turn on *gA*. Furthermore, with the $\overline{\text{AND}}$-element fed by $\gamma$ going to 0, the $\delta$ flip-flop is set to have $\delta = 1$, $\bar{\delta} = 0$. When $\bar{\delta}$ goes to 0, if *gAr'* is still equal to 0, the $\gamma$ flip-flop can be reset to $\gamma = 0$, $\gamma = 1$, which would then, through the $\overline{\text{AND}}$-element and AND-element, turn off *gA*. Thus *gA* has been turned on and off without proper control by the *gAr* signal, and this is an error. Note also that the added delay element could have been excited and then been unexcited without acting in this sequence of changes and thus the circuit is no longer semi-modular.

The sequence of changes just examining is extremely unlikely to occur in practice, however, since eight changes have to occur before the *gAr'* signal changes once from 0 to 1 to the OR-element. In practice, this separation by eight changes is sufficient for correct operation since the line delay takes much less time to change than eight element changes. Thus the circuit of Figure 10.7.4 is not truly speed independent because an element delay of any length of time less than infinity is allowed in the theoretical model; but for correct operation here, the added delay element in this circuit must have a delay less than that required for the sequence of eight changes described.

## 10.8  CONCLUDING REMARKS

In concluding this chapter we discuss some relative advantages and disadvantages of speed independent versus synchronous sequential circuits which should be weighed when considering using speed independent circuits for any particular application.

Some of the advantages of speed independent circuits are the following

1. The circuit will perform a desired sequence of operations even when the operating speeds of the individual decision elements are not known or changes with time because of tolerance, aging of components, or other effects.

2. From the interpretation of reply back signals in semi-modular circuits, it is clear that if some element fails to act when it becomes excited, the reply back signal will never indicate completion of the operation containing this element. This causes the circuit to stop. For diagnosis of the failure, this stop condition makes it quite simple to analyze the circuit and find the failing element.

3. Since each operation generates its own completion signal, in operations that may require a variable length of time one can proceed to the next operation immediately on receiving the completion signal of the previous operation, rather than having to wait the maximum length of time that the operation might take before proceeding.

4. In semi-modular and distributive circuits, using interconnection Theorem 10.5.2, one obtains great flexibility in allowing parallel unhazardous operations.

5. No basic timing signal (or clock) is required as a common input to all elements of the circuit as is required in synchronous circuits.

There are also some disadvantages in using speed independent circuits.

1. It is much more difficult to design speed independent circuits, in general, than synchronous circuits, except where the flow chart and a few basic circuits are all that is required for some specialized type of design.

2. It takes some circuitry and time to generate and transmit the reply back signals between interconnected circuits. The increased circuit complexity may be undesirable, especially when generating replies from very parallel operations like arithmetic registers. Also, the time to produce the replies may be less than, or greater than, normal safety factors required for synchronous operation for some applications. If the time required to generate and transmit replies is greater, the resulting slower operation of the speed independent circuit may be undesirable.

3. Since certain parts of large systems, such as memory units, seem to be inherently synchronous in operation, if speed independent circuits are used in such systems, there must be circuits to provide a suitable interconnection of the synchronous and speed independent circuits.

4. Finally, since the theory for equivalence of speed independent circuits has not been totally developed, it is more difficult to find and compare the cost of various possible circuit designs for any desired operation.

**Exercises**

1. Prove that if $C$ is a circuit which is semi-modular with respect to state $u$ and state $a$ is related to $u$ by $u \mathscr{F} a$, $C$ is also semi-modular with respect to state $a$.
2. (*a*) Determine what race conditions, if any, occur on the following circuit and the possible transient response of the output, when the circuit is initially in the equilibrium condition $x_1 = 1$, $x_2 = 0$, $x_3 = 1$, $x_4 = 0$, $\alpha = 0$, $\beta = 1$, $\gamma = 1$, and $z = 0$, and the input $x_3$ is changed from 1 to 0.

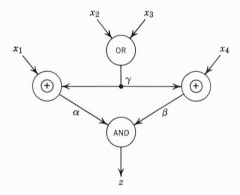

(*b*) Another circuit having the same output function $z = f(x_1, x_2, x_3, x_4)$ is shown here. With this circuit initially having equilibrium values $x_1 = 1$, $x_2 = 0$, $x_3 = 1$, $x_4 = 0$, $\alpha = 1$, $\beta = 0$, $\gamma = 1$, $z = 0$, analyze this circuit for transient output response when $x_3$ changes from 1 to 0.

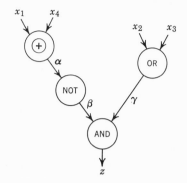

(c) Is either circuit free of output transients for all possible equilibrium conditions followed by a single input value change?

3. For the complete circuit shown determine:
   (a) The state diagram for the circuit.
   (b) Which states, if any, are equilibrium states.
   (c) The states *u* for which the circuit is semi-modular with respect to *u*.

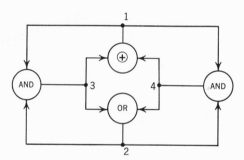

4. Using two binary signals, design a complete circuit realizing the following state diagram, where state *a* is encoded as (0, 0).

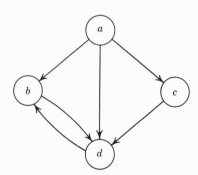

5. (*a*) Give the state diagram for the following circuit.

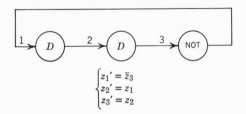

$$\begin{cases} z_1' = \bar{z}_3 \\ z_2' = z_1 \\ z_3' = z_2 \end{cases}$$

   (*b*) Determine all states of the circuit for which the circuit is
   (1) Totally sequential.
   (2) Distributive.
   (3) Semi-modular.
   (4) Speed independent.
   (5) Nonspeed independent.
6. For the two node circuit described by the equations

$$z_1' = \bar{z}_1 \vee z_2,$$
$$z_2' = z_1 \vee z_2,$$

   (*a*) Determine the state diagram.
   (*b*) Find the equivalence classes of states.
   (*c*) Classify each equivalence class as terminal, or nonterminal, and the terminal classes as maximal or pseudo-maximal.
7. (*a*) Analyze the following circuit, determining its state diagram.

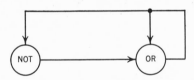

   (*b*) Is this circuit totally sequential with respect to state $(0, 0)$?

REFERENCE NOTATIONS

   The development of speed independent switching circuit theory is due to Muller [8–12]. The discussion of Sections 10.2 to 10.4 is primarily based on [9]. A short introduction to speed independent circuits is also given in [7]. Interconnection theorems, as discussed in Section 10.5 appear in [8]. Counting circuits are considered in some detail by Nelson [14]. The flow chart methods of design are discussed in Gillies [4] and Swartwout [18, 19]. Shelly discusses change chart synthesis in [17]. Other work on synthesis procedures can be found in [2] and [20].
   The practical circuit problems discussed in Section 10.7 follow the work of Robertson [15]. Several computer programs for testing a circuit for speed independence are discussed in [1] and [3]. Finally, in [13], Muller considers an extension of regular expressions which are closely related to allowed sequences of speed independent circuits.

## REFERENCES

1. Bartky, W. S. and D. E. Muller, "An Illiac Program for Simulating the Behavior of Asynchronous Logical Circuits and Detecting Undesirable Race Conditions," File Report No. 221, University of Illinois, Digital Computer Laboratory, and Presented at the ACM National Meeting, Houston, Texas, June 1957.
2. Bartky, W. S., "A Theory of Asynchronous Circuits III," Report No. 96, University of Illinois, Digital Computer Laboratory, January 1960.
3. Frazer, W. D. and D. E. Muller, "A Method for Factoring the Action of Asynchronous Circuits," *Proceedings of the First Annual AIEE Symposium on Switching Circuit Theory and Logical Design*, Vol. S-134 pp. 246–249, October 1961.
4. Gillies, Donald, B., "A Flow Chart Notation for the Description of a Speed-Independent Control", *Proceedings of the Second Annual AIEE Symposium on Switching Circuit Theory and Logical Design*, Detroit, Michigan, Vol. S-134, October 1961.
5. Huffman, D. A., "The Synthesis of Sequential Switching Circuits," *Journal of the Franklin Institute*, Vol. 257, Nos. 3 and 4, pp. 161–190 and 275–303, March and April 1954.
6. Huffman, D. A., "The Design and Use of Hazard-Free Switching Networks," *Journal of the ACM*, Vol. 4, No. 41, pp. 47–62, January 1957.
7. Miller, R. E., "An Introduction to Speed Independent Circuit Theory," *Proceedings of the Second Annual AIEE Symposium on Switching Circuit Theory and Logical Design*, Detroit, Michigan, Vol. S-134, pp. 87–93, October 1961.
8. Muller, D. E., "A Theory of Asynchronous Circuits," Report No. 66, University of Illinois, Digital Computer Laboratory, December 1955.
9. Muller, D. E., "Lecture Notes on Asynchronous Circuit Theory," Spring 1961, University of Illinois, Digital Computer Laboratory.
10. Muller, D. E. and W. S. Bartky, "A Theory of Asynchronous Circuits," *Proceedings of an International Symposium on the Theory of Switching*, Vol. 29 of the *Annals of the Computation Laboratory of Harvard University*, pp. 204–243, Harvard University Press, 1959.
11. Muller, D. E. and W. S. Bartky, "A Theory of Asynchronous Circuits I, " Report No. 75, University of Illinois, Digital Computer Laboratory, November 1956.
12. Muller, D. E., and W. S. Bartky, "A Theory of Asynchronous Circuits II," Report No. 78, University of Illinois, Digital Computer Laboratory, March 1957.
13. Muller, D. E., "Infinite Sequences and Finite Machines," *Proceedings of the Fourth Annual IEEE Symposium on Switching Circuit Theory and Logical Design*, Vol. S-156, pp. 9–16, September 1963.
14. Nelson, James C., "Speed Independent Counting Circuits," Report No. 71, University of Illinois, Digital Computer Laboratory, July 1, 1956.
15. Robertson, James E., "Problems in the Physical Realization of Speed-Independent Circuits," *Proceedings of the Second Annual AIEE Symposium on Switching Circuit Theory and Logical Design*, Detroit, Michigan, Vol. S-134, pp. 106–108, October 1961.
16. Seshu, S., "Mathematical Models for Sequential Machines," *IRE National Convention Record*, Vol. 7, Part 2, pp. 4–16, 1959.
17. Shelly, J. H., "The Decision and Synthesis Problems in Semi-Modular Switching Theory," Report No. 88, University of Illinois, Digital Computer Laboratory, May 20, 1959.

18. Swartwout, Robert E., "One Method for Designing Speed-Independent Logic for a Control," *Proceedings of the Second Annual AIEE Symposium on Switching Circuit Theory and Logical Design*, Detroit, Michigan, Vol. S-134, pp. 94–108, October 1961.

19. Swartwout, Robert E., "Further Studies in Speed-Independent Logic for a Control," Report No. 130, University of Illinois, Digital Computer Laboratory, December 13, 1962.

20. Swartwout, Robert E., "New Techniques for Designing Speed-Independent Control Logic," *Proceedings of the Fifth Annual IEEE Symposium on Switching Circuit Theory and Logical Design*, Vol. S-164, pp. 12–29, November 1964.

21. Unger, S. H., "Hazards and Delays in Asynchronous Sequential Switching Circuits," *IRE Transactions on Circuit Theory*, Vol. CT-6, pp. 12–26, March 1959.

# Index